HELIUM-3 AND HELIUM-4

THE INTERNATIONAL CRYOGENICS MONOGRAPH SERIES

General Editors | Dr. K. Mendelssohn, F. R. S.
The Clarendon Laboratory
Oxford, England
Dr. K. D. Timmerhaus
University of Colorado
Boulder, Colorado

H. J. Goldsmid
Thermoelectric Refrigeration, 1964
G. T. Meaden
Electrical Resistance of Metals, 1965
E. S. R. Gopal
Specific Heats at Low Temperatures, 1966
M. G. Zabetakis
Safety with Cryogenic Fluids, 1967
D. H. Parkinson and B. E. Mulhall
The Generation of High Magnetic Fields, 1967
W. E. Keller
Helium-3 and Helium-4, 1969

In preparation | A. J. Croft
Cryogenic Laboratory Equipment

HELIUM-3 AND HELIUM-4

by William E. Keller
Los Alamos Scientific Laboratory
Los Alamos, New Mexico

ℚPLENUM PRESS • NEW YORK • 1969

CHEMISTRY

Library of Congress Catalog Card Number 68-25382

Preface

The title of this monograph certainly deserves qualification—so small a package could scarcely contain all that its label advertises.

I have constructed the book so that each chapter is much like a short review article on some aspect of helium at low temperature, with the ordering of the chapters intended to produce a logical structure. Although space limitations have dictated a certain amount of selectivity in the topics included here, many of the important ones are discussed; nevertheless, for those that have been neglected references are provided to other up-to-date accounts. While the choice of what is important is admittedly a personal one—and the emphasis even more personal—I have been guided in this choice by the current literature.

The enigmas of liquid helium at low temperatures have attracted the interest of scientists of diverse backgrounds and preparation: experimental and theoretical physicists, physical chemists, and, more recently, cryogenic engineers. For the expert there appears to be no dearth of excellent and thorough accounts on the subject, but the novice might find many of these hard going, especially if he is not well acquainted with the astonishing physics of quantum phenomena on a macroscopic scale. It is for the latter reader that I have primarily, but by no means exclusively, tried to write. Toward this end, throughout the work distinctions are drawn between the properties of helium and of those substances we ordinarily meet—"classical" substances—and then further, between the two stable isotopes of helium, He^3 and He^4. We may understand these distinctions through quantum mechanics; and therefore while at least an elementary grasp of this subject is assumed, I have included various definitions and conclusions from the quantum mechanics to make the arguments appear plausible to the initiate. For such additions I beg the indulgence of the more knowledgeable readers.

v

293

Experimental results and their interpretation form the basis for discussion, with little reference to application of the results to practical problems. In many instances histories of the attempts at solving various problems are cited, for two main purposes: firstly, to indicate where the thinking went wrong and to point out some of the fallacies that may have erroneously persisted: and secondly to emphasize that our present far-from-perfect understanding is highly susceptible to amendment. Extensive tables of data are not included. The tables that do appear—and the drawings as well—have been mainly selected to illustrate and amplify arguments in the text, and serious effort was made to use the most reliable data available. Finally, I have tried to present broad outlines of theoretical principles and experimental methods rather than many complicated equations, rigorous derivations and details of laboratory techniques. Even with all the above omissions there is more than plenty to write about helium.

In producing this book I of course owe much to many. Particularly, I am indebted to Dr. E. F. Hammel, who has critically reviewed several sections of the manuscript and made many constructive comments.

I am also grateful to Prof. M. Cohen and Dr. L. Campbell for reading and commenting on portions of the manuscript and to Prof. E. Huggins and Drs. C. Ackerman, L. Goldstein, E. Grilly, R. Mills, W. Overton, and S. Larsen for joining in illuminating discussions and for pointing out material which I otherwise might have overlooked.

About 150 of the drawings are new, and for inking these onto linen I wish to thank Miss G. Basmann, Mr. R. Davis, and Mr. P. Stibbard.

It is to my wife, Helen, that I owe my greatest appreciation. Her encouragement and understanding during the difficult periods of the writing were invaluable; but in addition she has borne with composure and good humor the task of typing the several drafts of the manuscript. Her skill and patience proved exceptional.

In spite of all the good counsel I have received, errors undoubtedly remain; needless to say, the full responsibility for these is mine.

Santa Cruz, N.M.   W. E. KELLER
May, 1968

Contents

Chapter 1

Introduction: The Helium Problem

The history of attempts to understand the behavior of helium at low temperatures has been full of surprises, and this factor, probably more than any other, has stimulated the continuous and accelerating growth of helium research since 1908 when Kamerlingh Onnes first liquefied He^4. The liquefaction itself, occurring at the then incredibly low temperature of $4°K$, was indeed a triumph and perhaps the first of the surprises, since at that time the idea of "persistent gases" was still prevalent—and helium was the last of these to undergo reduction to the liquid state. However, subsequent investigations of this apparently simple substance have uncovered an abundance of complexities and surprises which in turn have sustained a remarkably high interest in the subject.

The challenge of the helium problem has attracted a significant number of leading experimentalists and theorists. A roll call of those who have tried their hands at solving it is impressive and includes several Nobel Laureates in addition to those who were specifically so honored for their helium work (Kamerlingh Onnes and L. Landau). In short, ever since the early days, helium research has been "in fashion," and it is likely to remain so for some time to come, since it is certain that the bag of surprises is far from exhausted.

1.1. VERY EARLY LIQUID HELIUM RESEARCH

By now we have learned to expect the unexpected, but this was not always so. In the years immediately following 1908, the school under Kamerlingh Onnes at Leiden concentrated upon determining the state properties of fluid helium. There was little reason to expect other than routine results from this colorless, electrically neutral, seemingly ordinary liquid composed of spherically symmetrical and chemically inert atoms. Whenever strange effects were observed, there was a natural reluctance to consider them meaningful. Thus the discovery in 1911 by Kamerlingh Onnes that the liquid density displayed a sharp maximum at about 2.2°K undoubtedly caused consternation and disbelief. The latter persisted until 13 years later when Onnes and Boks repeated the measurements and obtained the original results. Yet this did little to dispel the mystery as to why there should be a maximum.

In 1926, Dana and Onnes reported the first measurements of the liquid specific heat, omitting from the publication certain data obtained in the temperature region of the density maximum, since these did not conform to results at higher temperature. These anomalous points were also subsequently verified (Keesom and Keesom, 1936), but not before Wolfke and Keesom (1928) concluded from their studies of the dielectric constant that liquid He, in contrast to all other known liquids, must exist in two modifications, with the transition temperature occurring at the same temperature as the density maximum.

Thus, nearly 20 years separated the discovery of the first symptom and the bold preliminary diagnosis that some extraordinary condition was present in liquid He. Following this realization, additional indications of the abnormality were sought; in fact, the search continues. However, it is interesting to note in passing that a considerable induction period was required for the fundamental significance of the transition to be appreciated. This in no way deprecates the efforts of the early investigators, who had to overcome tremendous experimental difficulties, a fact we are apt to overlook in the face of the present development of the state of the art. But significant progress was not made until the decade beginning in 1938—which really was a "golden era" of liquid He research, and this despite the intervention of World War II.

In the following sections, we shall discuss the temperature dependence of some of the more interesting properties of liquid He at saturated vapor pressure conditions, with the primary purposes of, first, examining the extent to which liquid He conforms to our notions concerning more familiar fluids, and second, pointing out significant differences that require special additional concepts and assumptions for their understanding. Since the following sections are intended both as a review of several well-established liquid He properties for readers already somewhat familiar with the subject and as an introduction to those first encountering it, the treatment will intentionally be quite elementary and far from complete. As guides to many of the original papers, as well as for excellent summaries of these papers, the extensive texts by Keesom([1]) and by Atkins([2]) are recommended. A few additional references will be given here to material not covered by these texts and as well to other pertinent books.

1.2. SOME EXPERIMENTAL RESULTS CONCERNING THE PROPERTIES OF He I AND He II AT SATURATED VAPOR PRESSURES

1.2.1. The Lambda-Point

Experiments have shown that for temperatures above the transition point, some of the liquid properties are like those of ordinary liquids, while others are more gaslike; however, below this point, many characteristics of liquid He undergo drastic qualitative changes and still others are unique to this substance. The properly behaved high-temperature form was called originally by Keesom "He I" and the low-temperature deviate form "He II." We use the term "λ-point" to designate the transition location on the phase diagram, a recognition of the resemblance of the Greek letter to the shape of the specific heat curve in the vicinity of the transition. The transition occurs at a saturated vapor pressure of 38.05 mm Hg and a temperature $T_\lambda = 2.171°K$.

Some of the most important bits of information we can seek about liquid He are also some of the most tantalizingly difficult to obtain: these are the properties by which the precise characterization of the λ-point may be made. It has been realized that the λ-point is a singular point in that several of the thermodynamic properties which define the transition have very large and increasing temperature coefficients (positive or negative) as the transition is approached. Therefore, the experiments must be made infinitesimally close to the singularity in order to make this definition. Historically, it has turned out that as the measurements have become more precise and have been made closer and closer to the λ-point, we have had to change our ideas about the nature of the transition. In Chapter 7, we shall consider this problem in greater detail and present interpretations of the λ-phenomena in terms of the most recent results. Here, however, we are interested in contrasting the behavior of He I and He II, and for this it will be convenient to treat the λ-point as an indeterminate region, especially in those instances for which the experimental data are still ambiguous.

1.2.2. State Properties of Liquid He⁴

In order to orient our discussion, let us look at the phase diagram projected onto the $P–T$ plane, schematically shown in Fig. 1.1. Aside from the λ-point and its extension (the λ-line) forming the phase boundary between He I and He II, undoubtedly the most startling feature of this diagram is the absence of a triple point at which solid, liquid, and vapor coexist at equilibrium. Of all known substances, helium alone remains a liquid under its own vapor pressure extending down

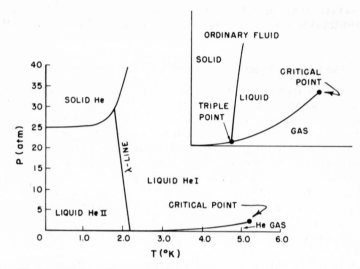

Fig. 1.1. P–T phase diagram for He^4 contrasted to that for an ordinary fluid (upper right).

in temperature to absolute zero. In general terms, we interpret this radical behavior as an indication that the net attractive forces between the helium atoms are exceedingly weak—so weak that we may appreciate how really close the believers in the persistent-gas theory were to being correct; and so weak that at $T = 0°K$, a pressure of approximately 25 atm is required to maintain the system in the orderly structure of a solid. Among the interesting consequences of this feature of helium is the opportunity we are afforded of studying the liquid state literally from its simplest beginnings and largely stripped of thermal chaos, whereas with ordinary liquids we have to deal with a hopelessly complicated assembly of particles in a highly disordered condition.

Again reflecting the weak interatomic attractive forces, the vapor pressure curve ends at a comparatively low critical point: 2.26 atm at $5.20°K$. The normal boiling point is at $4.215°K$. As we continue to lower temperature, we find that P_{sat} $vs.$ T, the relation of vapor pressure to temperature, is continuous through the λ-point, and only in higher derivatives is it affected by the transition. Likewise, σ_l, the surface tension of the liquid, behaves fairly normally. It rises with decreasing T, varying roughly as $\sigma_l = \sigma_l(0°K) - AT^{7/3}$, with A a constant, and a limiting low-temperature value of $\sigma_l(0°K) \approx 0.37$ erg/cm^2. Through the λ-region, σ_l is continuous, but the most recent experiments[3] suggest a discontinuity in slope $d\sigma_l/dT$ of approximately 20% at T_λ. The molar polarization, α_M, remains sensibly constant at a value of

~0.123 on both sides of the λ-point, thereby excluding the possibility that the transition is associated with any change in molecular structure, such as dimerization. On the whole, the gentle behavior of P_{sat}, σ_l, and α_M indicates that the forces responsible for the λ-transition are also considerably more subtle than those associated with usual first-order changes, a conclusion additionally confirmed by the absence of a latent heat accompanying the transformation from He I to He II.

The density of the liquid along the saturation curve, ρ_{sat}, passes through the λ-point more dramatically, as we may see from the plot against temperature in Fig. 1.2a. A maximum in the density occurs ([4]) some 0.006°K above T_λ rather than at the transition, but at T_λ there is a discontinuity of slope. Toward higher temperatures, ρ_{sat} decreases quite rapidly, but is otherwise well-behaved. On the low side of T_λ, ρ_{sat} passes through a shallow minimum near 1.17°K, then a point of inflection, and, in accordance with the third law of thermodynamics, approaches its value at $T = 0°K$ with zero slope. The expansion coefficient along the saturation curve reflects, and even magnifies, these variations in the density. From thermodynamics, we have

$$\alpha_{sat} \equiv -\frac{1}{\rho_{sat}}\left(\frac{d\rho_{sat}}{dT}\right) = \alpha_P - \beta_T\left(\frac{dP_{sat}}{dT}\right) \tag{1.1}$$

where α_P is the isobaric expansion coefficient, (dP_{sat}/dT) is the slope of the vapor pressure curve, and $\beta_T \equiv -V^{-1}(\partial V/\partial P)_T = \rho^{-1}(\partial \rho/\partial P)_T$ is the isothermal compressibility. Figures 1.2b and 1.2c show, respectively, α_{sat} (which differs but little from α_P but is more easily measured) and β_T, both as functions of T. The latter quantity has a cusplike character in the λ-region and is, of course, everywhere positive.

1.2.3. Thermal Properties of Liquid He[4]

The molar entropy, S, of liquid helium is continuous through the λ-point, but shows remarkably different behavior above and below the transition. As can be seen in Fig. 1.3a, this property in the He I region rises slowly with temperature, as one might expect, whereas the entropy for He II has a much stronger temperature dependence than usually found for a liquid. Between T_λ and about 0.9°K, S is roughly proportional to T^6; as the temperature is lowered, the power decreases, until, at about 0.6°K, the functional dependence of S is quite accurately T^3.

Since the entropy generally measures the degree of order in a system, with S decreasing as the order increases, we might be led to conclude from the features shown in Fig. 1.3a that the λ-transition marks an enormous change in the system's configuration. Actually, the structural differences between He I and He II, as determined by the

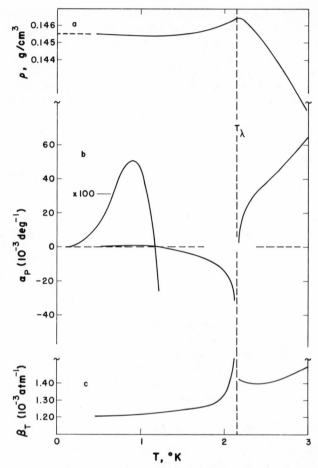

Fig. 1.2. Some *P–V–T* properties (schematic) of liquid He⁴ along
the saturation curve: (a) density; (b) expansion coefficient; and (c)
compressibility coefficient.

scattering of X-rays and neutrons,* are quite subtle, and, if anything,
indicate that the spatial order of the liquid is *greater* above T_λ than
below. Hence, the cause for the dramatic change in the entropy's
character must be sought elsewhere. The neutron data, however, do
give some hint that the atomic *motions* become more orderly below
T_λ; and, as we shall soon discover, He II admits of a very peculiar type
of ordering process for these motions.

The entropy also reflects the manner in which the energy of a

* See, for example, Henshaw (⁵).

system is partitioned among the various types of thermal excitations possible for that system, and the temperature dependence of S gives additional clues about the nature of these excitations. Thus, the T^6 behavior above $0.9°$K suggests an unusual mode of excitation not encountered in any other system, while the T^3 character below $0.6°$K is reminiscent of that for sound waves, or phonons, in a Debye solid.

Although the entropy is a primary thermodynamic quantity, it is experimentally most accessible through measurements of the specific heat, e.g., from the relation defining the heat capacity per mole at constant pressure:

$$C_P \equiv T(\partial S/\partial T)_P \qquad (1.2)$$

For liquid He, the most accurate measurements have been made along

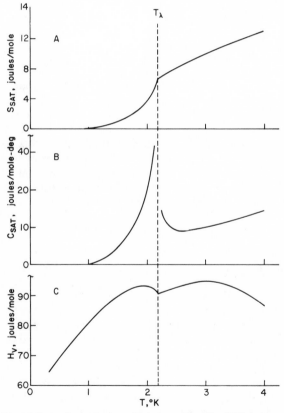

Fig. 1.3. Some thermal properties (schematic) of liquid He^4 along the saturation curve: (a) entropy; (b) specific heat; and (c) heat of vaporization.

the vapor pressure curve, giving C_{sat}, where, V_l being the molar volume of the liquid,

$$C_{sat} = C_P - \alpha_{sat} T V_l \left(\frac{dP_{sat}}{dT}\right) \tag{1.3}$$

However, the numerical differences between C_{sat} and C_P are rather small, amounting to somewhat less than 1 % of C_P near the λ-point. In either case, as in the relation between ρ_{sat} and α_{sat}, the derived quantity accentuates the λ anomaly, and this behavior for C *vs.* T is shown in Fig. 1.3b. At temperatures below $0.6°K$, the most recent experiments ([6]) give

$$C = 0.0816 \, (\pm 0.0016) \times T^3 \quad \text{J/mole-deg} \tag{1.4}$$

Through the Clausius–Clapeyron equation

$$\left(\frac{dP_{sat}}{dT}\right) = \frac{H_v}{T(V_g - V_l)_{sat}} = \frac{h_v}{T(\rho_g^{-1} - \rho_l^{-1})_{sat}} \tag{1.5}$$

the latent heat of vaporization per mole, H_v (or per gram, h_v) (see Fig. 1.3c) is expected to reflect the behavior of ρ_{sat} near T_λ, since neither the slope of the vapor pressure nor the density of the vapor, ρ_g, exhibits any first-order irregularities (V_g is the molar volume of the saturated vapor). However, direct measurements of H_v are very difficult and have not been made with sufficient precision to define the behavior in the transition region. Most liquids conform within $\pm 20\%$ to Trouton's law, i.e., $H_v/T_B \approx 23$, where T_B is the normal boiling point temperature; however, for liquid He, the ratio is about 5.2. Once more the weak binding energy of the liquid is manifested, providing a major source of deviation from classical behavior.

1.2.4. Transport Properties of Liquid He^4

The character of the coefficient of viscosity η of liquid He^4 is quite unlike that of a typical liquid. For He I, as may be readily seen from Fig. 1.4, η more resembles a gas than a liquid in its magnitude (of the order 3×10^{-5} g/cm-sec, or about 1000 times less than η for water) and in its temperature dependence (nearly constant above $2.6°K$). Below the λ-point, the results of early attempts to measure η were most confusing. Three different methods known to be successful when applied to classical liquids yielded the three different sets of values sketched in Fig. 1.4. The first of these measured the damping by the liquid of oscillating systems—cylinders and disks—and gave the results labeled (1) in the figure, η dropping at first rapidly with temperature, and then more slowly, reaching an estimated value of 10^{-9} g/cm-sec. On the other hand, Kapitza and others observed the pressure drop accompanying the flow of the liquid through narrow channels. Here [curve

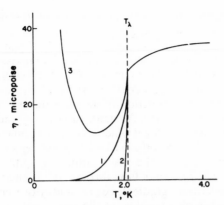

Fig. 1.4. The apparent viscosity coefficient of liquid He[4] as measured by three different methods: curve 1, by oscillating systems; curve 2, by flow through channels; and curve 3, by rotating viscometers. Above T_λ, the three methods give essentially the same results.

(2)], the viscosity apparently decreased quite rapidly just below T_λ to a surprisingly low upper limit of $\sim 10^{-11}$ g/cm-sec. Finally, measurements of the drag on a cylinder rotating in He II with a constant angular velocity have given the results of curve (3), showing a minimum value of $\sim 1.2 \times 10^{-5}$ g/cm-sec near 1.7°K and then a steep increase as the temperature is lowered.

No less startling are the observations made of the thermal conduction by the liquid. We usually define the coefficient of thermal conductivity λ through the relation

$$\lambda \equiv -\bar{q}/\nabla T \qquad (1.6)$$

where $\bar{q}$ is the mean heat current density and ∇T the temperature gradient. In He I, we again find a transport property characteristic of a gas, λ being quite small, of the order 2×10^{-4} W/cm-deg; in fact, at 3.0°K, λ is very nearly given by $(5/2)\eta C_V$, as predicted for an ideal classical gas. However, as the temperature is lowered into the He II region, the liquid becomes capable of transporting enormous amounts of heat even though driven by only small temperature gradients.

This phenomenon is easily made evident to an observer watching a dewar full of liquid He: if the vapor pressure is reduced by pumping, the liquid boils vigorously as expected; however, upon passing through the λ-point pressure, the visible signs of boiling—bubbles—no longer appear, the liquid being unable to support the temperature difference necessary for the formation of superheated vapor. A very popular comparison asserts that He II conducts heat 1000 times better than does copper at room temperature, and although this statement must be qualified, it is hardly an exaggeration. Under certain conditions, $\bar{q}$ may reach values as high as several W/cm^2, depending upon the geometry of the system as well as upon the imposed temperature difference. For these high heat currents, the observed heat conduction departs markedly from the behavior predicted by equation (1.6) by being a strong nonlinear function of the temperature gradient as well as a function of the geometry. At small values of $\bar{q}$, and hence also of ∇T, an effective λ can be defined which has a most remarkable temperature dependence, going something like T^{12} in the region $1°K < T < T_\lambda$. Even more astonishing was the observation by Kapitza that in narrow channel geometries, heat may flow through the liquid in the *complete absence* of a temperature gradient, i.e., reversibly or isentropically.

An observation closely allied to the heat conductivity is that the existence of a temperature difference ΔT in He II implies a pressure difference ΔP. The experiment considered in Fig. 1.5 has very often been used to illustrate this effect, but remains a dramatic one. Here we have a tube plugged at the bottom with packed powder to form a series of narrow channels. When heat is supplied to the region above the plug, a temperature difference develops between the fluid inside the tube and the He bath ; the accompanying pressure difference then forces a fountain of liquid He to squirt from the open end of the tube. Although

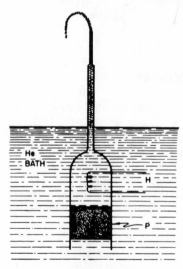

Fig. 1.5. The fountain effect. H is a heater and P is fine powder packed to form narrow channels.

the results may bring to mind the familiar sight of a coffee percolator, the He fountain is in no way related, but is a result of the interaction of the flow of heat and the flow of matter, usually referred to as the "thermo-molecular pressure" effect.

Although He II is the only liquid known to respond so vigorously to a temperature difference in the manner described by the above experiment, the same sort of behavior has long been associated with a Knudsen gas. When two vessels containing the gas are held at different temperatures and are connected by a hole or tube the radius of which is long compared with the mean free path of the gas molecules, then a pressure difference is established so that $P_1/P_2 = (T_1/T_2)^{1/2}$, the familiar thermal transpiration formula. The general phenomenon is described by the relation

$$\Delta P/\Delta T = -\rho Q/T \qquad (1.7)$$

where Q is the amount of heat transferred per unit mass through the orifice or narrow channel. This relation is valid independent of the size of the connection between the two parts of the system, but the effect becomes observable only under the special geometrical cir-cumstances mentioned above.

For bulk liquid He I, the thermomolecular pressure effect has not been observed; but for He II, the quotient on the left side of equation (1.7) can be maximized if ΔT is kept small and the channels very narrow—effective diameter of the order of microns or less. With these conditions satisfied, it has been shown that $-Q/T = s$, the entropy per gram of liquid He, so that equation (1.7) becomes

$$\Delta P/\Delta T = \rho s \qquad (1.8)$$

This relation was first derived for liquid He II by H. London in 1939 on the basis of essentially reversible thermodynamics. It represents the stationary value of ΔP reached by the system after the imposition of a constant ΔT. Here, no flow of matter results as in the squirting foun-tain, but a flow of energy is required, heat being exchanged with the sur-roundings in order to maintain the steady state. The relationship in equation (1.8) under these conditions is called the "thermomechanical effect" and the pressure difference $\Delta P = P_f$ the "thermomechanical pressure difference" or simply the "fountain pressure." A more rigorous derivation based on irreversible thermodynamics has been given by de Groot ([7]).

One of the most spectacular transport properties of liquid He II was first noticed in 1922 by Kamerlingh Onnes, but not properly identified until nearly 15 years later by Rollin and Simon. Kamerlingh Onnes' observation was essentially that if an open container is partially immersed in a bath of He II so that the liquid levels inside and outside

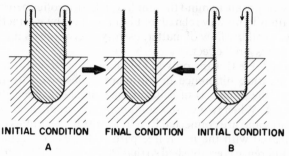

INITIAL CONDITION   FINAL CONDITION   INITIAL CONDITION

A   B

Fig. 1.6. Flow of the mobile He II film in (A) emptying and (B)
filling a beaker.

the container are initially different, then the two levels equilibrate
surprisingly rapidly. This phenomenon is illustrated in Fig. 1.6 for
the two possible types of initial conditions. During the course of an
experiment in which He was used only as a heat-conducting medium,
Rollin and Simon were led to the unusual conjecture that a thick
mobile film covers all surfaces in contact with bulk He II and that such
a film was responsible for the rapid level equilibration observed by
Kamerlingh Onnes. While adsorption is a familiar phenomenon,
ordinarily, vapors adsorbed on a surface are but a few molecular layers
thick, and although molecules of the adsorbate may undergo random
thermal motion, they are not known to participate in directed mass
motion. An ingenious series of experiments by Mendelssohn and
Daunt, as well as by Atkins, has confirmed the ideas of Rollin and Simon
and provided much information concerning the nature of the film's
mobility. The experimental difficulties in obtaining quantitative information about the film are indeed considerable, since such effects as
small temperature gradients, surface imperfections (for example, cracks
or even minute amounts of dirt or condensed gases), and mechanical
agitation may significantly perturb the results. Consequently, the
numerous investigations of the film have yielded few hard and fast
rules concerning its behavior.

The properties of the film which have been of chief interest are its
thickness, d, as a function of height and of temperature and the transfer
rate, R, under varying conditions. Measurements of film thickness,
primarily by Jackson and co-workers, have given the following results:
In the He II region, d decreases with H, the height of the film above the
liquid surface, according to the relation

$$d = k/H^n \quad \text{cm} \tag{1.9}$$

where $k \approx 3 \times 10^{-6}$ cm^{n+1} nearly independent of temperature, and n
is a constant between 0.3 and 0.45. Thus, for $H = 1$ cm, the film is about

300 Å thick and is comprised of something like 80 atomic layers. As T increases through the λ-point, d does not change very much, a thick film having been observed at as high a temperature as 3.4°K. In the He I region, small amounts of stray radiation can easily reduce the film thickness.

Only below T_λ is the film mobile, and under these conditions it may transport heat much like a narrow channel and may support the thermomechanical effect. The mobility may be measured by the transfer rate, which is the product of the film thickness and the average particle velocity; usually R is given in cm³/sec per cm perimeter of the flow vessel. Typical results of R vs. T are shown in Fig. 1.7, although we emphasize that the values given are hardly unique.

The several properties of films described above refer to those films connected to the liquid at P_{sat}. It is also possible to form helium films under less-than-saturated conditions, as in conventional adsorption experiments. Long and Meyer have demonstrated the mobility of unsaturated films and have shown that the apparent T_λ at which mobility begins is depressed as the number of atomic layers covering the surface is reduced. For a coverage of only two layers, the onset of mobility occurs at about 1.4°K. Specific-heat measurements of unsaturated films on jeweler's rouge have been reported by Frederickse, who found that not only was the cusp of the C vs. T curve shifted to lower temperatures with decreasing coverage, but also that the sharpness of the peak was lost. These results reinforce the notion of a depressed λ-point for liquid helium in very restricted geometries. [Chapter 7

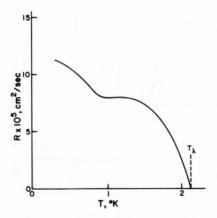

Fig. 1.7. The transfer rate R of the film as a function of temperature T.

of Atkins (^{2}) presents a useful summary of experiments and theories on the film up to 1959.]

1.2.5. Wave Propagation in Liquid He^4

Liquid helium is capable of supporting several sorts of wave motion. In order to simplify the notation applicable to the various modes, all are called "sound" but are differentiated by a numerical prefix. Thus, the isentropic propagation of a compressional wave—an ordinary acoustic wave—is called "first sound," with a velocity u_1 given by

$$u_1^2 = (\partial P/\partial \rho)_S = \gamma/\rho\beta_T \tag{1.10}$$

Here, $\gamma = C_P/C_V$, the ratio of specific heats at constant pressure and constant volume. Figure 1.8 shows the temperature variation of u_1 for liquid He, and it is seen that in the λ-region, the cusplike character of β_T is reflected in u_1. Other than this, u_1 shows no unusual behavior. As $T \to 0°K$, an extrapolation of the data gives a limiting value of $u_1 = 239$ m/sec.

In 1938 Tisza predicted, on the basis of a theory which we shall subsequently discuss, that bulk He II should be capable of transmitting

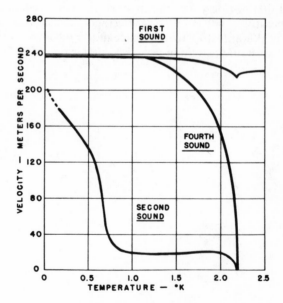

Fig. 1.8. Sound velocities in He II as a function of temperature: u_1, first sound; u_2, second sound; u_4, fourth sound.

another type of wave motion—namely, temperature waves. Such a mode is referred to as "second sound" and is manifested by the fact that the signal from a temperature pulse or oscillation generated in one part of the system by, for example, a modulated heater, may be received essentially undistorted in another part of the system. Second sound in He II was observed first by Peshkov in 1944.

The propagation of thermal waves is not something we would expect to encounter for dielectric substances, especially liquids. If, for instance, we have a rod of some ordinary dielectric heat-conducting material, a thermal pulse introduced at one end would be received at the other spread out over a time interval considerably longer than the input. This we understand in terms of phonons, or acoustic wave packets, which, having been excited by the energy pulse, traverse the solid conductor in a sort of diffusion process and scatter off one another. Thus, even though the phonons might have emanated from the source simultaneously, their mutual interactions cause delays en route resulting in a distribution of arrival times at the receiver. But in the case of liquid He II, it appears as if the carriers of thermal energy possess an exceedingly long mean free path and may traverse the fluid without the type of collision encountered in an ordinary conductor. The propagation of second sound and thermal conduction by He II have this feature in common, and, indeed, the latter may in a rough way be considered equivalent to second sound of zero frequency. In addition, both the unusually large thermal conduction and second sound appear only below T_λ.

The velocity u_2 of second sound has been found to be a complicated function of temperature, rising from its value of zero at $T = T_\lambda$ to a plateau of about 20 m/sec extending from $\sim 1.8°$ down to $\sim 1.0°K$. At lower temperatures, there is a subsequent rise, and at $T = 0°K$, the expected value is $u_1/\sqrt{3}$. These features are depicted in Fig. 1.8. Whereas u_1 is given by the variation of pressure with density at constant entropy, u_2 is defined by the variation of temperature with entropy at constant density.

Under certain geometrical conditions, He II may support additional types of wave motion. One of these has been predicted by Atkins ([8]), who advanced the numerical nomenclature in calling the propagation of surface waves on the helium film "third sound." About three years later, Atkins and co-workers ([9]) reported success in detecting this mode. In 1948, Pellam ([10]) discussed briefly the consequences of a second sound wave propagated through He II constrained in narrow channels. He concluded that when the channel width was significantly smaller than the viscous penetration depth of the wave, the propagation velocity of a thermal wave should be given by a temperature-dependent linear combination of u_1 and u_2. Atkins ([8]) later elaborated upon

Pellam's remarks, calling this new mode "fourth sound," and refined the derivation for the velocity u_4. A wave having the characteristics predicted by Atkins has been observed by Rudnick and Shapiro (1962) ([11]); their results for u_4 are also shown in Fig. 1.8. In the fourth sound mode there are simultaneous variations in the pressure, density, temperature, and entropy per unit mass.

1.3. BEGINNINGS OF A THEORY FOR LIQUID He II

In the foregoing, we discussed several unusual features of liquid He II which distinguish it from other liquids. Even before the discovery of many of these remarkable properties, as early as 1938, a few theoreticians appreciated that He II could not be understood in the same terms nor by using the same methods as applied to ordinary liquids. Actually, our knowledge concerning details of the liquid state is exceedingly incomplete; the high-order interactions among the disordered particles complicates the problem of understanding liquids. However, through a novel approach developed by London, Landau, and Tisza and their successors, we have been able to gain a significantly deeper insight into the nature of liquid helium than of any other liquid. London considered the behavior of He II so strange that he was once led to refer ([12]) to it as a "fourth state of aggregation." On the other hand, we have come to realize that despite its unusual properties, in some respects He II is quite probably the most nearly ideal and simplest of all liquids. Even so, our understanding of liquid He II is still quite limited.

The advent of quantum mechanics in the middle 1920's provided spectroscopists with powerful tools for describing the energy spectrum of systems composed of a few particles. Exact solutions were obtained for the two-body problem, such as the proton–electron pair comprising the hydrogen atom. Interactions between three bodies and more have not proven tractable to the same degree of exactness, but nevertheless have been approximated through the application of perturbation and variational techniques. These methods, combined with the principles of exchange energy and electron spin, have allowed a fairly quantitative description for more complicated systems, such as the hydrogen molecule and the helium atom.

It is a very large step, however, from producing a theory for describing a single He atom to considering one for a collection of 10^{23} He atoms. A start in this direction was made by London, who suggested that the behavior of He II could be explained as the macroscopic manifestation of quantum effects and that a significant fraction of the liquid, or even the entire liquid at absolute zero, might exist in a single quantum state. The idea that nurtured this hypothesis had originated in a statistical scheme invented by the mathematician Bose and employed subsequently by Einstein to describe an assembly of photons. As contrasted to the familiar rule governing electrons—the Pauli principle, which excludes more than one particle (neglecting spin) from occupying the same energy level—the Bose–Einstein rule permits unlimited occupation of any energy level. The condition for gaining this additional freedom is that the particles involved be composed of an even number of elementary subparticles—electrons, neutrons and protons—the net spin (both nuclear and electronic) being either zero or an even multiple of the spin unit. The wave function for a collection of atoms or molecules with this property remains unchanged in sign when any two of the particles are interchanged. Such an assembly of particles is said to obey Bose–Einstein (BE) statistics—or symmetric statistics, corresponding to the symmetric or even nature of the wave-functions—and the particles themselves are often referred to as "bosons." Clearly, He^4, having two neutrons, two protons, and two electrons, meets these qualifications.

The mathematical consequences of the treatment of a large number of noninteracting bosons—an ideal BE gas—is that for certain sets of critical values of the state properties for the gas, a significant fraction of the particles may occupy the ground-state energy level. This phenomenon is known as Bose–Einstein condensation (BEC). Thus, if the condensation begins at the critical temperature $T = T_c$, as the temperature is lowered, more and more particles fall into the ground state, until, at $T = 0°K$, all of them occupy this level. As London described this condensation, the separation of phases in ordinary space is not involved, but rather a "condensation" in momentum space wherein the condensed particles occupy the *same* momentum state. In Section 1.2.3, in connection with the entropy of liquid He, we mentioned that the λ-point was associated with a type of ordering other than spatial. Now we may speculate as a consequence of BEC that this different type of ordering is one in momentum space, i.e., that particles, even though separated by large distances in the fluid, may be correlated in their momenta. London fully realized the many highly nonphysical aspects of the properties of the ideal BE gas, but at the same time perceived in these properties the basis for a model to describe liquid He—the two-fluid model.

1.3.1. The Phenomenological Two-Fluid Model for He II

Before discussing the elements of the two-fluid model, we mention some of the pitfalls that are associated with models in general. A model is devised to represent a physical phenomenon because the actual situation is far too complicated to be handled directly; the model then incorporates the simplifying assumptions that make the problem tractable. The first danger, then, is one of oversimplification, and this is an especially hazardous possibility when quantum effects are involved. Our models are invariably classical ones derived from the framework of our experience, to which quantum phenomena are completely foreign; the validity of the model is thus limited from the start. On the other hand, the better the model, the more aspects of the problem are describable in terms of it, and a good model should be able to predict effects not already experimentally verified. When such a model exists, there is a tendency to take it too literally, to promote it to too high a status, and then, finally, to forget that it is only a model. The two-fluid model for liquid He II has proved to be a very good one and is highly subject to the two kinds of misinterpretation mentioned here. The idiom for speaking about He II has become greatly influenced by the success of the model, a defect which unfortunately will not be corrected in this book. *Caveat lector.*

The model for He II considers the liquid to be composed of two interpenetrating fluids, each with its own particle density and, to a first approximation, its own independent velocity field. One fluid is called the "normal fluid," with an effective density ρ_n and, in flow conditions, a velocity $\mathbf{v}_n$; the other is called the "superfluid," with density ρ_s and velocity $\mathbf{v}_s$. The total density of the liquid ρ_l, or simply ρ, is then given by

$$\rho_l = \rho_n + \rho_s = \rho \tag{1.11}$$

For any given temperature, a unique ratio exists between the amounts of normal fluid and superfluid present in the equilibrium system such that ρ_n/ρ_s may be determined by the temperature or, conversely, the ratio itself may determine the temperature. At the λ-point and for He I, the entire liquid is normal fluid, i.e., $\rho_n/\rho = 1$, so $\rho_s/\rho = 0$; at $T = 0°K$, the entire liquid is superfluid, indicating that $\rho_n/\rho = 0$ and $\rho_s/\rho = 1$; and at intermediate temperatures, each fraction is a strong function of T, ρ_n/ρ going something like $T^{5.6}$. A graph of the variation of the separate concentrations of the two fluids with T is given in Fig. 1.9.

The superfluid fraction plays a role corresponding to the atoms of the ideal BE gas which are condensed into the ground state; accordingly, the superfluid even at $T \neq 0°K$ has internal energy $E = 0$, though it may have, and certainly often does have, nonzero kinetic energy. Since $C_V = (\partial E/\partial T)_V$, the superfluid does not contribute to the specific heat, nor to the entropy of the liquid. Thus, all the static thermal properties of He II are attributable to the normal fluid.

The assumption of independent velocity fields for the two fluids allows a description for many of the unusual transport properties that were mentioned earlier and implies a separate equation of motion describing the hydrodynamic behavior of each fluid. Following the

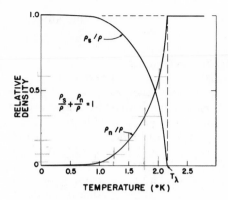

Fig. 1.9. The superfluid and normal fluid
fractions as a function of temperature.

ideas of London, Landau, and Tisza, the superfluid equation for low
velocities in the absence of external forces may be written as

$$\rho_s \, d\mathbf{v}_s/dt = -(\rho_s/\rho) \nabla P + \rho_s s \, \nabla T \qquad (1.12)$$

and that for the normal fluid under the same conditions as

$$\rho_n \, d\mathbf{v}_n/dt = -(\rho_n/\rho) \nabla P - \rho_s s \, \nabla T - \eta_n \nabla \times \nabla \times \mathbf{v}_n \qquad (1.13)$$

where s is the entropy per gram of liquid and η_n is the coefficient of
viscosity of the normal fluid. The significance of these relations will be
discussed more fully in Chapter 8; but here we wish to mention several
points.

First, we notice that both equations of motion include a contribution to the fluid acceleration which is essentially thermal in character,
so that the static thermal properties and hydrodynamic properties of
the liquid appear to have a certain equivalence as well as a definite
interrelation.

Second, taking into account this property of the thermal term,
each of these equations is analogous to expressions familiar in classical
hydrodynamics, equation (1.12) being essentially the Euler equation
for an ideal liquid and equation (1.13) the Navier–Stokes equation for
an incompressible viscous fluid.

Third, there are three possible assumptions that may be made in
considering the absence of superfluid viscous forces from equation
(1.12): either $\nabla \times \mathbf{v}_s = 0$, indicating that there is no volume vorticity
and hence the liquid may exhibit pure potential flow (Landau); or,
since the superfluid represents a condensation into a single quantum
state, it is reasonable to expect that collisions involving dissipative

interactions cannot occur between superfluid atoms (London), so that the superfluid viscosity $\eta_s = 0$; or perhaps both $\nabla \times \mathbf{v}_s = 0$ and $\eta_s = 0$. Clarification of this situation is an essential requirement for our understanding of He II thermodynamics.

Fourth, the experimental evidence concerning the He II transport properties appears to require that, as compared with the usual hydrodynamic formulation for a fluid, an additional hydrodynamic variable, and hence an additional independent equation, be introduced to describe the He II system. In the present formulation, $\mathbf{v}_s$ is the additional variable and equation (1.12) the additional relation; but this choice is not unique.

Fifth, equations (1.12) and (1.13) are in general appropriate only for the limit of low velocities; additional terms must be included in the equations in order to extend the range of validity to higher velocities. Several schemes have been proposed for doing this, but none has been altogether successful. The achievement of a complete and consistent hydrodynamic description of He II remains a central problem.

Despite shortcomings, such as those suggested above, the two-fluid equations of motion have been extremely successful in providing more than a superficial explanation for the remarkable transport properties of He II. First of all, we are now in a position to understand why the early viscosity measurements gave such cryptic results. The indications of extremely low viscosity as observed when liquid He II flows through narrow passages can be associated with the absence of the viscous term in the superfluid equation. Hence the superfluid may pass unimpeded, whereas under conditions of small gradients, the finite value of η_n effectively immobilizes the normal fluid, so that $\mathbf{v}_n = 0$. It was in fact the observations of these conditions that led Kapitza to describe He II as a "superfluid;" and we now use the term "superfluidity" to denote those classes of phenomena in which the motion of the superfluid fraction of the liquid has a predominating influence, including: flow through narrow channels and the film; thermal conduction; the fountain effect; and second, third, and fourth sounds.

When $\mathbf{v}_n \neq 0$, a proper solution to equations (1.12) and (1.13) is the usual Poiseuille relation. For example, if the flow is through a parallel-sided channel of width d, the average value of the normal fluid velocity is given by

$$\bar{\mathbf{v}}_n = -(d^2/12\eta_n)\,\nabla P \qquad (1.14)$$

But for determining η_n, the usual Poiseuille experiments are obviously meaningless, since the volume flow will still be almost entirely due to superfluid.

In the light of the two-fluid model, the difficulties associated with the oscillating-disk experiments also become evident: since what is measured is the product $\rho\eta$, it is necessary to specify correctly the density of the fluid contributing to the inertia acting on the disk. Prior to the two-fluid model it was wrongly assumed that the total density should be used, leading to the results shown as curve (1) in Fig. 1.4. The beautiful experiments of Andronikashvili, published in 1946, both settled this problem and produced the first measurements of ρ_n. In this study, a stack of closely-spaced disks was employed. When the assembly was immersed in the liquid and set into oscillation about its axis, only that part of the fluid possessing viscosity was dragged along between the disks to contribute to the effective moment of inertia of the system. Above the λ-point, the total liquid responded to the motion of the disks; but in He II, only the normal fluid fraction did so, the superfluid remaining essentially stationary, unable to interact with the disk surfaces. Thus, ρ_n was determined at various temperatures from the decrease in moment of inertia of the system relative to the He I value. Clearly then, the appropriate density for providing the damping in the single-disk experiments should be ρ_n; and with this substitution, the results shown as curve (3) in Fig. 1.4 were obtained. The rotating-cylinder experiments yield correct values of η_n, since these do not depend upon density and therefore determine the viscosity directly.

To explain the abnormal heat flow in He II, additional hypotheses are necessary, and these were supplied by Kapitza and Landau and further elaborated by London and Zilsel. The process is conceived as a sort of internal convection with the normal fluid being the carrier of heat, since it alone has thermal energy. When a temperature gradient is established in the liquid, the resulting average heat current density is given by

$$\bar{\mathbf{q}} = \rho s T \bar{\mathbf{v}}_n \tag{1.15}$$

The normal fluid flows from the heat source to the sink, and in order that momentum be conserved in the system, an equal flow of superfluid occurs in the reverse direction. Thus, in the steady state,

$$\rho_n \bar{\mathbf{v}}_n + \rho_s \bar{\mathbf{v}}_s = 0 \tag{1.16}$$

If we restrict our consideration to *small gradients only*, and continue to use the example of a parallel-sided channel (other simple geometries introduce no new principle), equation (1.14) may be substituted for $\bar{\mathbf{v}}_n$ in equation (1.15) to yield

$$\bar{\mathbf{q}} = -\frac{\rho s T d^2}{12\eta_n}\nabla P = -\frac{(\rho s)^2 T d^2}{12\eta_n}\nabla T \tag{1.17}$$

To obtain the heat flow in terms of the temperature gradient, the fountain-pressure relation of equation (1.8) has been used here. We see from equation (1.17) that it is the normal fluid viscosity which imposes the essential limitations upon the heat flow. With the entropy obtained calorimetrically, relation (1.17) may be used to provide an alternate method for determining values of η_n from heat flow measurements in narrow channels. Such experiments have been performed ([13]) and conclusively show that η_n is in excellent agreement with this quantity measured in the bulk fluid using oscillating and rotating systems. Finally, if we compare equations (1.6) and (1.17), λ is identified as

$$\lambda = (\rho s)^2 T d^2 / 12\eta_n \qquad (1.18)$$

To appreciate the extremely strong temperature dependence of λ, we may use a rough approximation for s in the form $s = s_\lambda \rho_n / \rho$, where s_λ is the entropy per gram of liquid at the λ-point. Then, since $\rho_n / \rho \propto T^{5.6}$, we have $\lambda \propto T^{12.2}$, as previously noted.

In section 1.2.4, we made the statement that in liquid He II, heat may flow reversibly in the absence of a temperature gradient, which may seem to contradict equations (1.15) and (1.17). The point we must realize here is that these equations apply only to the steady state, whereas the reversible flow can occur only for nonsteady-state conditions. Suppose we maintain two reservoirs A and B at the same temperature, $T_A = T_B$, connect them by a superleak, and insert a heat source in A. As we turn on the heater just a bit, superfluid will flow into A at such a rate that the amount of heat supplied, Q, produces the proper amount of normal fluid to keep T_A constant; i.e., $Q = T_A s$ per gram of superfluid entering A. Since reservoir B has lost superfluid, increasing ρ_n / ρ in B, we must remove the same amount of heat from B in order that $T_A = T_B$. Thus, under these nonequilibrium conditions, we may transport Q from A to B isothermally and reversibly.

If we now turn up the heater sufficiently high that the superfluid cannot enter A fast enough to prevent T_A from rising, we will produce the temperature difference $\Delta T = T_A - T_B$ and thus the fountain effect. Again consider Fig. 1.5. When heat is supplied above the powder section, the superfluid will continue to flow until the driving force $\rho s \Delta T$ is balanced by the column of liquid above the rouge, $\Delta P = \rho g \Delta H$ (g is the gravitational constant and ΔH is the height difference between the top of the column and the level of the surrounding bath). In many respects, the process is analogous to an osmotic pressure which occurs when fluid mixtures of different concentrations are separated by a semipermeable membrane, the net flow through the membrane being toward the mixture with lower solute concentration. Since the fluid which passes the barrier in the case of the fountain effect is devoid of entropy, an amount of heat $Q = Ts$ per gram must be supplied to maintain the temperature difference between the fluids until the maximum level difference ΔH is achieved. If the channels are sufficiently narrow that $\bar{v}_n = 0$, and if the walls of the tube are perfect insulators, once the maximum ΔH is reached no more heat need be supplied to maintain the ΔT; however, even though these adiabatic conditions are never reached in practice, the ideal fountain effect may be readily obtained. In fact, as we shall see later, relation (1.8) has been found valid (when integrated with respect to T and P) even when the normal fluid velocity is as high as 100 cm/sec. There are evidently complexities associated with the fountain effect that have not been considered in the usual simple derivations.

We also mention here the reverse of the fountain effect, the mechanocaloric effect. Suppose we have an adiabatic vessel fitted with a fine porous plug and immersed in a bath of He II so that the vessel is initially filled with liquid. Now we raise the vessel from the bath, allowing the superfluid to flow through the plug. Since the liquid left behind is being depleted of superfluid, the temperature in this section will rise. Thus, in London's words, we have an "entropy filter." A two-fluid theory of He II flow developed by Tisza in 1938, very shortly after London originally proposed the model, predicted the mechano-caloric effect before it was observed experimentally and provided some of the first indications of the power of the two-fluid model.

The most significant triumph of Tisza's theory, however, was the prediction of the phenomenon of second sound in He II. Whereas the compression waves of ordinary sound involve the oscillation of the fluid particles in phase, Tisza conceived that superfluid particles could oscillate against those of the normal fluid, or 180° out of phase, thereby giving rise to local fluctuations in the ratio ρ_n/ρ_s equivalent to temperature fluctuations. Tisza concluded that such an alternation of relative density could be propagated as a wave or a pulse—second sound—and produced a relationship for the temperature dependence of the propagation velocity u_2. The latter has subsequently been shown to be based on an erroneous assumption which nevertheless affects the predictions only at low temperatures; the correct expression was provided by Landau in 1941 as

$$u_2^2 = (\rho_s/\rho_n)(s^2 T/c) \tag{1.19}$$

(c is the specific heat per gram) which gives the limiting behavior shown in Fig. 1.8.

After several false starts, Peshkov in 1944 observed second sound. For the signal generator, he used a resistive wire fed with alternating current and for the receiver, a phosphor–bronze resistance thermometer. The system was sufficiently sensitive that signals could be produced in the range of 30 to 10,000 c/sec without loss of sharpness and could be received after suffering no apparent dispersion. Peshkov measured u_2 over the interval from 1.4°K to within a few millidegrees of the λ-point, and from knowledge of the thermal properties of the liquid, calculated the ratio ρ_s/ρ_n using equation (1.19). These results have been found to be in agreement with component density values determined by Andronikashvili using the oscillating disks.

Third and fourth sound were also predicted on the basis of the two-fluid model. In the former, the surface waves initiated by a thermal pulse on the stationary He II film are considered to be associated almost entirely with superfluid motion, since viscosity should effectively restrain the movement of the normal component. This superfluid motion may take place on an otherwise static film and is to be distinguished from the usual transfer processes. Thus, third sound is pictured as an oscillation of superfluid in a direction parallel to the wall supporting the film. The excess fluid at the crest of the surface wave is due to the accumulation of ρ_s and the temperature here is therefore lowered compared with the trough from which ρ_s has been depleted. From his analysis, Atkins [8] derived for the velocity of third sound

$$u_3^2 \approx (\rho_s/\rho)df[1 + (sT/h_v)] \tag{1.20}$$

where f represents the restoring force on the wave and the second term in the bracket is small compared with unity. Everitt et al. [9] detected the third-sound wave by observing the thickness changes of a film adsorbed on a horizontal surface when a small section of the film was periodically evaporated at a point relatively remote from the measurement location. The velocity of the wave was found experimentally to depend upon film thickness in the manner given by equation (1.20) but appeared about a factor of 2 too low. At $\sim 1.1°\mathrm{K}$ for $d \approx 3 \times 10^{-6}$ cm, the observed value of u_3 was 30 cm/sec.

Similarly, fourth sound represents the oscillation of ρ_s when ρ_n is clamped in the confines of a narrow channel such that the width d is much less than $(2\eta_n/\omega\rho_n)^{1/2}$, the viscous penetration depth of the wave with frequency ω. To a good approximation, the two-fluid model yields the relation for u_4:

$$u_4 \approx (\rho_s/\rho)^{1/2}u_1 \tag{1.21}$$

which was quantitatively confirmed by Rudnick and Shapiro [11].

1.3.2. Zero-Point Energy and van der Waals Forces

We have briefly considered some of the pioneering ideas and experiments that have contributed to the solid foundation of the two-fluid model upon which most theoretical treatments of He II ultimately rest. Through this model, diverse properties of the liquid may be interrelated and given significance. There are, however, other helium phenomena for which the model alone is simply incapable of providing a suitable description. Among these are included the origin of the extraordinary static thermal properties and the absence of a solid–liquid–vapor triple point. The two-fluid model must be supplemented by more fundamental principles, and evidently what is needed is a deeper probe, using quantum-mechanical techniques, into first the atomic interactions and then into the manner in which energy is distributed in the many-atom systems.

To describe most quantum-mechanical systems, only slight modifications of classical analogs are necessary. For helium, however, this approach is not adequate, and the reasons for failure may be traced to the low atomic weight and the extremely small interatomic forces characterizing the substance. If we consider systems at absolute zero, we ordinarily think of the atoms at rest in their equilibrium positions: the thermal energy of the ensemble of particles has been removed, so that the total energy is equal to the potential energy arising from the interaction between neighboring atoms. Usually, the total potential energy U is approximated as the sum of the forces $\Phi(r)$ between all pairs of the particles, where $\Phi(r)$ is a function only of the separation $r = |\mathbf{r}_i - \mathbf{r}_j|$ between two atoms i and j. Thus, if

$$U = \tfrac{1}{2} \sum_{i,j}^{N}{}' \Phi(|\mathbf{r}_i - \mathbf{r}_j|) \tag{1.22}$$

where the prime on the summation indicates $i \neq j$ and accounts for the factor $\tfrac{1}{2}$, then U will be a minimum $= U_0$ when all the N atoms of the system of volume Ω occupy their classical rest positions, thereby forming a close-packed lattice. Such a description is not appropriate for liquid helium at $0°K$, and we must look for some modification to bring our model more closely in line with reality. Suppose in the next approximation we place each of the N particles in a potential well created by its neighbors. Then, if we assume the resulting potential to be parabolic about the minimum and consider only small displacements of the atoms from their equilibrium position, the system behaves as if it were composed of N independent harmonic oscillators. The quantum-mechanical energy of the nth harmonic oscillator is quantized in units of Planck's constant h and is given by

$$\epsilon_n = (l_n + \tfrac{1}{2})h\nu_n \tag{1.23}$$

where the quantum number $l_n = 0, 1, 2, 3$, etc. and the frequency ν_n is given by

$$\nu_n = \frac{1}{2\pi}\left(\frac{f_n}{m}\right)^{1/2} \tag{1.24}$$

in terms of the force constant f_n and the mass m of the particle. The result that for the lowest state, $l_n = 0$,

$$\epsilon_n^0 = \tfrac{1}{2}hv_n \tag{1.25}$$

has its origins in the uncertainty relations and is purely a quantum-mechanical effect. The ϵ_n^0 is the "zero-point energy" of the oscillator. Because m is small for helium, the zero-point energy is significant for an assembly of helium atoms, whereas for heavier atoms and molecules it is not, and is often neglected. In this approximation, the total energy of N helium atoms at $0°K$ can be written as

$$E_0 = U_0 + \tfrac{1}{2}\sum_{n=1}^{N} hv_n = U_0 + E_0^0 \tag{1.26}$$

This expression describes the energy of a monatomic crystal lattice, which, together with a particular assumed (parabolic) distribution function for the frequencies v_n, forms the basis for the Debye theory of solids. It is paradoxical that in some respects, liquid He II resembles a gas, while in others, it is quite solidlike; however, although many of the theories for describing the liquid proceed from one of these models, neither viewpoint is completely satisfactory. For liquid He, E_0 is the binding energy of the particles and is equivalent to the latent heat of vaporization at $T = 0°K$.

The evaluation of the sums for both U_0 and the zero-point energy E_0^0 are very complicated and the results so far are at best crude approximations. In his book, London ([12]) has discussed various approaches to the problem. A brief summary of his analysis will be considered here.

We know that X-ray scattering experiments may be interpreted as showing that, on the average, each He atom in the liquid at $P = 0$ and $T = 0°K$ has six nearest-neighbors with centers at a distance of 3.16 Å. A suitable spatial model can be devised to make this figure consistent with the observed molar volume $V = 27.6 \text{ cm}^3/\text{mole}$. In these terms the liquid structure is very open, greatly expanded compared with what might be expected in the absence of zero-point energy, so that each atom may vibrate with considerable amplitude in the cage formed by its nearest neighbors. These considerations led London to replace the harmonic oscillator zero-point energy E_0^0 of the Debye model by the kinetic zero-point energy, K_0, defined semiempirically by

$$K_0 = \frac{h^2 d}{2\pi m(R - 0.891d)^2(R + 0.713d)} \tag{1.27}$$

Here, each atom of diameter d is thought of as confined to a spherical cage formed by its neighbors, and $R = (\Omega/N)^{1/3}$; expression (1.27) resembles the familiar particle-in-a-rectangular-box zero-point energy,

$(Nh^2/8m)(4\pi/3\Omega)^{2/3}$. The principal effect of the substitution of K_0 for E_0^0 is to change the dependence upon mass from $m^{-1/2}$ to m^{-1}.

An estimate of V based solely on a reasonable potential energy U_0 gives a value several times too small; but if U_0 is now modified to be consistent with the experimental value of V, calculation of the quantities entering into relation (1.26) gives $E_0 = U_0 + K_0 = -47.2 + 28.6 = -18.6$ cal/mole, in fair agreement with the observed ground state energy, -14.3 cal/mole. The zero-point energy is a large positive quantity and is therefore repulsive in character. It counterbalances to a considerable extent the attractive forces associated with U_0, thereby making the net binding energy weak and accounting for the extraordinary volume expansion. In terms of this description, we are now able to understand qualitatively that due to the small net attractive forces and an open atomic configuration the liquid should have gaslike properties and, as well, should be difficult to bring into the order of a solid lattice.

The principal forces of attraction between any two nonpolar molecules such as helium are those named after van der Waals, who first introduced the concept of attractive forces into the equation of state for a gas. The van der Waals forces arise from the mutual polarization when the two molecules are brought close together. The transient electric dipole arising from the unsymmetrical instantaneous electronic configuration of each molecule displays a motion similar to that of a three dimensional harmonic oscillator. When two such oscillators interact, the resulting in-phase vibration (resonance) produces a net attraction. The quantum-mechanical description for this coupling leads to a term in the potential proportional to $-r^{-6}$, or an attractive force proportional to r^{-7}, with the constant of proportionality given essentially by the ground-state static polarizability α^0,

$$\alpha^0 = \frac{e^2}{4\pi^2 m_e} \sum_n \frac{f_n}{v_n^2} \tag{1.28}$$

Here, e and m_e are the charge and mass of the electron, respectively, and f_n is the force constant or oscillator strength associated with the frequency v_n, corresponding to transitions between the ground state E_0 of the molecule and the excited electronic state E_n. We recall that $hv_n = (E_0 - E_n)$. The coupling energy entering into $\Phi(r)$ from these considerations is given by the interaction energy of the oscillator system minus the zero-point energy of the oscillators. The force derived from this part of $\Phi(r)$ has also been called either the "London force," after London who, in 1930, first made the quantum-mechanical calculations, or the "dispersion force," arising from the fact that the oscillator frequencies contributing to α^0 are the same ones which are responsible for the dispersion of light.

The potential function between two He atoms will be more fully treated in Chapter 3; but here we wish to emphasize that the attractive parts arising from the polarization forces are exceedingly weak and are nearly balanced by the repulsive effects of the zero-point energy. This can be further appreciated by comparing He with H_2 in these respects, as has been pointed out by London ([12]). Since the zero-point energy for these light molecules is considered proportional to m^{-1}, and $m_{H_2}/m_{He} = 0.5$, we should expect K_0 for H_2 to be twice as large as for He. On this basis, we should predict liquid H_2 to be even more "blown up" and even more difficult to solidify than He. However, the attractive part of $\Phi(r)$ for H_2 is some 12 times stronger than for He, so that the dilation due to zero-point energy is, in the case of H_2, overshadowed by this attraction, the net result being that liquid H_2 is easily solidified and has only about one-third as much excess volume as liquid He.

In a rather different context, the van der Waals forces are believed to play an essential role in the formation of the thick He film as well as in the determination of its properties. Equation (1.9) relating the film thickness to its height has been derived by balancing the gravitational forces acting on an element of film against the van der Waals forces between the substrate and the helium atoms. This gives directly an exponent n exactly equal to $\frac{1}{3}$ and a value of k which varies slightly with the material of the substrate, both in qualitative agreement with experiment. Other more subtle but nonetheless significant considerations may also enter into the d vs. H relation, as discussed by Atkins ([2]).

1.3.3. Landau's Theory of the Thermal Excitations

The two-fluid model for He II as developed by London and Tisza is based to a large extent upon analogy with the condensation of an ideal Bose–Einstein gas. This treatment emphasizes the importance of the statistics obeyed by the particles and attributes much of the superfluid behavior of the liquid to the unusual properties of the condensed particles. A different approach has been taken by Landau, who discounted the importance of particle statistics and instead stressed the significance of the thermal excitations in the liquid. In this respect, Landau shifted the emphasis of the two-fluid model from ρ_s to ρ_n and pictured the normal fluid as existing in an inert background sea of the superfluid. His theory is an attempt to develop a phenomenological microscopic description of a quantum liquid through the quantization of hydrodynamics, and its final form was achieved by obtaining the best fit to the relevant experimental data. Although it is now generally agreed that the BEC is an essential ingredient of superfluid systems, many of the predictions that resulted from Landau's profound physical insight have been subsequently verified by direct experiment as well as by more fundamental theoretical studies. The differing viewpoints of London–Tisza and Landau were developed independently and nearly simultaneously. Initially, they were considered competitive, but with the perspective of time and through careful exploration of the underlying principles, it has become clear that they are instead complementary.

Landau, in two important papers (1941 and 1947), proposed that the thermal excitations of liquid He II possessed a spectrum with the form pictured in Fig. 1.10. Here, the energy ϵ of the elementary excitations is expressed in temperature units ϵ/k_B, where k_B is the Boltzmann constant, and is plotted against the momentum p given in wave numbers, i.e., $p/\hbar$ cm^{-1} ($\hbar = h/2\pi$). According to this spectrum, if we begin with the liquid at $0°$K and then add to the system a small amount of thermal energy, this energy will be distributed over the most easily excited modes, that is, the lowest-lying energy levels, which are evidently those near the origin in the figure. Here, the energy is proportional to the momentum

$$\epsilon(p) = Kp \tag{1.29}$$

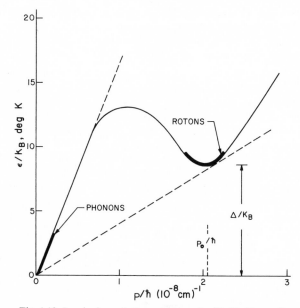

Fig. 1.10. Landau's excitation spectrum for He II. Heavy lines indicate regions of largest excitation concentration. Dotted lines show $|\epsilon(p)/p|_{\min}$ for phonons and rotons.

This form of dispersion relation is characteristic of sound waves transmitted through a solid. Such modes involving the coordinated or collective motion of all the atoms in the solid we call "phonons." Here, we find for liquid He II its closest approach to solidlike behavior. For a solid, three acoustical branches are possible, corresponding to one set of longitudinal modes and two sets of transverse modes of oscillation of the lattice. For a liquid, the shear modulus is zero, so that transverse or torsional waves cannot be supported, but the bulk modulus is not zero, and longitudinal compression waves can certainly be propagated. According to Landau, for He near $0°K$, the lowest-lying excitations are quantized longitudinal sound waves, or phonons, of very long wavelength.

For higher values of the momentum, Landau suggested that a different type of excitation might be present in the liquid. These were called "rotons," since they were pictured as involving a few atoms undergoing a sort of rotational motion perhaps somewhat like the curling of a smoke ring. Whereas the description of phonons in liquid He rests upon the well-established model of a solid lattice, no such physical analog is available for rotons. In effect, Landau has considered the experimentally determined properties of the liquid and by some sort of intuition asserted that "this is what the spectrum must be." The result is that the roton region of the $\epsilon-p$ curve is characterized by a dip and that the form of the curve near the minimum is described by

$$\epsilon(p) = \Delta + (p - p_0)^2/2\mu \tag{1.30}$$

The quantities Δ, μ, and p_0 are constants to be determined from experimental thermal data, Δ is essentially an activation energy for the formation of a roton, with Δ/k_B found to be about $9°K$; μ is the reduced mass of the excitation, is about one-quarter the mass of the helium atom, and determines the curvature near the minimum; and p_0 locates the position of the minimum, placing it at $p/\hbar = p_0/\hbar \approx 2.0 \text{ Å}^{-1}$ (wavelength comparable to the interatomic spacing). Although the form of equation (1.30) is suggestive of a single-particle-like excitation, rotons are, like phonons, collective motions of the atoms of the whole liquid, but in the case of rotons, the amplitude of the excitation is highly localized.

Collective excitations such as phonons and rotons have many properties in common with individual particles, and because of this they are often referred to as *quasiparticles*. Phonons, and most probably rotons also, obey BE statistics, a consequence which is independent of and to be distinguished from the type of statistics governing the individual particles. Since the energy of a roton is at least Δ, which is large compared with $k_B T$, rotons may be treated without loss of accuracy by the classical Boltzmann statistics.

The distinction between phonons and rotons is artificial, since the spectrum is really continuous; but Landau supposed that the populations of the excitations were concentrated near the linear portion and near the minimum of the spectrum. The good account which the theory gives for the thermal properties of the liquid appears to justify somewhat the simplifications brought about by dealing only with the limiting features of each type of excitation. In this way, the expressions (1.29) and (1.30) involving but four empirical constants are taken to describe *all* the excitations even though they apply only to very restricted momentum regions. A corollary to this approximation is the noninteraction between the two types of excitations, so that we may speak, for instance, of the heat capacity due to phonons as entirely separate from that due to rotons. Or putting it still another way, the phonons and the rotons may be considered as two distinct dilute gases; so long as the concentrations of the two gases remain low, the interactions between them may be neglected.

The thermodynamic functions of the liquid are readily obtained from the above suppositions concerning the spectrum by the methods of statistical mechanics. For the phonon contribution to the thermodynamic quantities, the treatment follows very closely that of the well-known Debye theory of solids, in which the specific heat of a solid is derivable from its phonon spectrum. In the case of the present theory of He II, the phonon spectrum is approximated by a linear dispersion relation, so that in equation (1.29) K is replaced by the velocity of sound u_1 at $0°K$. The free energy of the liquid is then calculated and from this, by the usual thermodynamic relations, all the other thermal properties are obtained. For F_ϕ, the phonon free energy per gram of liquid, we get

$$F_\phi = -\tfrac{1}{6}\Phi T^4 \tag{1.31}$$

where

$$\Phi = \pi^2 k_B^4 / 15\hbar^3 u_1^3 \rho \tag{1.32}$$

By successive differentiations with respect to T, we obtain the phonon entropy and specific heat,

$$S_\phi = -\partial F_\phi/\partial T = \tfrac{2}{3}\Phi T^3 \tag{1.33}$$

and

$$C_\phi = T\,\partial S_\phi/\partial T = 2\Phi T^3 \tag{1.34}$$

The corresponding quantities for rotons are calculated by considering them as an ideal Boltzmann gas of N_r particles in a volume Ω. Here, N_r is a function of T and is determined by the condition of minimum free energy. The results are (with all quantities per gram of liquid):

$$N_r = (k_B T)^{1/2} R_0 \exp(-\Delta/k_B T) \tag{1.35}$$

$$F_r = -(k_B T)^{3/2} R_0 \exp(-\Delta/k_B T) \tag{1.36}$$

$$S_r = \left(\frac{k_B}{T}\right)^{1/2} \Delta R_0 \left(1 + \frac{3 k_B T}{2\Delta}\right) \exp(-\Delta(k_B T) \tag{1.37}$$

and

$$C_r = \frac{\Delta^2 R_0}{k_B^{1/2} T^{3/2}} \left[1 + \frac{k_B T}{\Delta} + \frac{3}{4}\left(\frac{k_B T}{\Delta}\right)^2\right] \exp(-\Delta/k_B T) \tag{1.38}$$

where

$$R_0 = 2\mu^{1/2} p_0^2/(2\pi)^{3/2} \rho \hbar^3 \tag{1.39}$$

If we consider, for example, the specific heat C of the whole liquid, from the model of independent excitation gases we find that

$$C = C_\phi + C_r \tag{1.40}$$

This and similar expressions for the other quantities remain quite accurate for temperatures up to within several tenths of a degree of the λ-point, where the independent gas model for the excitations breaks down and details of the shape of the spectrum become important. For the roton quantities in equations (1.35)–(1.38), the exponential $\exp(-\Delta/k_B T)$ is the principal factor determining the temperature dependence. Since at low temperatures, $\Delta \gg k_B T$, the roton contribution to the properties of liquid helium in the neighborhood of $0°$K is negligible. Thus, the specific heat has the T^3 dependence characteristic of the Debye theory, and below $0.6°$K it is calculated to be

$$C = C_\phi = 0.0204 \times T^3 \quad \text{J/g-deg} \tag{1.41}$$

when u_1 extrapolated to $T = 0°$K is taken as 239 m/sec (u_1 in the region in question varies only slightly). The calorimetric determination of C for $T < 0.6°$K made by Wiebes et al. [6] is described by precisely the same expression (1.41). Near $T = 0.6°$K, the effect of the rotons becomes evident and by about $1°$K, $C_\phi \approx C_r$; above $1°$K, the roton contribution relative to that of the phonons rises very rapidly and displays the extremely large temperature dependence noted earlier in Section 1.2.3.

The ratio ρ_n/ρ may also be calculated from the excitation spectrum within the same approximation as made for the thermodynamic quantities just discussed. Again the phonon and roton parts of ρ_n are considered separately, the results being

$$\rho_n = (\rho_n)_\phi + (\rho_n)_r$$

$$= \frac{2\rho}{3u_1^2}\Phi T^4 + \frac{\rho p_0^2}{3(k_B T)^{1/2}}R_0 \exp(-\Delta/k_B T) \qquad (1.42)$$

The roton contribution to ρ_n is calculated to be negligible at very low temperatures, but is comparable to the phonon part at about $0.6°K$, and at $1°K$ is some 60 times larger than $(\rho_n)_\phi$. Experimentally determined values of u_2 and of C when inserted into equation (1.19) yield values of ρ_n/ρ in reasonable agreement with equation (1.42) for the temperature range below about $1.5°K$, above which the simplifications made for excitation spectrum are once more inadequate.

The Landau model, even in the approximate form described above, has been extremely successful in describing the thermal properties of liquid He II. Since the time of Landau's original proposal, however, considerable progress has been made in refining the theory and in improving the fit with experiment by means of direct determination of the dispersion relation from neutron scattering measurements. These matters will be discussed more fully in Chapter 5.

1.3.4. Landau's Explanation of Superfluidity

We have already mentioned that the equation of motion (1.12) for the superfluid is valid only for small velocities v_s. If we consider a situation in which the normal fluid is held fixed and v_s is gradually increased, a value of this velocity will be reached for which purely potential flow will cease and dissipative processes will set in. We call the value of v_s at which this occurs the "critical velocity," $v_{s,c}$, and we consider this to signal the destruction of superfluidity. On the basis of the excitation spectrum just described, Landau has discussed the special reasons that He II should exhibit superfluidity and under what conditions superfluidity should be destroyed. Although a large number of authors have elaborated upon Landau's original proposal, providing separate routes to the same conclusions, the situation is still not entirely clear, nor is it certain that the conclusions are correct. Here we summarize Landau's viewpoint.

We first consider the processes which might lead to the destruction of superfluidity. If we have an ordinary liquid flowing through a long tube, its velocity is described by frictional forces originating at the wall and within the liquid itself. Through friction, mechanical energy is ultimately converted into heat. For liquid He at $0°K$ flowing in such a tube, Landau has argued that the superfluid should flow as a perfect liquid, and therefore be curl-free $(\nabla \times v_s = 0)$ until a v_s is reached which corresponds to the minimum velocity required to create a single thermal excitation from the flowing fluid. That is, the energy required for the production of an excitation must be removed from the kinetic energy of the flow, thereby causing the *entire* fluid to slow down by an amount corresponding to this energy loss. The appearance of an excitation of energy $\epsilon(p)$ and momentum $\mathbf{p}$ changes the energy of the liquid by the amount $\epsilon(p) + \mathbf{p} \cdot \mathbf{v}_s$, and this change must be negative, so that

$$\epsilon(p) + \mathbf{p} \cdot \mathbf{v}_s < 0 \tag{1.43}$$

the minimum value obtaining when $\mathbf{p}$ and $\mathbf{v}_s$ are antiparallel. From Equation (1.43), it is seen that for an excitation to be produced in the fluid, the condition imposed upon the velocity becomes

$$\mathbf{v}_s > |\epsilon(p)/p|_{min} = [\partial \epsilon(p)/\partial p]_{min} \tag{1.44}$$

Here, $\partial \epsilon(p)/\partial p$ is the group velocity of the excitation produced and is represented on the plot of the spectrum by a line drawn from the origin to a point of tangency to the curve. Two such points of the spectrum shown in Fig. 1.10 satisfy this criterion; these are at the origin in the phonon region,

$$\mathbf{v}_\phi = |u_1 p/p|_{min} = u_1 \approx 2 \times 10^4 \text{ cm/sec} \tag{1.45}$$

and the other slightly to the right of the minimum in the roton region,

$$\mathbf{v}_r = \left| \frac{\Delta}{p} + \frac{(p - p_0)^2}{2\mu p} \right|_{min} \approx 6 \times 10^3 \text{ cm/sec} \tag{1.46}$$

A very serious deficiency of the theory becomes apparent if, along with Landau, we interpret either of these values of $\mathbf{v}_\phi$ or $\mathbf{v}_r$ as the critical velocity, $\mathbf{v}_{s,c}$. Then we would expect that superfluid flow could occur for all velocities less than those necessary to produce the elementary excitations. Such an estimate is unrealistically high by several orders of magnitude, since the largest observed critical velocities appear to be only about 50 cm/sec. This is the value found in film flow, whereas for flow of the liquid through channels, the values are even lower and decrease as the size of the channel becomes larger. While it is true that these measurements have been made at nonzero temperatures, this does not explain the large disparity between the experiments and the theory. We may expect that a different amount of energy is required for the production of an excitation depending on whether or not there are other excitations already present; but this effect is so slight that it should not materially alter either the nature of Landau's argument or the numerical predictions.

A resolution of this difficulty could be brought about if still other excitations for which $|\epsilon/p|_{min}$ is very small could be identified in the liquid. This might arise if the energy were low and the momentum were high and hence if there were another minimum in the excitation spectrum far out to the right in the plot in Fig. 1.10. The considerable effort expended in exploring the liquid for such excitations have resulted in some hope for success. Evidence has been found for quantized vortex-line states which possess some of the required characteristics. Further investigation of this possibility provides one of the most active areas for current research, the status of which will be reviewed in Chapter 8.

While there is still speculation over the mechanism by which superfluidity is destroyed, there is considerably more confidence in Landau's picture concerning the reasons He II should exhibit super-fluidity in the first place. If $|\epsilon(p)/p|_{min}$ were zero, implying no critical velocity and hence no superfluidity, this would require the accessibility of very low, almost zero, energy states with finite momentum. Such a system would have a nonlinear dispersion relation near the origin, so that the curve would be tangent to the momentum axis at the origin. Since for liquid He, the Landau spectrum admits of no such low-lying states, $|\epsilon(p)/p|_{min}$ cannot be zero. And so, in fact, it is due to the scarcity of such states that in one respect helium owes its superfluid properties. Chester ([14]) has discussed at some length the application of the Landau criterion to common systems showing no critical velocity, and, further, emphatically points out that this criterion can be applied to liquid He only if the assumption is valid that the production of excitations is alone responsible for slowing down the liquid as it flows through a tube. There are other conceivable ways in which the entire liquid might be slowed down by an opposing force, one being if the liquid possessed the sort of rigidity usually ascribed to solids; and although such a distinction between liquid He and a solid seems reasonable, it has yet to be rigorously proved.

1.4. HELIUM THREE

Until about 1946, if one spoke of liquid helium, it was naturally assumed that the reference was to the isotopic species with four mass units, He^4. Although since the middle 1930's other helium isotopes were known to exist, they were available in such trivial amounts as to make the specification of mass unnecessary insofar as low-temperature research was concerned. A heavier isotope, He^6, could be produced through nuclear reactions, but this atom is exceedingly unstable, and its short half-life ($\tau = 0.82$ sec) as well as its scarcity nearly precluded its use in cryogenic experiments. On the other hand, a lighter species, He^3, was known to be stable, and not only could it be produced from a variety of nuclear reactions, but it was also found to occur in nature (Alvarez and Cornog, 1934). Even so, the difficulties associated with obtaining enough He^3 for studying its low-temperature properties rendered such projects extremely unattractive.

The sole commercially feasible sources of helium gas are certain favored natural gas wells. In these wells, the He^4 content, which may be as high as 1 or 2%, is accompanied by very small amounts of He^3. While the ratio He^3/He^4 varies from well to well, it is generally only about $1/10^7$. Small occurrences of terrestrial helium are also found associated with radioactive minerals, but without exception, He^3 is absent from these deposits. Among the gases that comprise the lower strata of the earth's atmosphere, a meager 0.0005% is composed of He, and of this, approximately $1/10^6$ is He^3. At much higher altitudes, recent evidence gained from artificial satellites (especially Explorer XVII, launched April 1963) has indicated that the earth is enveloped by a helium mantle (at extremely low pressures) beginning at ~ 500 km and extending to as much as ~ 5000 km, depending on the cycle of solar activity. One conjecture is that this helium originates from primary cosmic ray bombardment, and it has been verified experimentally that about 0.4% of the helium produced from such processes is He^3. Clearly, at present, this could not represent a practical source of He^3, but it may be that this isotope is not such a rare commodity in nature as was once believed.

A proposal by Franck ([15]) in 1946 spurred efforts to concentrate the He^3 fraction of helium obtained from the atmosphere. It was expected that in dilute He^3–He^4 solutions, the lighter isotope should behave much like the normal fluid below the λ-point and would therefore not partake in superflow. Hence, Franck suggested that in the emptying of a vessel containing He II, superfluidity should provide a filtering mechanism for enriching the He^3 content of the residue. These conjectures were confirmed in 1947 in a series of experiments by Johnston and Daunt and co-workers, who observed upwards of a five-fold enhancement of He^3 concentration during a single pass in He II transport experiments involving film flow, flow through narrow slits, and the mechanocaloric effect.

Fortunately, however, it has not been necessary to resort to such difficult schemes for collecting significant amounts of He^3 from its dispersed state in nature. Instead, the high-flux neutron sources available from nuclear reactors may be used to exploit the $Li^6(n, \alpha)H^3$ reaction, which as early as 1940 was believed to be the principal source of atmospheric He^3. The Li^6, having an abundance of 7.5%, is readily obtainable, and the tritium resulting from the slow-neutron bombardment can be efficiently separated from the ejected α-particle (He^4) by selective diffusion through a heated palladium barrier. The tritium subsequently decays by β^- emission ($\tau = 12.5$ yr) to He^3, which can from time to time be "milked" off by the diffusion method.

Even with this new source of He^3, the pure gas was for some time in very short supply, and that which was available was very costly, of the order of \$100/cc STP. The price by 1966 for 99.98 % He^3 had fallen to \$0.135/cc STP, and use of a rotating gas centrifuge for purification promises to make the price for the rare isotope considerably lower still. Nevertheless, beginning in 1947, a substantial number of low-temperature experiments on the properties of dilute He^3–He^4 mixtures were attempted, largely on the expectation that they might clarify some of the mysteries of superfluidity in He II. Justification for this optimism has not yet been fully realized, but in their own right the mixtures have become fertile ground for research.

1.4.1. Mixtures of He^3 and He^4

Many aspects of mixtures of He^3 and He^4 will be omitted from the present volume. A recent review article by Taconis and De Bruyn Ouboter ([16]) provides an excellent systematic summary of interesting facets of the subject. Nevertheless, the remarkable composition vs. temperature phase diagram at low pressure, shown in Fig. 1.11, is

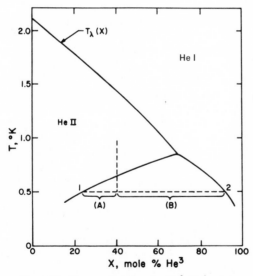

Fig. 1.11. Phase separation in He^3–He^4 mixtures. $T_\lambda(x)$ shows how the λ-point temperature varies with He^3 concentration. See text for explanation of other features; also see Fig. 6.18.

worthy of special mention here, and from time to time other features of mixed systems will be introduced.

Ordinarily, isotopic mixtures exhibit few if any gross properties which differentiate them from the pure components. Again helium is the exception, as may readily be seen from the phase diagram. We first of all notice that beginning with pure He^4, as He^3 is added to the system, the λ-transition is depressed in temperature and apparently disappears at a new phase boundary, indicating there should be no such transition for pure He^3.

The second striking feature of Fig. 1.11 is this new boundary, which tells us that below about 0.8°K, He^3 and He^4 liquids are not miscible in all proportions—a most anomalous behavior indeed! In the region of phase separation, the stratification of the system into two layers can be made visually apparent. If, for example, we begin with a mixture of 60 mole-% He^4 and 40 mole-% He^3 at, say, 1°K, the system will exhibit the usual superfluid properties, albeit additionally complicated because the system is a mixture. Next, as we cool the system just below 0.7°K, a nonsuperfluid phase, rich in He^3, will begin to appear with a distinct meniscus at the top of the liquid. With further reductions in temperature, the composition and volume of the two phases will change relative to one another. Thus, at 0.5°K, the original mixture can be described by the construction shown in Fig. 1.11: the ratio of volumes of the upper phase A to the lower phase B is the ratio of lengths $(A)/(B)$; the composition of phase A is given by the intersection at point 2, i.e., about 90% He^3, and similarly that of phase B by point 1, indicating about 20% He^3. Phase B is always superfluid and phase A never superfluid.

A particularly spectacular observation is sketched in Fig. 1.12, where the system just discussed is used in a film-flow experiment. The small bucket is initially filled with a mixture of the same composition as contained in the larger vessel. When the bucket is raised, phase B helium flows up the bucket wall as a superfluid film and collects as droplets which then fall from the outside of the bucket's bottom. The droplets of phase B pass through phase A in the larger vessel as distinctly visible spheres, shattering as they strike the meniscus.

In the theory of nonideal solutions, the existence of a phase separation implies a heat of mixing, and conversely (actually, a positive heat of mixing was measured for the addition of liquid He^3 to He^4 before the first direct determination of phase stratification). Now, the heat of mixing for the helium isotopes is being put to practical use as the design basis for a refrigerator ([17]).* Mixture refrigerators have been successfully built and operated in the region near 0.010°K and

* A review of mixture refrigeration has been given by D. S. Betts, *Contemp. Phys.* **9**, 97 (1968).

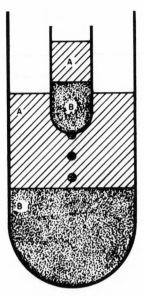

Fig. 1.12. Film-flow experiment in He^3–He^4 mixtures. A is nonsuperfluid phase; B is superfluid.

are helping to open up the entire field of research at ultralow temperatures.

The phase diagram and its ramifications furnish impressive evidence that He^3 and He^4 are distinctly different species, and as well suggest that just because they are so different we should not expect the mixtures to yield critical information about the pure isotopes. However, quite recently, indications have been reported that mixtures of low He^3 concentrations should remain superfluid down to extremely low temperatures, perhaps to $0°K$. Oddly enough, it turns out that these dilute-solution investigations give promise of elucidating the nature of pure He^3. Some details concerning this interesting notion will be discussed in Chapter 6.

1.4.2. Some Properties of Liquid He^3

The probability that pure He^3 would become available stimulated theoretical speculations as to whether the gas could be liquefied under normal conditions. From an estimate of zero-point energy, London concluded that the repulsive force should exceed the attractive van der

Waals interaction and thereby prevent the condensation of He³, except perhaps under applied pressure. He was not alone in this belief. On the other hand, measurements of the vapor pressure of dilute solutions of He³ in He⁴ made by H. Fairbank *et al.* in 1948 suggested that He³ should exist as a stable liquid with a boiling point of 2.9°K. Also in 1948, de Boer and Lunbeck ([18]), on the basis of de Boer's theory of the quantum-mechanical law of corresponding states ([19]), predicted the vapor pressure of liquid He³, placing the critical point at $3.2° < T_c < 3.5°K$, $0.9 < P_c < 1.2$ atm. The controversy was resolved when Sydoriak, Grilly, and Hammel reported in 1949 the first successful attempts at producing liquid He³. At the same time, the vapor pressure of the liquid was measured, with the results in remarkable agreement with de Boer's prediction.

Since 1949, He³ has become more readily available in quantities sufficient for many laboratories to explore the character of this substance. As suspected, significant differences have been discovered in the behavior of the two isotopes He³ and He⁴, and in the remainder of this book, two of our primary concerns will be first to compare where possible the properties of the isotopes and then to examine the reasons

Table 1.I.   Comparison of some Properties of Liquids He³ and He⁴

Property	He⁴	He³
Normal boiling point (°K)	4.215	3.191
Critical constants:		
T_c (°K)	5.20	3.324
P_c (atm)	2.26	1.15
ρ_c (g/cm³)	0.0693	0.0413
Density at 0°K (g/cm³)	0.146	0.0823
Compressibility at 0°K (cm³/J)	0.120	0.361
Binding energy at 0°K		
(minus the heat of vaporization at 0°K)		
(J/mole)	−59.62	−20.56
Entropy at 2.0°K (J/mole)	1.19	12.95
Surface tension at 0°K (extrapolated) (erg/cm²)	0.37	0.16
Velocity of sound at 0°K (extrapolated) (m/sec)	239	183
Thermal conductivity at normal boiling point		
(mW/cm² deg)	0.26	0.20
Viscosity at normal boiling point (μP)	36	19
Magnetic moment (nuclear magnetons)	0	−2.127
Molar polarization at $\lambda = 5462$ Å	0.125	0.125
λ-point parameters:		
P_λ (mm)	37.80	
T_λ (°K)	2.1720	

underlying the similarities or differences that appear. The present section gives a brief review to indicate the extent of the dissimilarity between the properties of the two liquids. Again the reader is referred to several excellent review articles ([20]) for additional details of the early researches.

A glance at Table 1.I immediately discloses the dramatically contrasting behavior of the two liquids with respect to several equilibrium and transport properties. Of special interest and importance is the contrast in specific heats, shown in Fig. 1.13. At the same time, there is one very significant quantity which is essentially the same in both substances—namely $\alpha_M = N\alpha^0$, the molar polarization. Because of this, we expect the interatomic forces to be unaffected by isotopic interchange, and we must therefore look elsewhere for the differences that do exist in the other properties of liquid He^3 and He^4. Three fundamental sources for these are the differences in *mass, statistics*, and *nuclear spin*.

The most significant direct consequence of the mass difference is the considerable increase of kinetic zero-point energy, K_0, for He^3 over that for He^4, which, according to the discussion in Section 1.3.2, should be by a factor of $\frac{4}{3}$. Since U_0 remains unchanged, this larger zero-point energy for He^3 means that the net ground-state energy, or binding

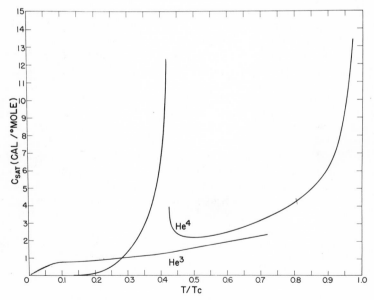

Fig. 1.13. Comparison of heat capacities of liquids He^3 and He^4 as a function of the reduced temperature T/T_c, where T_c is the critical temperature.

energy, for this liquid is even less than that for liquid He^4. This in turn implies that liquid He^3 should have a molar volume that is even more "blown up" than for liquid He^4 and should at a given temperature have a larger vapor pressure. These expectations have been confirmed by experiment, as can be seen from Table 1.I and also from Table 4.I, where the vapor pressures, latent heats, and molar volumes are compared. From the experimental evidence, it is now possible to understand that the failure of London's original prediction of the noncondensibility of He^3 was due to an overestimation of the zero-point energy. This error can be traced to two sources: first, there was considerable uncertainty in the value of K_0 for He^4 upon which he based his prediction; and second, the molar volume of liquid He^3 has been found to be larger than expected, and, as we have seen, the zero-point energy decreases with increasing volume. In any event, it is clear that He^3 just barely, by a fortuitous combination of circumstances, exists as a liquid, and that its large zero-point energy and small binding energy are exceedingly important in determining many of the properties of the liquid. The P–V–T properties are particularly sensitive to changes in the zero-point energy, as already indicated with respect to the molar volume and the vapor pressure, and as shown by the additional comparisons given in Table 1.I of the critical constants and liquid compressibility for the two isotopes. A further prominent feature resulting from these considerations is that He^3, like He^4, remains a liquid under its own vapor pressure all the way down to $0°K$. Some 30 atm are required to produce the solid at that temperature.

Since the He^3 atom is composed of an odd number of elementary particles, the Pauli exclusion principle is applicable to a collection of such atoms and the wavefunction for the system must change sign whenever two particles are spatially interchanged. These are the same rules that apply, for example, to electrons, and the corresponding statistics are known as Fermi–Dirac (FD) or antisymmetric statistics. Accordingly, we call particles that obey FD statistics "fermions."

Either BE or FD statistics are required to describe situations where quantum effects are important. The differences between the two types of statistics become apparent only at low temperatures, whereas at higher temperatures, both merge into the classical Boltzmann statistics. But what do we mean by "low" and "high" temperature? A very useful measure of this distinction is given by the so-called "thermal wavelength," λ_T, which is the de Broglie wavelength for a particle of mass m:

$$\lambda_T = (h^2/2\pi m k_B T)^{1/2} \qquad (1.47)$$

λ_T represents the quantum-mechanical uncertainty in the position of a particle; or alternatively, since the wavefunction describing the particle changes significantly over distances less than λ_T we may expect quantum effects to become important when λ_T becomes comparable to or larger than the average spacing of the particles. This condition, i.e., $\lambda_T \geqslant (\Omega/N)^{1/3}$, where Ω is the volume of the container and N is the number of particles in Ω, is termed the "degeneracy condition," and we may therefore distinguish between "low" and "high" temperature depending upon whether or not the system is degenerate. Electrons in a metal, for example, may be considered as being at "low" temperature even though in the usual sense the metal may be quite hot, since the degeneracy condition is satisfied for electrons in all metals below their melting points. Conversely, we have seen that the behavior of He I, which exists only under conditions normally thought of as "cold," is virtually uninfluenced by the symmetry of the statistics. Only in the region of the λ-point and below, where the degeneracy condition is satisfied, do these effects begin to become prominent. Likewise, at higher temperatures, the character of He^3 is unaffected by the statistics, with the evidence of degeneration appearing only below about 0.5°K.

There is a significant difference in the manner in which bosons and fermions become degenerate, and this is a direct consequence of the type of statistics which apply, even though in both cases, the transition involves a sort of momentum ordering. For He^4, the BEC at the λ-point occurs suddenly and spectacularly, whereas for He^3—and for all truly FD systems— the onset of degeneration is gradual as a function of temperature and is not accompanied by discontinuities in either the thermal or transport properties of the liquid. But below about 0.5°K, these properties are affected by statistics.

Because He^3 obeys FD rather than BE statistics, it seems reasonable to expect that no λ-type anomaly and no superfluid properties should be exhibited by the liquid. And, in fact, these expectations have been experimentally verified down to temperatures as low as 0.005°K, as illustrated by the heat capacity shown in Fig. 1.13. Further evidence that liquid He^3 does not show superfluidity has also been obtained from flow measurements extending to below 1°K. In general, the behavior found for liquid He^3 is gaslike and qualitatively similar to that of He I, having none of the anomalous transport characteristics of He II. Several theoretical studies* have suggested that at very low temperatures, He^3 should transform to a "correlated" phase characterized by a special type of superfluidity. Peshkov [22] has reported specific-heat measurements which give evidence that the transition temperature should be located at about 0.0035°K, whereas Abel et al. [23] have investigated this region and report no anomaly. No other properties of a correlated phase have been observed, and as yet no other corroborative information has been obtained for its existence.

* See, for example, the review by Sessler [21].

A more detailed examination of this interesting controversy will be given in Chapter 6.

There is some confusion possible when we say that superfluidity is characteristic of bosons and not possible for fermions, while it may be observed that some property of the electron gas in certain metals is intimately responsible for a sudden complete loss of electrical resistance at low but finite temperatures. This phenomenon, known as "superconductivity," apparently provides a contradiction to our earlier statement concerning the differing symptoms of degeneration in FD and BE systems. While we do not intend to enter here into a discussion of the theory of superconductivity, we can in general terms resolve this paradox quite simply. The more recent theories on superconductivity, such as those proposed by Bardeen, Cooper, and Schrieffer ([24]) (BCS) and summarized by, for example, Blatt ([25]), have been quite successful in explaining the older observations and predicting new ones. They indicate that the interaction between two conduction electrons with opposite spins should be sufficiently correlated that the formation of electron pairs is highly likely, and that the fundamental "particle" for superconductivity should not be the single electron but rather the bound electron pair. The onset of superconductivity is then conceived to occur through the condensation of electron pairs, in very close analogy to BEC of single-particle bosons. The Pauli principle applies only to single-particle electron states and does not restrict the occupation number of electron pairs of a given pair state. As a result, FD statistics are not applicable and therefore cannot forbid such a condensation; instead, rules more akin to BE statistics should apply. Admittedly, the picture as given here is rather incomplete. However, the successive refinements and elaborations of these ideas have shown that the essential character of superconductivity lies very close to that of superfluidity in He II. While this behavior may appear at first sight to be foreign to the nature of Fermi systems, it is believed to occur for all such systems at sufficiently low temperatures, and it forms the basis for predictions of the correlated phase in liquid He^3.

A final remark we wish to make here with respect to statistics concerns the existence of "statistical forces." An example illustrating the origin of these forces will be given in Chapter 3; but briefly, the correlations between bosons are attractive while those between fermions are repulsive. The former situation is well illustrated by the crowding together of the particles, as mentioned earlier, in the condensation of an ideal BE gas. An example of the FD repulsion is given by the so-called "Fermi hole" representing the improbability of close approach of two electrons of like spin, this repulsion being in addition to that of the Coulomb forces. For liquid helium, the statistical forces become operative only at low temperature and even then their effects are secondary to those of the intermolecular forces and the zero-point energy, but for gaseous helium the statistical correlations assume greater importance. Some of the early conjectures that He^3 should not liquefy under its own vapor pressure gave too much weight to the FD repulsion as exhibited by the ideal FD gas and insufficient regard for the many-body interactions that are possible for a liquid.

The third conspicuous difference between the two helium isotopes is their respective nuclear spins. It is a general property of the statistics that integral multiples of spin angular momentum are associated with bosons and half-integral multiples with fermions. Thus, the He^4 atom with two protons and two neutrons has a resultant spin of zero, while He^3 with two protons and one neutron has a net of one-half unit of spin angular momentum, $\hbar/2$ (spin quantum number $\sigma = \frac{1}{2}$). Here, we will be concerned with how the spin system influences the magnetic properties of He^3, and in later chapters, with how in turn these are closely allied to other properties, especially the thermal properties, of the liquid and also of the solid.

Since the He^4 nucleus has no angular momentum and therefore no magnetic moment, its magnetic behavior is entirely determined by the diamagnetism of the electrons, which has an inconsequential effect upon the fluid properties. However, as shown in Table 1.I, the nuclear magnetic moment, μ_M, of He^3 is -2.127 nuclear magnetons, so that we may expect significant magnetic effects in the neighborhood of the He^3 atom. Since the degeneracy g of spin states is given by quantum mechanics as $g = (2\sigma + 1)$, which for He^3 equals two, there are two possible nuclear spin orientations for a free He^3 atom, and these are spoken of as being "plus" or "minus," or, alternatively, "up" or "down." For a collection of He^3 atoms in the absence of an external field, the internal field due to the nuclear magnetism induces spins of different sign to pair up in an antiparallel configuration. This pairing is opposed by the disordering effect of temperature, so that the higher the temperature, the fewer the pairs and the larger the number of free or unpaired spins. If we now apply a weak external magnetic field, the unpaired nuclear spins tend to line themselves up in the direction of the field. A measure of the fraction of nuclear spins that are free to line up with the field is the susceptibility χ, which in the low field limit, is given by the ratio of magnetic moment per unit volume M to the applied external field H. The classical Curie–Langevin law relates the susceptibility to the effect of temperature upon pairing, and at high temperatures ($T \gg T_F$, where T_F is the FD degeneracy temperature) liquid He^3 should at least approximately obey this law. Thus

$$\chi = \mu_M^2/3k_B T v = \mathscr{C}/T \qquad T \gg T_F \tag{1.48}$$

where χ is the paramagnetic volume susceptibility, $v^{-1} = N/\Omega$ is the atomic concentration, and $\mathscr{C}$ is the Curie constant $\mu_M^2/3k_Bv$.

An ideal FD fluid at 0°K should, on the other hand, have all of its spins paired off so that the resultant angular momentum and magnetic moment both should vanish. However, through the presence of interactomic forces the possibility arises that the system may exhibit a spontaneous magnetism, i.e., ferromagnetism with parallel alignment of spins, as opposed to the antiferromagnetic configuration of completely antiparallel alignment. In the former case, the total moment would be $N\mu_M$, and therefore the susceptibility should be large; and in the latter case, the moment should be zero and χ vanishingly small. Goldstein and Goldstein in 1950, using several different reasonable potential functions, concluded that the conditions of minimum energy were satisfied by the antiferromagnetic configuration. Experimental confirmation of this prediction was first obtained in 1952 by Hammel et al., who showed that down to 0.9°K, the volume susceptibility of liquid He^3 was less than 5×10^{-6}.

The total susceptibility χ_T is the sum of χ and χ_d, the latter being the electronic diamagnetic susceptibility, which is the same for He^3 and He^4 within a factor of the relative mass densities. For He^3 χ turns out to be more than ten times smaller than χ_d, so that the classical methods for obtaining susceptibilities, which measure only χ_T, are very insensitive for determining χ. On the other hand, nuclear magnetic resonance techniques measure χ directly and these were first employed to study He^3 by Fairbank et al. [26]. Values of χ were obtained over

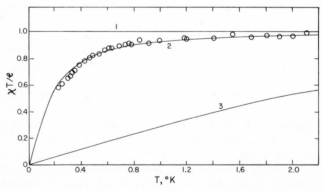

Fig. 1.14. Paramagnetic susceptibility of He^3 plotted as $\chi T/\mathscr{C}$ vs. temperature. $\mathscr{C}$ is a normalizing Curie constant such that if equation (1.48) were obeyed, curve 1 would result. Curve 3 is calculated using the degeneracy temperature, $T_F \approx 5°K$, for an ideal FD gas with density of liquid He^3. Curve 2 passing through the data points [Fairbank et al. [26]] is calculated using $T_F = 0.45°K$.

the temperature range 0.1° to 2.0°K, and the results are shown in Fig. 1.14 plotted as $\chi T / \mathscr{C}$ vs. T, where $\mathscr{C}$ is a normalizing Curie constant. An ideal FD gas with the density of liquid He^3 would have a degeneracy temperature $T_F \approx 5°K$. The susceptibility calculated using this model is also shown in Fig. 1.14 as curve 3, and it can be seen that it is indeed a very poor representation of the data. However, if T_F is taken instead to be 0.45°K, the corresponding calculated χ, given by curve 2 in the figure, provides a very good fit to the experimental points. It should be noted nevertheless that this T_F is still for the ideal FD gas with a mass about ten times the He^3 atomic mass. Unfortunately, other observed properties of the liquid, such as the entropy, are not consistent with this simple ideal-gas model. This provides us with a rather complicated situation which we shall consider further in Chapter 6.

1.5. THE HELIUM PROBLEM

The preceding sections of this chapter presented an elementary and abbreviated survey of some of the prominent properties exhibited by the helium isotopes. We have also mentioned some concepts basic to our attempts at understanding the origin of these properties. Up to this point, the emphasis has been upon how the liquids behave as the temperature is varied under conditions of the saturated vapor pressures; other dimensions of the helium problem, such as the compressed liquids, the solids, the gases, have been neglected almost entirely. Use of the temperature variable has served as a convenient way of introducing the reader to the anomalous world of quantum fluids, and, historically, the phenomena we have described were usually the first to be investigated, since the regions along the vapor pressure curves are experimentally most accessible. However, these conditions represent only a very small part of the whole phase diagram, and therefore our failure to mention other phases and state variations should in no way be interpreted to mean that we consider them of less significance.

We shall make amends for these omissions in the following chapters. Our plan is to begin with the gaseous phase, proceed through vapor–liquid equilibria to the liquid phase under saturated conditions, then to the liquid under pressure, and finally to the solid.

From what has already been said, it is evident that the literature concerning the helium isotopes is rich indeed and that the investigative tools brought to bear upon the helium problem are of tremendous variety and include sophisticated experimental and theoretical techniques. It will be equally evident that many unresolved problems remain. Some of the most important of these form the subject matter to be treated in the rest of this monograph, though, unfortunately, it will not be possible in the space available to treat all of the questions now outstanding. However, our scope is even more limited than would appear, since, in the past, the elucidation of one aspect of the helium problem has almost invariably uncovered one or more new mysteries hitherto unsuspected. How much of the surface has been scratched is difficult to say, so we must approach our task with considerable humility as well as with the awareness that some of the results and notions we have gained so far may be deceptive. We shall try to describe the more recent advances in what is believed to be the right direction without being dogmatic in this belief.

REFERENCES

1. W. H. Keesom, *Helium*, Elsevier, Amsterdam (1942).
2. K. R. Atkins, *Liquid Helium*, Cambridge University Press (1959).
3. K. R. Atkins and Y. Narahara, *Phys. Rev.*, **138**, A437 (1965).
4. E. C. Kerr and R. D. Taylor, *Ann. Phys. (N.Y.)*, **26**, 292 (1964).
5. D. G. Henshaw, *Phys. Rev.*, **119**, 9 (1960).
6. J. Wiebes, C. G. Niels-Hakkenberg, and H. C. Kramers, *Physica*, **23**, 625 (1957).
7. S. R. de Groot, *Thermodynamics of Irreversible Processes*, Chapter III, North Holland, Amsterdam (1952).
8. K. R. Atkins, *Phys. Rev.*, **113**, 962 (1959).
9. C. W. F. Everitt, K. R. Atkins, and A. Denenstein, *Phys. Rev. Letters*, **8**, 161 (1962); *Phys. Rev.*, **136**, A1494 (1964).
10. J. R. Pellam, *Phys. Rev.*, **73**, 608 (1948).
11. I. Rudnick and K. A. Shapiro, *Phys. Rev. Letters*, **9**, 191 (1962); K. A. Shapiro and I. Rudnick, *Phys. Rev.*, **137**, A1383 (1965).
12. F. London, *Superfluids*, Vol. II, John Wiley, New York (1954).
13. D. F. Brewer and D. O. Edwards, *Proc. Roy. Soc. (London)*, **A251**, 247 (1959); W. E. Keller and E. F. Hammel, *Ann. Phys. (N.Y.)*, **10**, 202 (1960).
14. G. V. Chester, in *Liquid Helium* (G. Careri, ed.), p. 51, Academic Press, New York (1963).
15. J. Franck, *Phys. Rev.*, **70**, 983 (1946).
16. K. W. Taconis and R. De Bruyn Ouboter, in *Progress in Low Temperature Physics* (C. J. Gorter, ed.), Vol. IV, p. 38, North Holland, Amsterdam (1964).
17. H. E. Hall, in *Superfluid Helium* (J. F. Allen, ed.), p. 7, Academic Press, London (1966).
18. J. de Boer and R. J. Lunbeck, *Physica*, **14**, 510 (1948).
19. J. de Boer, *Physica*, **14**, 139 (1948).
20. E. F. Hammel, in *Progress in Low Temperature Physics* (C. J. Gorter, ed.), Vol. I, p. 78, North Holland, Amsterdam (1955); V. P. Peshkov and K. N. Zinov'eva, *Reports on Progress in Physics*, **22**, 504 (1959); E. R. Grilly and E. F. Hammel, in *Progress in Low Temperature Physics* (C. J. Gorter, ed.), Vol. III, p. 113, North Holland, Amsterdam (1961).
21. A. M. Sessler in *Helium Three* (J. G. Daunt, ed.), p. 81, Ohio State University Press (1960).
22. V. P. Peshkov, *Zh. Eksperim. i Teor. Fiz.*, **46**, 1510 (1964) [English translation, *Soviet Phys.—JETP*, **19**, 1023 (1964)]; *Zh. Eksperim. i Teor. Fiz.*, **48**, 997 (1965) [English translation, *Soviet Phys.—JETP*, **21**, 663 (1965)].
23. W. R. Abel, A. C. Anderson, W. C. Black, and J. C. Wheatley, *Physics*, **1**, 337 (1965).
24. J. Bardeen, L. N. Cooper, and J. R. Schrieffer, *Phys. Rev.*, **108**, 1175 (1957).

25. J. M. Blatt, *Theory of Superconductivity*, Academic Press, New York (1964).
26. W. M. Fairbank, W. B. Ard, and G. K. Walters, *Phys. Rev.*, **95**, 566 (1954); W. M. Fairbank and G. K. Walters, Proc. of Symposium on Solid and Liquid He^3 (Ohio State University, Columbus, 1957), p. 205; *Suppl. Nuovo Cimento*, **9**, 297 (1957).

Chapter 2

Ideal Quantum Gases

Although the noninteracting BE and FD gases are not in themselves suitable representations for their quantum liquid counterparts, the ideal-gas model serves in both instances as a necessary starting point for theoretical investigations of the liquids. An appreciation of the features of the ideal gases is indeed indispensable if we are to attempt an understanding of the real fluids, and for this reason we include here a brief summary of some of the more important properties of ideal BE and FD systems. There are several approaches in statistical mechanics that may be appropriately applied to these problems to achieve essentially the same results. The philosophy and much of the mathematics of these methods will be omitted here but may be found in standard texts of statistical physics [see, for example, Eyring *et al.* [1] and Huang[2]]. For the present purposes, it will be convenient to develop simultaneously some preliminary results for the BE and FD systems and then later to distinguish between the two in greater detail. In order to achieve a degree of consistency with at least one standard text, the notation used here will to a large extent follow that of Huang[2]. However, the elegant discussion of the BE gas by London [3] ought not to be overlooked.

2.1. IDEAL GASES

Our first task is to determine in what ways quantum gases differ from classical gases obeying Maxwell–Boltzmann (MB) statistics. In all cases, the systems we consider are composed of a constant number N of point particles, which we may divide into smaller groups of particles according to the energy levels that they may occupy. Thus, if in the ith energy level ϵ_i there are n_i particles, we say that the *occupation number* of this level is n_i. Furthermore, it is appropriate to specify the state of the entire system by indicating for it the set of

51

occupation numbers $\{n_i\}$. The first distinction we must make is that the **MB** particles are *distinguishable* from one another: without any loss of generality we may "tag" a given particle and unambiguously follow it in its peregrinations through the system. Because of this, if we exchange two particles belonging to different energy groups, say n_j and n_k, a new state of the system is obtained even though the set $\{n_i\}$ remains unchanged. On the other hand, quantum particles are *indistinguishable*: they cannot be tagged, nor can the state of the system be altered by interchanges among the n_i. Thus $\{n_i\}$ uniquely specifies the state of a quantum system.

Both quantum and classical gases may be treated as ensembles of particles subject to the following constraints:

$$\sum_i n_i = N = \text{constant} \tag{2.1}$$

and

$$\sum_i n_i \epsilon_i = E = \text{constant} \tag{2.2}$$

where E is the total energy. However, when we take the next step and inquire as to how the particles for a given system are distributed among the various energy levels, we find important differences depending upon the distinguishability of the particles and their symmetry properties. The results for the three cases of $\langle n_i \rangle$, the most probable occupation number for the ith level, are

$$\langle n_i \rangle = \frac{g_i}{\exp(-\alpha + \beta \epsilon_i) - \gamma} \qquad \gamma = \begin{matrix} -1 & \text{for FD} \\ +1 & \text{for BE} \\ 0 & \text{for MB} \end{matrix} \tag{2.3}$$

where $\beta = 1/k_B T$ and $\alpha = \mu/k_B T$, μ being the chemical potential per particle; and g_i represents the degeneracy of the ith level, i.e., the number of eigenstates available to the $\langle n_i \rangle$ particles. At all but very low temperatures, g_i is much greater than $\langle n_i \rangle$, and by expressing equation (2.3) alternatively as

$$(g_i/\langle n_i \rangle) + \gamma = \exp(-\alpha + \beta \epsilon_i) \tag{2.4}$$

we may appreciate that **MB** statistics will provide a good approximation whenever the choice of γ becomes insignificant, i.e., when $g_i/\langle n_i \rangle$ or $\exp(-\alpha + \beta \epsilon_i) \gg 1$, and thus when $(\epsilon_i - \mu) \gg k_B T$. At low temperature and high density, these conditions do not hold and it then becomes essential to use the appropriately symmetrized quantum statistical scheme.

For ideal systems, the potential energy is zero, so that the Hamiltonian depends only upon the translational energy levels of the particles. Each particle of mass m in a volume Ω has, in terms of its momentum $\mathbf{p}$, or its momentum eigenvalue $\hbar k/\Omega^{1/3}$, the kinetic energy

$$\epsilon_{\mathbf{p}} = p^2/2m = h^2 k^2/2m\Omega^{2/3} \qquad (2.5)$$

with the vector $\mathbf{k}$ taking on integral values when cyclic boundary conditions are imposed. Each momentum state $\epsilon_{\mathbf{p}}$ of the system is occupied by $n_{\mathbf{p}}$ particles under the conditions of equations (2.1) and (2.2). Then the weight function g_i can be evaluated to give the number of single-particle states, $g(\epsilon_{\mathbf{p}})$, which lie between $\epsilon_{\mathbf{p}}$ and $\epsilon_{\mathbf{p}} + d\epsilon_{\mathbf{p}}$ (neglecting internal degeneracy)

$$g(\epsilon_{\mathbf{p}}) = \frac{2\pi\Omega}{h^3}(2m)^{3/2}\epsilon_{\mathbf{p}}^{1/2} \qquad (2.6)$$

Upon combining equations (2.1), (2.3), and (2.6), we find

$$N = \sum_{\mathbf{p}} n_{\mathbf{p}} = \sum_{\mathbf{p}} \frac{2\pi\Omega}{h^3}(2m)^{3/2}[\exp(-\alpha + \beta\epsilon_{\mathbf{p}}) - \gamma]^{-1}\epsilon_{\mathbf{p}}^{1/2} \qquad (2.7)$$

To evaluate equation (2.7), we let N and Ω go to infinity. Under these conditions, the energy levels become sufficiently close-spaced to make the replacement of the sum by an integral a good approximation. Then equation (2.7) becomes

$$\frac{N}{\Omega} \equiv \frac{1}{v} = \frac{2\pi(2m)^{3/2}}{h^3}\int_0^\infty \frac{\epsilon^{1/2}\,d\epsilon}{e^{-\alpha+\beta\epsilon} - \gamma} \qquad (2.8)$$

where v is the volume per particle.

For the MB gas with $\gamma = 0$, the integral in equation (2.8) may be expressed as a Γ-function and directly evaluated simply as

$$\frac{1}{v} = \frac{2\pi(2m)^{3/2}}{h^3}z\int_0^\infty \epsilon^{1/2}\,e^{-\beta\epsilon}\,d\epsilon$$

$$= \left(\frac{2\pi mk_B T}{h^2}\right)^{3/2} z$$

$$= \lambda_T^{-3}z \qquad (2.9)$$

Here, $z = e^\alpha$ is the fugacity and λ_T the thermal wavelength [equation (1.47)].

2.2. THE IDEAL FERMI–DIRAC GAS

With the requirements $n_{\mathbf{p}} = 0$ or 1 and $\gamma = -1$ for a system of spinless fermions, the integral in equation (2.8) becomes more complicated than for the MB case. For the ideal FD gas, it becomes

$$1/v = \lambda_T^{-3}f_{3/2}(z) \qquad (2.10a)$$

which, together with the expression

$$P/k_B T = \lambda_T^{-3} f_{5/2}(z) \qquad (2.10b)$$

provides us with a parametric form for the equation of state. The function $f_m(z)$ explicitly represents the integral by the series

$$f_m(z) = - \sum_{l=1}^{\infty} (-z)^l l^{-m} \qquad (2.11)$$

which converges for values of $z \geqslant 0$.

The equations (2.10) are valid only under two circumstances. The first is sometimes called the case of weak degeneracy, when $\lambda_T^3/v \ll 1$; since the average interparticle separation is much longer than the thermal wavelength, the behavior of the system departs but little from that of a classical gas. The second case is that of strong degeneracy, when the temperature is low and the density high such that $\lambda_T^3/v \gg 1$. The former is of interest to us primarily because the equation of state may be expressed in the following form:

$$\frac{Pv}{k_B T} = \frac{v}{\lambda_T^3}\left(z - \frac{z^2}{2^{5/2}} + \cdots \right) = 1 + \frac{1}{2^{5/2}} \frac{\lambda_T^3}{v} + \cdots \qquad (2.12)$$

where we have used, to a good approximation, the result of equation (2.9). This series in powers of $1/v$ is known as a virial expansion and will be discussed more fully in Chapter 3.

The strong degeneracy case, however, is of more interest and will be useful as a background for future discussions of Fermi liquids. It is convenient to consider first the case at $T = 0$ where all of the N lowest momentum states are filled, the highest filled level being designated the Fermi energy ϵ_F. The distribution of occupation numbers $\langle n_\mathbf{p} \rangle$

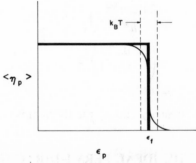

Fig. 2.1. Distribution of occupation numbers for the ideal FD gas. At $T = 0$, all levels less than the Fermi energy ϵ_F are filled (heavy line); at $T \neq 0$ (lighter lines), particles from the corner are excited above ϵ_F, the spread being characterized by $k_B T$.

as a function of ϵ_p is shown for this situation in Fig. 2.1. Then, using equation (2.6), we may find

$$\int_0^{\epsilon_F} g(\epsilon)\, d\epsilon = \frac{4\pi}{3}\Omega\left(\frac{2m\epsilon_F}{h^2}\right)^{3/2} = N \qquad (2.13)$$

for spinless fermions. For fermions with spin σ, equation (2.13) is to be multiplied by $(2\sigma+1)$, and thus with $\sigma = \frac{1}{2}$, we may obtain ϵ_F, which may equivalently be expressed in terms of a temperature, the Fermi temperature T_F, as

$$\epsilon_F = \frac{h^2}{8m}\left(\frac{3N}{\pi\Omega}\right)^{2/3} = k_B T_F \qquad (2.14)$$

The energy of the system at $T = 0$ is prevented by the Pauli exclusion principle from being zero and is given by

$$E_0 = \int_0^{\epsilon_F} \epsilon g(\epsilon)\, d\epsilon = \frac{3}{5}N\epsilon_F \qquad (2.15)$$

For T finite, but still near zero, the distribution of occupation numbers smears out, as shown in Fig. 2.1, and it becomes possible to express the chemical potential, through its relation with $f_n(z)$, as the expansion*

$$\mu = k_B T \ln z = \epsilon_F[1 - (\pi^2/12)(\epsilon_F\beta)^{-2} + \cdots] \qquad (2.16)$$

which in turn leads to the energy expression

$$E = \tfrac{3}{5}N\epsilon_F[1 + \tfrac{5}{12}\pi^2(\epsilon_F\beta)^{-2} + \cdots] \qquad (2.17)$$

From equation (2.17), we may easily obtain a series approximation for the specific heat, the leading term of which is

$$\frac{C_V}{Nk_B} = \frac{1}{Nk_B}\left(\frac{\partial E}{\partial T}\right)_V \approx \frac{\pi^2}{2}\frac{k_B T}{\epsilon_F} \qquad (2.18)$$

showing that C_V approaches $T = 0$ linearly with T. This behavior is illustrated in Fig. 2.2a.

Other thermodynamic quantities may be derived from these formulas in a straightforward manner; in particular, we find for the pressure the classical relation with E and Ω, that is,

$$P = \frac{2E}{3\Omega} = \frac{2N\epsilon_F}{5\Omega}\left[1 + \frac{5\pi^2}{12}(\epsilon_F\beta)^{-2} + \cdots\right] \qquad (2.19)$$

* Exact and detailed numerical calculations for the Fermi–Dirac functions $f_m(z)$ for use in the thermodynamic functions of the ideal gas have been given by McDougall and Stoner [4].

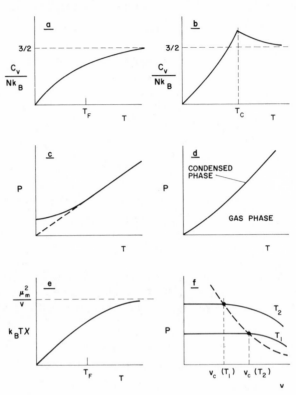

Fig. 2.2. Comparison of some properties of ideal FD and BE gases: (a) and (b), specific heat—note that $C_V/Nk_B = \frac{3}{2}$ for the ideal MB gas; (c) and (d) P–T phase diagram; (e) Pauli paramagnetism for the FD gas; (f) typical P–v isotherms for the BE gas.

But equation (2.19) tells us that, contrary to the classical case, at $T = 0$, P for the FD gas remains finite (Fig. 2.2c), and this we understand from the apparent repulsion as a consequence of the Pauli principle. As can be seen from equations (2.10) and (2.19), no unusual features are associated with the onset of degeneration, as contrasted to the BE case, and·at constant T, P decreases monotonically with Ω.

We shall be especially interested in the Pauli paramagnetism arising from the nuclear spin, $\sigma = \frac{1}{2}$, for liquid He^3 at low temperature. While at high temperatures, the susceptibility χ_{FD} for an ideal FD gas has as its limiting value the Curie–Langevin law [equation (1.48) as modified by quantum mechanics no longer has the factor $\frac{1}{3}$], as T

approaches $T_F = \epsilon_F/k_B$ (weak degeneracy), χ_{FD} begins to depart from this law; and finally, when $T \ll T_F$, χ_{FD} may be approximated by a series expansion, the leading term of which is the Pauli temperature-independent susceptibility:

$$\chi_{FD} = \frac{3\mu_M^2}{2\epsilon_F v}\left[1 - \frac{\pi^2}{12}(\epsilon_F\beta)^{-2} + \cdots\right] \qquad (2.20)$$

The temperature dependence of χ_{FD} is shown in Fig. 2.2e.

2.3. THE IDEAL BOSE–EINSTEIN GAS

For a system of spinless *bosons*, we set $\gamma = 1$ and allow $n_p = 0, 1, 2,\ldots$ in equation (2.7). Under these conditions, we cannot directly substitute the integrated form (2.8) for the summation since this process excludes the contribution from the $\epsilon_p = 0$ (or, $p = 0$) level. For FD or MB statistics, this omission is inconsequential because only an infinitesimal number of the particles occupy the zero energy (or momentum) level; but in the case of BE statistics, this number may become significantly large. To account properly for the ground state we must then add a corresponding term to the integral (2.8). We then may arrive at the BE analogs for equations (2.10), namely,

$$\frac{1}{v} = \lambda_T^{-3}g_{3/2}(z) + \frac{1}{\Omega}\frac{z}{1-z} \qquad (2.21a)$$

$$\frac{P}{k_BT} = \lambda_T^{-3}g_{5/2}(z) - \frac{1}{\Omega}\ln(1-z) \qquad (2.21b)$$

where the second term on the right of each expression represents the contribution from the $\epsilon_p = 0$ level, and

$$g_m(z) = \sum_{l=1}^{\infty} z^l l^{-m} \qquad (2.22)$$

Here, in contrast to the FD case, z is restricted to the values $0 \leqslant z \leqslant 1$ in order that the series (2.22) converge.

The quantity $z/(1 - z)$ gives $\langle n_0\rangle$, the average occupation number of the $p = 0$ state, and with this notation, equation (2.21a) may be recast as

$$\frac{\langle n_0\rangle}{\Omega} = \frac{\lambda_T^3}{v} - g_{3/2}(z) \qquad (2.23)$$

We next inquire about the interesting consequences of equation (2.23) as $z \to 1$, where $g_{3/2}(z)$ diverges. At $z = 1$, the latter function has an infinite slope but a finite value which is

$$g_{3/2}(1) = \zeta(\tfrac{3}{2}) = 2.612$$

$\zeta(m)$ being the Riemann zeta function of m. Thus, whenever $(\lambda_T^3/v > 2.612$, a finite fraction of the particles will occupy the lowest single-particle momentum state, characteristic of Bose–Einstein condensation. In short, BEC will occur under the following conditions: when the number of particles N exceeds the critical number $N_c = 2.612\Omega\lambda_T^3$, or when the volume per particle is less than $v_c = (2.612\lambda_T^3)^{-1}$, or when the temperature is below $T_c = (h^2/2\pi m k_B)$ $\times (N/2.612\Omega)^{2/3}$.

The condensation occurs with considerable suddenness. An ideal BE gas at some $T > T_c$ is not much distinguished from a similar classical gas, the N particles being distributed over the various momentum states such that $\langle n_0 \rangle$ is very small compared with N. As the temperature is lowered and the conditions for condensation are met, the properties of the gas become enormously altered and influenced by the finite value of $\langle n_0 \rangle/N$, the fraction of particles in the condensed state. The temperature dependence of this latter quantity when $\Omega/N = v$ is fixed is given by

$$\langle n_0 \rangle/N = [1 - (T/T_c)^{3/2}] \tag{2.24}$$

so that $\langle n_0 \rangle/N$ increases from 0 at T_c to 1 at $T = 0°\text{K}$.

A consequence of the abruptness of the condensation process is the requirement that all of the thermodynamic properties of the system be described by different functional forms depending upon whether the system is above or below the transition. These may be derived by standard methods starting from the energy expression, E/N, formulated in terms of the functions $g_m(z)$. We note, first of all, that the energy of the ideal BE system, unlike that for the FD gas, can be taken as zero at $T = 0°\text{K}$. However, the usual relation $E = \tfrac{3}{2}PV$ remains valid. From equation (2.21b), we may write*

$$\frac{P}{k_B T} = \begin{cases} \lambda_T^{-3} g_{5/2}(z) & v > v_c \tag{2.25a} \\ 1.342\lambda_T^{-3} & v < v_c \tag{2.25b} \end{cases}$$

since $g_{5/2}(1) = \zeta(\tfrac{5}{2}) = 1.342$; and since the thermodynamic properties are defined for the conditions $N \to \infty$, $\Omega \to \infty$, but N/Ω fixed, the second term in equation (2.21b) becomes negligible. Then we find directly that the energy expression is

$$\frac{E}{N} = \tfrac{3}{2}P\Omega = \begin{cases} \tfrac{3}{2}\lambda_T^{-3} k_B T v g_{5/2}(z) & T > T_c \tag{2.26a} \\ \tfrac{3}{2}\lambda_T^{-3} k_B T v(1.342) & T < T_c \tag{2.26b} \end{cases}$$

* Numerical calculations for the Bose–Einstein functions $g_m(z)$ for use in the thermodynamic functions of the ideal BE gas have been given in the appendix of London's book ([3]).

Of special interest is the specific heat, obtained from equations (2.26) by differentiation with respect to T:

$$\frac{C_V}{Nk_B} = \begin{cases} \dfrac{15}{4}\lambda_T^{-3}vg_{5/2}(z) - \dfrac{9}{4}\dfrac{g_{3/2}(z)}{g_{1/2}(z)} & T > T_c \quad (2.27a) \\[3mm] \dfrac{15}{4}\lambda_T^{-3}v(1.342) & T < T_c \quad (2.27b) \end{cases}$$

Thus, it can be seen that C_V is proportional to $T^{3/2}$ as $T = 0°K$ is approached, which is an essential consequence of the independent particle spectrum [equation (2.5)] and the manner in which particles are removed from excited momentum states, i.e., the temperature dependence of $1 - \langle n_0 \rangle/N$. Equations (2.27) are plotted in Fig. 2.2b, where it is evident that C_V and therefore also S_V are continuous through the transition, with a discontinuity in the slope of C_V at T_c.

The true nature of the transition is, however, masked by the above constant-volume expressions. If we return to consider the isotherm formulas, equations (2.25), for $v > v_c$, the situation is rather normal, and it becomes possible to expand $g_{5/2}(z)$ in a power series in $1/v$ to obtain a virial expression analogous to equation (2.12). However, for the region of condensation where $v < v_c$, an isotherm is quite anomalous in that P no longer depends upon the volume per particle, or, in even more startling terms, that the condensed phase occupies zero volume. The typical isotherm behavior is shown for two arbitrary temperatures below T_c in Fig. 2.2f, where the transition line is inferred as the locus of points at which $(\partial P/\partial v)_T$ becomes zero. In the P–T plane (Fig. 2.2d), this transition line appears as the boundary between the gas phase and a meaningless region, since the condensed phase exists only and entirely on the line itself. Despite the unusual features of this phase diagram, it is possible to ascribe a vapor pressure P_{sat} to the condensed phase and also to determine (dP_{sat}/dT). This gives essentially the Clausius–Clapeyron equation, which defines a latent heat per particle between the gas and condensed phases as

$$h_v = \left(\frac{1.342}{2.612}\right)\left(\frac{5}{2}\right)k_B T \tag{2.28}$$

Therefore, the BEC can be classified as a first-order phase transition when P and T are considered the independent variables. Incidentally, at constant pressure, the heat capacity C_P, in contrast to C_V, becomes infinite at T_c.

Although, as we have already cautioned, the ideal BE gas exhibits many properties not shared with liquid He^4, it is interesting to note that if the mass of the atom and the density of the liquid are inserted into the expression for T_c, the result is a transition temperature of $3.14°K$. This is encouragingly close to the observed λ-point temperature and leads us to pursue the model further.

REFERENCES

1. H. Eyring, D. Henderson, B. J. Storer, and E. M. Eyring, *Statistical Mechanics and Dynamics*, John Wiley, New York (1964).
2. K. Huang, *Statistical Mechanics*, John Wiley, New York (1963).
3. F. London, *Superfluids*, Vol. II, John Wiley, New York (1954).
4. J. McDougall and E. C. Stoner, *Phil. Trans. Roy. Soc.* (*London*), **237**, 67 (1938).

Chapter 3

Gaseous Helium

It is hardly surprising that of all the phases in which the helium isotopes exist, the gas is the best understood. Even so, there remain significant gaps in our knowledge concerning the gas. While the specific properties of this phase are of interest in their own right, study of the gas has been exceedingly rewarding for several other reasons. One of these is that the features distinguishing He^3 from He^4 can be most readily sorted out into the effects due to differences in mass, statistics, and nuclear spin. Also, because of the weakness of the interaction between two helium atoms, a gaslike model has usually been the starting point for theoretical treatments of the liquid phases, so that detailed knowledge of the gas can be of tremendous importance in gaining insight into the properties of the liquids. On the other hand, a correct microscopic description of the condensed phases will ultimately depend upon taking into account the exact nature of the intermolecular interactions. Here again studies of the gas can be extremely helpful.

This chapter will summarize some of the important theoretical and experimental results which lead to our present understanding of the equilibrium and transport properties of helium gas. Emphasis will be placed on the effects of quantum phenomena in connection with gas imperfection and the kinetic coefficients of viscosity, thermal conductivity, and diffusion. We first consider the potential function appropriate for the interaction between a pair of helium atoms, one of the areas in which our knowledge is least adequate, and then indicate to what extent the theoretical predictions based on the various potentials agree with experimental results. An excellent and exhaustive treatise on the general subject matter of this chapter is the work of Hirschfelder *et al.* ([1]).

3.1. THE PAIR POTENTIAL FOR TWO HELIUM ATOMS

3.1.1. Quantum-Mechanical Calculations

Two sentences which begin and end a recent discussion of inter-molecular forces given by Hirschfelder [2] pinpoint our requirements in this subject and emphasize our deficiencies:

> "It is surprising how little is known about intermolecular forces when you consider their importance in a wide variety of problems."
> "Right now an accurate calculation of the interaction of two helium atoms is long overdue!"

In attacking the problem of two interacting helium atoms, we consider the Schrödinger equation for a system of two nuclei and four electrons with mutual interactions governed by the Coulomb law. Even with the simplifications afforded by the Born–Oppenheimer approximation and the Hellmann–Feynman theorem, this solution presents formidable difficulties. The Born–Oppenheimer approximation allows the separation of nuclear and electronic motions so that the Schrödinger equation may be quite accurately solved for the electrons at various fixed values of the internuclear distance r; the Hellmann–Feynman theorem permits the forces upon the nuclei to be calculated from classical electrostatic formulas once the electron probability density has been determined quantum-mechanically. Hence the first step is to obtain a solution of the Schrödinger equation for the electrons for one fixed atomic configuration by using one of several approximation methods, such as the variational or perturbation techniques, or a combination of these two, or the generalized self-consistent field method of Slater [3]. Then the same process must be repeated for a wide range of different values of r, from which may be obtained the total potential energy, $\Phi_T(r)$.

The components of $\Phi_T(r)$ are the self-energies, or ionization potentials, Φ_1, of each atom plus the interaction energy, $\Phi_{12}(r)$ [or simply $\Phi(r)$], such that for two helium atoms,

$$\Phi(r) = \Phi_T(r) - 2\Phi_1 \tag{3.1}$$

Here is where the difficulty arises, since the desired result, $\Phi(r)$, is obtained from the difference of two large, nearly equal quantities. In the case of the helium isotopes, the maximum interaction energy occurring at r_m is of the order of -1.4×10^{-15} erg, while the ionization potential is 3.9×10^{-11} erg. Therefore if we wish to calculate $\Phi(r_m)$ to, say, only two significant figures, we must first calculate $\Phi_T(r_m)$ to six significant figures. At other values of r, the requirements are even more stringent. These comparisons assume that Φ_1 can be determined even more accurately, and thanks to several recent extensive calculations this is probably true. Scherr and Knight ([4]) have recently extended the variational perturbation procedure invented by Hylleraas ([5]) to obtain estimates of the energy to 13th order, and Pekeris ([6]) has attacked the problem using the purely variational method with a trial wave function containing 1078 terms. Both calculations agree with the experimentally determined value of Φ_1 to seven significant figures. While these results on a three-body problem could not have been accomplished without modern giant high-speed electronic computers, the solution of the six-body problem involved in obtaining $\Phi_T(r)$, and hence $\Phi(r)$, being a considerably larger task, has been prevented essentially due to limitations on computer capacity. On the more optimistic side, progress in extending computer technology has been rapid, so that it may not be too long before Hirschfelder's invocation for an accurate He–He potential will receive an acceptable reply.

Since efforts have so far failed to produce an He–He interaction potential starting from first principles, there have been numerous attempts to calculate the potential piecemeal. The forces at large, small, and intermediate separation distances are considered as separate problems with the expectation that a synthesis of the several answers will produce a realistic total potential function. The composition of $\Phi(r)$ may be considered approximately as

$$\Phi(r) = \phi_V + \phi_{E\text{-}2} + \phi_{D\text{-}6} + \phi_{D\text{-}8} \tag{3.2}$$

Here, ϕ_V arises from the valence or short-range repulsive forces, $\phi_{E\text{-}2}$ is the second-order exchange energy which becomes important at intermediate ranges, $\phi_{D\text{-}6}$ is due to the induced-dipole–induced-dipole London dispersion forces which become dominant at large separations, and $\phi_{D\text{-}8}$ is derived from the induced-dipole–induced-quadrupole dispersion forces, also long-range effects. While at very small r the potential may be fairly well represented by the valence term and at large r by the dispersion terms, in the intermediate range where these forces overlap, expression (3.2) does not give a realistic account of the interaction. This is very unfortunate, since the intermediate range of the potential is extremely important in determining the physical properties of the gas, liquid, and solid. Nevertheless, it will be instructive to examine briefly each of the components of the relation (3.2).

In treating molecular interactions, the variational procedure is valid over the whole range of intermolecular spacings. However, at short ranges for helium, since $\Phi(r)$ is indeed very small compared with the ionization energy, a perturbation scheme with $\Phi(r)$ as the perturbation potential is also appropriate and is more easily applied. For small r it has been usual to expand $\Phi(r)$ in powers of r, though Hirschfelder ([2]) has indicated the limited validity of this expansion. Beginning in 1928, several first-order perturbation calculations of the repulsive term ϕ_V

were carried out, the most complete being that of Rosen [7] who was the first to evaluate all the necessary Coulomb and exchange integrals. More recent developments in molecular quantum mechanics have indicated that the Hartree–Fock approximation, including the superposition of electron configurations to account for electron correlation effects, is a more rapidly converging method, and hence potentially more accurate than either the variational or perturbation methods when applied to small separations. Using the Hartree–Fock scheme with up to 64 configurations, Phillipson [8] has calculated ϕ_V for the range $0.5 \leqslant r \leqslant 1.0$ Å. The result is

$$\phi_V = 3.0635 \times 10^{-10} \exp(-3.8486\, r) \quad \text{erg} \tag{3.3}$$

with an estimated maximum error of about 1×10^{-12} erg. (Here and in the following formulas of this section, r is given in angstroms.)

The most successful method for treating long-range intermolecular forces has involved the perturbation solution for the Schrödinger equation of the two-molecule system, where the perturbation is the interaction potential expanded in inverse powers of the separation distance. At large distances, the problem is simplified because the exchange integrals, which decrease exponentially with distance, become negligible compared with the Coulomb integrals. It then becomes possible to choose as the zero-order wave function for the system the product of the wave functions appropriate for the isolated molecules without the necessity of antisymmetrizing the representation for the total electronic configuration. If the net angular momentum of the isolated molecules is zero—and this is true for helium—the first-order perturbation energy is also zero. The second-order energy is not zero and leads to the result

$$\phi_D = Cr^{-6} + C'r^{-8} + C''r^{-10} + \cdots$$
$$= \phi_{D\text{-}6} + \phi_{D\text{-}8} + \phi_{D\text{-}10} + \cdots \tag{3.4}$$

known as the London dispersion energy. The first term is by far the most important; the second is not negligible, but higher terms may, for our purpose, be dropped from consideration.

In Section 1.3.2, it was noted that the inverse-sixth-power dispersion energy was negative, and therefore attractive, and that $\phi_{D\text{-}6}$ should be given in terms of the polarizability α^0. Actually, the second-order perturbation calculation gives $\phi_{D\text{-}6}$ directly in terms of oscillator strengths f_i, and when certain well-founded assumptions are made, the representation in terms of α^0, equation (1.28), becomes a very good approximation. Thus, for interaction of two ground-state helium atoms i and j,

$$\phi_{D\text{-}6} = -\frac{3}{2} \frac{(e\hbar)^4}{r^6 m_e^2} \sum_{i,j} \frac{f_i f_j}{(E_0 - E_i)(E_0 - E_j)(2E_0 - E_i - E_j)} \tag{3.5}$$

where the notation follows that of equation (1.28). In calculating ϕ_{D-6} a difficulty arises in determining the quantum-mechanical oscillator strengths. At present, the best estimate of these quantities comes from experimental measurements of the variation of the index of refraction of light as a function of frequency. The final result for ϕ_{D-6} for helium is

$$\phi_{D-6} = -3E_I(\alpha^0)^2/4r^6 = C/r^6 \tag{3.6}$$

where E_I is an empirical constant approximately equal to the ionization energy. Early work by Margenau ([9]) gave for helium a value of $C = -1.39 \times 10^{-12}$ erg/Å^6 from a consideration of the oscillator strengths for transitions between the ground state and all excited states, requiring a summation over the discrete states and integration over those in the continuum. Dalgarno and co-workers and others have made more refined estimates of C using carefully determined oscillator strengths; representative of them is the value obtained by Chan and Dalgarno ([10]): $C = -1.408 \times 10^{-12}$ erg/Å^6. It should be noted that second-order perturbation theory indicates that the difference between C for He^3 and C for He^4 is about 1 part in 10^4 and arises from the differences in reduced mass of the electron-nucleus pairs. With the experimental techniques now available, this difference in C should just barely be observable in measurements of the polarizability.

The second term, ϕ_{D-8}, in the series (3.4) for the dispersion energy has been calculated by Page ([11]) using a variational method. His result for the constant C' is -3.0×10^{-12} erg/Å^8.

The three quantities of equation (3.2) that we have considered so far involve the extremes of separation distance. At intermediate distances, these terms should overlap; however, they do not, because the different procedures used to obtain the results involve different representations of the wave function for two helium atoms. The wave function obtained at short ranges by Phillipson ([8]) cannot be extended beyond about 1 Å because the convergence of the Hartree–Fock scheme becomes poor. Likewise, there is difficulty in extending the second-order perturbation method for the dispersion forces to shorter distances. The first source of this difficulty arises from the neglect of the exchange terms, which do become important in the intermediate range (in fact, the beginning of this range with decreasing r may be defined by the value of r at which exchange terms first become required). Hence, in equation (3.2), a term ϕ_{E-2} is included to represent these second-order exchange effects. An attempt to evaluate ϕ_{E-2} has been made by Margenau ([9]), with the result

$$\phi_{E-2} = -5.60 \times 10^{-10} \exp(-5.33\,r) \quad \text{erg} \tag{3.7}$$

However, this value, when combined with other terms of equation (3.2), inadequately represents $\Phi(r)$, as indicated earlier. The second difficulty in extending the second-order perturbation method has origins in the fact that the inverse-power expansion of the perturbation potential is not strictly valid ([2]).

To obtain a wave function appropriate for both intermediate distances and the limiting separations poses a very challenging problem. A promising approach has been presented by Kestner and Sinanoglu ([12]), who divide the interaction into two parts, one representing the electron correlations and the other treated by the Hartree–Fock approach. This method, by using the many-electron theory of atoms and molecules, calculates most of the interaction directly, thereby avoiding the difficulties associated with the subtraction in equation (3.1). However, as yet, good quantitative results have not been obtained. Several authors have prepared a "hybrid" potential by using the theoretical results for short-range repulsion and long-range attraction and by joining these in the region near the minimum with an empirically determined curve. The most recent such attempt, by Bruch and McGee ([13]), appears to have considerable merit.

3.1.2. Empirical Potentials

Since the theoretical calculation of the interaction potential between two helium atoms is in an unsatisfactory state, it has been necessary to resort to the use of empirically determined potentials possessing relatively simple analytical forms. Several of the more useful examples of these potentials are pictured in Fig. 3.1.

Probably the most elementary of all potentials is one applicable to rigid spheres whose centers can approach one another no closer than the sphere diameter a_0 and otherwise have no interaction. This potential is defined by

$$\Phi(r) = \infty \qquad r < a_0$$
$$= 0 \qquad r > a_0 \tag{3.8}$$

The hard-sphere potential has been most useful in development of microscopic theories of helium by making possible calculations for the approximation of interparticle forces which are primarily strongly repulsive at short distances. The value taken for a_0 is usually related to N/Ω, depending upon the specific nature of the problem. Clearly, this potential is very unrealistic, since it contains no attractive part.

The next step toward realism involves the addition to the rigid-sphere model of a negative, or attractive, square well. This potential

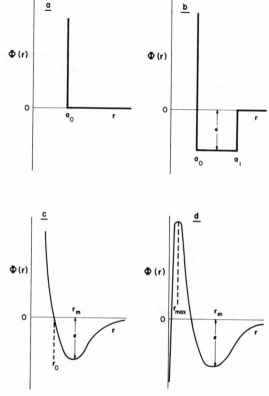

Fig. 3.1. Examples of empirical pair-potentials $\Phi(r)$ as a function of particle separation r: (a) for hard spheres of diameter a_0; (b) square well; (c) Lennard-Jones (12-6); (d) Buckingham Exp-6.

is described by the relations

$$\Phi(r) = \infty \qquad r < a_0$$
$$\Phi(r) = -\epsilon \qquad a_0 < r < a_1 \qquad (3.9)$$
$$\Phi(r) = 0 \qquad r > a_1$$

This crude model gives surprisingly good results in certain calculations which depend importantly upon either the strength ϵ of the attractive core or the area of the well. The parameters of the square-well potential are usually chosen to simulate the interaction given by other more realistic potentials which are analytically too complicated for the problem at hand.

The Lennard–Jones (12-6) potential

$$\Phi(r) = 4\epsilon[(r_0/r)^{12} - (r_0/r)^6] \tag{3.10}$$

has the virtues of being mathematically fairly simple, physically realistic, and theoretically rather faithful in representing the interaction between spherical nonpolar molecules. In addition, the parameters r_0 (the value of r for which $\Phi(r) = 0$) and ϵ (the maximum depth of the potential, which occurs at $r_m = 2^{1/6}r_0$) are readily obtainable from experimental data. This potential may be generalized by considering the powers of r as variable parameters, but the choice of the combination (12-6) facilitates calculations without undue sacrifice of accuracy. The inverse sixth power of r, of course, reproduces the functional dependence of the leading term of the London dispersion forces, and the inverse twelfth power of r approximates the exponential repulsive forces. For many problems involving helium, the Lennard–Jones (12-6) potential has been a useful and successful representation.

An empirical potential which more closely approximates the theoretical form is the four-parameter function proposed by Buckingham:

$$\Phi(r) = c_1 \exp(-c_2 r) - c_3 r^{-6} - c_4 r^{-8} \tag{3.11}$$

It is often more convenient for calculations to omit the induced-dipole–induced-quadrupole term and recast equation (3.11) in the form

$$\Phi(r) = \frac{\epsilon}{1 - (6/\alpha)} \left\{ \frac{6}{\alpha} \exp\left(\alpha\left[1 - \frac{r}{r_m}\right]\right) - \left(\frac{r_m}{r}\right)^6 \right\} \tag{3.12}$$

This expression is known as the modified Buckingham or Exp-6 potential. The parameter α describes the steepness of the repulsive part and r_m is the value of r for which $\Phi(r)$ is a minimum. Both equations (3.11) and (3.12) possess the nonphysical property of exhibiting a maximum at some small $r = r_{max}$. This is usually of little consequence; but when it is significant, auxiliary conditions may be imposed to restrict these equations to the range $r > r_{max}$ and to set $\Phi(r) = \infty$ for $r < r_{max}$.

3.1.3. Determination of the Parameters of Empirical Potentials Useful for Helium

We now consider briefly the problem of assigning numerical values to the parameters of the Lennard-Jones (12-6) and Buckingham (Exp-6) potentials applicable to the helium isotopes. The experimental data most useful for this purpose are obtained from (1) measurements of transport properties, especially viscosity, (2) measurements of the scattering of a beam of helium atoms, and (3) the temperature dependence of the experimentally determined second virial coefficient and

Joule–Thompson coefficient. A certain amount of care is required in using the results, since, for a given potential, the parameters derived from the different kinds of data are generally not consistent. Hence, a set of constants obtained from, for example, viscosity measurements alone will be suitable for representing other transport properties, but may be unsuitable for virial coefficients and other state properties. This selectivity arises from the fact that different physical properties depend more or less importantly on different parts of the potential and in different ways. For instance, the second virial coefficient is sensitive only to the area of the attractive (negative) part of the two-body potential. Furthermore, it is likely that a set of parameters which fits one type of measurement in one temperature range will need modification when extreme temperature ranges are considered. This is especially true for light gases such as helium at low temperatures, when quantum effects must be taken into account. The true potential is, of course, invariant, appropriate for all physical properties, and independent of temperature; but since the empirical potentials attempt to simulate a very complicated function with but a few parameters, the choice of these parameters based upon experimental data always involves some sort of compromise.

It might appear that theoretical calculations of the potential should be helpful in determining the constants necessary to fit experimental results, at least in the ranges of small and of large r. Unfortunately, although the theoretical results may be used as a guide, in practice, the comparisons fall short of our expectations. For example, the scattering measurements for He should give a good account of the short-range repulsive forces to agree with the calculation of Phillipson [8]. However, the disparity between the two results is quite a bit greater than the estimated errors in both. Dalgarno [14] has discussed this point and has raised a doubt as to whether the collision processes considered here are correctly described by an intermolecular potential. [*Added in proof*: See, however, J. E. Jordan and I. Amdur, *J. Chem. Phys.* **46**, 165 (1967).] In a somewhat different way, there is also difficulty at large separations. Because of the inflexibility of the functional form of the empirical potentials, it is not possible to separate out the London dispersion contribution without affecting the repulsive term. Hence, use of the theoretical value may result in a poor overall potential.

Buckingham [15] has reviewed these problems associated with deriving parameters for empirical potentials and has picturesquely summarized the dilemma:

> "We are thus in the awkward position that a bend of the head of the curve makes the tail wag, and a twist of the tail causes the head to nod! However, if we are in earnest about deriving potentials which are physically significant and which correlate the widest variety of

properties of a substance, it is very necessary to be able to vary the two ends of the curve independently of each other and independently of the position of the minimum."

This we cannot do with only three or four constants at our disposal.

The net effect of all of the above arguments is that there does not exist a unique, or even a "best," empirical intermolecular potential for helium. Instead, there are several which are useful for various purposes. A summary of the parameters for seven of these is given in Table 3.I, together with data for a hybrid potential ([13]) and the theoretical value of the constant C of the r^{-6} term. Graphical comparison of three of these is made in Fig. 3.2. In the table, three different Lennard-Jones (12-6) potential functions are listed, the parameters of the first two being determined from two types of high-temperature data, and those of the third being applicable for all low-temperature properties. The latter set, which for convenience we designate LJ-1, was determined first at high temperatures by de Boer and Michels ([16]) and later slightly refined by de Boer and Lunbeck ([17]) to make $\Phi(r)$ as consistent as possible for both high- and low-temperature experimental data. (The procedure is briefly described in Hirschfelder et al. ([1]), p. 420 ff.) Two sets of parameters for the Exp-6 potential are given. The first of these, MR-1, was determined by Mason and Rice ([18]) using high-temperature data with α determined from viscosity measurements. The second, MR-5, was obtained by Kilpatrick et al. ([19]) by keeping α constant to the MR-1 value and varying ϵ and r_m to fit the low-temperature second virial coefficient data of He^4. Buckingham (private communication to the author) has criticized this procedure on the basis that α determines

Table 3.I. Parameters for Several He–He Interaction Potentials

Potential	ϵ/k_B (°K)	r_m (Å)	$-C \times 10^{12}$ (ergs/Å^6)	α	References
Lennard-Jones (12-6)					
Classical (viscosity)	10.22	2.89	1.65	—	([22])
Classical (2nd virial coefficient)	6.03	2.95	1.10	—	([23])
Quantum parameters (LJ-1)	10.22	2.869	1.573	—	([16,17])
Exp-6					
MR-1	9.16	3.135	2.325	12.4	([18])
MR-5	7.56	3.189	2.127	12.4	([19])
Buckingham et al.	9.97	2.976	1.50	13.5	([20])
Yntema–Schneider	9.06	2.99	1.24	—	([21])
Hybrid	12.53	2.975	1.41	—	([13])
Theoretical	—	—	1.408	—	([10])

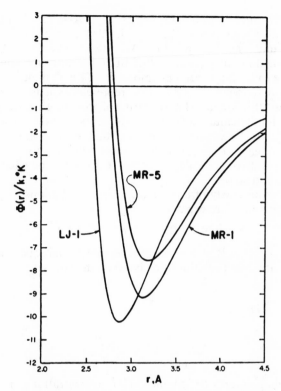

Fig. 3.2. Comparison of the LJ-1, MR-1, and MR-5
potentials [from Kilpatrick *et al.* ([19])].

the curvature of the minimum as well as the repulsive steepness and is
therefore important for low-temperature properties; he considers that
a value of 12.4 for α is too low to give realistic results. Thus, in the
Buckingham potential ([20]), the value of α is taken to be 13.5, which
gives a curvature at the minimum very similar to that of the LJ-1
function. Yntema and Schneider ([21]) have, from high-temperature
second virial coefficient data of He⁴, also obtained parameters appropriate for equation (3.11).

3.2. THE EQUATION OF STATE OF He³ AND He⁴ AT LOW TEMPERATURES

The equation of state of a real gas may be expressed in a form first
proposed on empirical grounds by Kamerlingh Onnes:

$$PV = N_A k_B T[1 + BV^{-1} + CV^{-2} + DV^{-3} + \cdots] \qquad (3.13)$$

Here V is the molar volume of the gas, N_A is Avogadro's number, and B, C, D, etc., are known as the second, third, fourth, etc., virial coefficients, all functions of temperature. With this terminology, $A = N_A k_B T$ may be called the first virial coefficient and is, of course, the ideal gas term. The units for B are $cm^3/mole$; for C, $cm^6/mole^2$; and so on. In addition to being a convenient representation for experimental P–V–T data, this equation has the virtue of providing a close connection with the fundamental sources of gas imperfection. The physical significance of the virial coefficients is that B represents corrections to the ideal-gas PV product due to the interactions occurring for encounters of two molecules at a time; C includes the effects of triple collisions; and so on.

An alternate way of formulating the contributions to gas imperfection is in a pressure expansion:

$$PV = A' + B'P + C'P^2 + D'P^3 + \cdots \qquad (3.14)$$

Both equations (3.13) and (3.14) are called the "virial equation of state," and there are direct relationships between the two sets of coefficients. In particular,

$$A = A' \qquad (3.15)$$

$$B = B' \qquad (3.16)$$

$$C = (B')^2 + A'C' \qquad (3.17)$$

etc.

At low pressures or low molecular concentrations, the principal source of nonideality of a gas arises from the binary collision processes. The dynamics of systems interacting only through two-body forces can be treated exactly in classical mechanics with the result that the second viral coefficient $B_{(cl)}$ is given simply by

$$B_{(cl)} = -\frac{N_A}{2} \int_0^\infty [e^{-\beta\Phi(r)} - 1] 4\pi r^2 \, dr \qquad (3.18)$$

where the temperature dependence of $B_{(cl)}$ is introduced through $\beta = (k_B T)^{-1}$. The accuracy for the calculation of $B_{(cl)}$ on this basis is limited only by the extent to which the pair potential $\Phi(r)$ represents the true potential. As the pressure or density is increased, C and higher coefficients become more important but calculations of these coefficients using realistic potential functions present formidable difficulties which as yet have not been satisfactorily overcome. Our treatment here will emphasize the development of the equation of state terminating with the second virial coefficient, which, fortunately, is a very useful approximation for many purposes; progress in the determination of C will also be discussed briefly.

3.2.1. Quantum-Mechanical Formulation of the Second Virial Coefficient

For light molecules, such as helium, at low temperatures, relation (3.18) no longer adequately represents B. Instead, B must be calculated by methods which take into account not only the interaction potential but also the quantum effects associated with the mass, the spin, and the statistics of the particles. A pioneering work discussing this problem and its solution has been given by Kahn [24], and an excellent development of the subject is given in Hirschfelder et al. [1]—Chapter 3 for the classical equation of state and Chapter 6 for the quantum-mechanical case. We first present here a brief summary of the steps necessary to make the transition from classical to quantum statistical mechanics. In general, we follow the notation of Hirschfelder et al. [1].

We consider the distribution function characterizing the canonical ensemble description of statistical mechanics (N identical particles of mass m with specified Ω and T). The partition function in the semi-classical case with elementary phase space cell volumes h^3 is

$$Z_N = \sum_i \exp(-\beta E_i)$$

$$= \frac{1}{N! h^{3N}} \int_{\mathbf{r}} \int_{\mathbf{p}} \exp[-\beta \mathbf{H}(\mathbf{r}^{(N)}, \mathbf{p}^{(N)})] \, d\mathbf{r}^{(N)} \, d\mathbf{p}^{(N)} \qquad (3.19)$$

where E_i is the energy of the ith state of the system, $\mathbf{r}^{(N)}$ and $\mathbf{p}^{(N)}$ stand for the entire collections of position and momentum vectors of the N particles, $\beta = 1/k_B T$, and the Hamiltonian $\mathbf{H}(\mathbf{r}^{(N)}, \mathbf{p}^{(N)})$ is the sum of the total kinetic and potential energies of the system, that is,

$$\mathbf{H}(\mathbf{r}^{(N)}, \mathbf{p}^{(N)}) = \sum_{j=1}^{N} \frac{p_j^2}{2m} + \Phi(\mathbf{r}^{(N)}) \qquad (3.20)$$

Equation (3.19) may be directly integrated over the momenta to yield

$$Z_N = \frac{1}{N! \lambda_T^{3N}} \int_{\mathbf{r}} W_N(\mathbf{r}^{(N)}) \, d\mathbf{r}^{(N)} \qquad (3.21)$$

where

$$W_N(\mathbf{r}^{(N)}) = \exp[-\beta \Phi(\mathbf{r}^{(N)})] \qquad (3.22)$$

is the *Boltzmann factor*. The partition function then depends only upon temperature and the total volume and is the sum of relative probabilities.

For the quantum-mechanical case, because of the uncertainty principle, it is no longer possible to simultaneously specify both the position and momentum of a particle. Instead, the distribution function for the system is stated in terms of the probability of finding the system in a particular configuration of the particles, which we recall are indistinguishable. Thus, if for the ith energy level, the state vector of the system, $\Psi_i(\mathbf{r}^{(N)})$, is expressed as a linear combination of orthonormal functions $\phi_i(\mathbf{r}^{(N)})$, the quantum-mechanical analog to Z_N becomes

$$Z_{Nq} = \sum_i \int [\phi_i^*(\mathbf{r}^{(N)})e^{-\beta\mathcal{H}}\phi_i(\mathbf{r}^{(N)})\,d\mathbf{r}^{(N)}] \tag{3.23}$$

with the Hamiltonian operator

$$\mathcal{H} = -\frac{\hbar^2}{2m}\sum_j \frac{\partial^2}{\partial r_j^2} + \Phi(\mathbf{r}^{(N)}) \tag{3.24}$$

replacing equation (3.20). Similarly, instead of the Boltzmann factor, equation (3.22), in quantum mechanics we must use the *Slater sum*, $\mathcal{W}_N(\mathbf{r}^{(N)})$, given by

$$\mathcal{W} = N!\lambda_T^{3N}\sum_i \phi_i^* \exp[-\mathcal{H}/k_B T]\phi_i \tag{3.25}$$

or, when we replace the Hamiltonian operator by its eigenvalues,

$$\mathcal{W} = N!\lambda_T^{3N}\sum_i |\Psi_i|^2 \exp(-E_i/k_B T) \tag{3.26}$$

A simple result using the Slater sum is instructive. If we consider an ideal quantum gas $[\Phi(r) \equiv 0]$ of just two particles without spin, equation (3.26) becomes (see Hirschfelder *et al.* ([1]), p. 401 *ff*)

$$\mathcal{W} = 1 \pm \exp(-2\pi r_{12}^2/\lambda_T^2) \tag{3.27}$$

For the classical case, the Boltzmann factor is just unity, so that the exponential term in equation (3.27) is of purely quantum-mechanical origin, arising from the indistinguishability of the particles. It is often called the "exchange term." When the eigenfunctions Ψ_i in relation (3.26) are symmetric, we are to take the positive sign, and when the Ψ_i are antisymmetric, we take the negative sign. Thus, if the particles obey BE statistics, equation (3.27) indicates that $\mathcal{W}$ is always greater than unity and approaches 2 as $r_{12} \to 0$. This increased probability for the particles to be near one another accounts for attractive statistical forces and, indeed, provides the rudiments of the BE condensation. On the other hand, for two FD particles, $\mathcal{W}$ vanishes as $r_{12} \to 0$, indicating an apparent mutual repulsion of the particles.

The equation of state of an ideal quantum gas of N particles may be derived following the ideas outlined in Section 2.2 to yield a virial form.

The second virial coefficient, B^0, now including the spin σ, is given by

$$B^0 = \mp \frac{N_A \lambda_T^3}{2^{5/2}(2\sigma + 1)}$$

$$= \mp \frac{N_A}{2^{5/2}(2\sigma + 1)}\left(\frac{h^2}{2\pi m k_B T}\right)^{3/2} \tag{3.28}$$

with the negative sign for BE and the positive sign for FD statistics. The ideal-quantum-gas second virial coefficient is due entirely to the exchange term, and we see from equation (3.28) that B^0 becomes important whenever $\lambda_T^3/v > 1$, i.e., when λ_T is large compared with the average distance between particles. This occurs for small m and low T, and therefore B^0 is significant primarily for the helium isotopes.

For the real gas, it is possible to write the equation of state as a simple power series in the fugacity z [cf. equations (2.10) and 2.21)]:

$$\frac{1}{v} = \sum_{l=1}^{\infty} l b_l z^l$$

$$\frac{P}{k_B T} = \sum_{l=1}^{\infty} b_l z^l \tag{3.29}$$

The coefficients b_l are the cluster integrals representing the interactions among l particles at a time; under the assumption that $\Phi(\mathbf{r}^{(N)})$ can be expressed as a sum of pair potentials $\Phi(r_{ij})$, we may obtain the cluster integrals in terms of the partition functions. The first three b_l are (in the classical case)

$$b_1 = 1 \tag{3.30}$$

$$b_2 = (1/2\Omega)\lambda_T^6(2Z_2 - Z_1^2) \tag{3.31}$$

$$b_3 = (1/3\Omega)\lambda_T^9(3Z_3 - 3Z_2Z_1 + Z_1^3) \tag{3.32}$$

In terms of these, the second and third virial coefficients can be written as

$$B_{(cl)} = -N_A b_2/b_1^2 \tag{3.33}$$

and

$$C_{(cl)} = -2N_A^2(b_3 - 2b_2^2) \tag{3.34}$$

when Ω is set equal to the molar volume V. Finally, for a monatomic gas with nuclear spin σ, the appropriate expression for the quantum-mechanical second virial coefficient is

$$B = -\frac{N_A \lambda_T^6}{2V} \frac{(2Z_{2q} - Z_{1q}^2)}{(2\sigma + 1)^2} \tag{3.35}$$

While equation (3.35) is valid for all temperatures, it is practical for calculations only at low temperatures. The central problem here lies in the evaluation of Z_{2q}. To accomplish this, the following strategem is useful: we first separate B into two parts, B^0 and $(B - B^0)$, with B^0 given by equation (3.28). Next, we factor the two-particle partition function into two parts, one associated with the translation of the center of mass of the two-molecule system and the other involving only the relative motion of the two molecules. Equation (3.35) can then be reduced to

$$B = B^0 + (B - B^0)$$

$$= B_0 - \frac{2^{3/2} N_A \lambda_T^6 [Z_{2q}(\text{rel}) - Z_{2q}^0(\text{rel})]}{V(2\sigma + 1)^2} \qquad (3.36)$$

where $[Z_{2q}(\text{rel}) - Z_{2q}^0(\text{rel})]$ describes the difference in the density of energy states of relative motion between the real gas and the ideal gas.

The energy levels of relative motion are the eigenvalues of the one-dimensional radial Schrödinger equation

$$-\frac{\hbar^2}{2\mu}\left[(r\Psi)'' + \frac{l(l+1)}{r^2}(r\Psi)\right] + \Phi(r)(r\Psi) = E(r\Psi) \qquad (3.37)$$

with $\mu = m_1 m_2/(m_1 + m_2)$ being the reduced mass of the two-particle system and l the angular momentum quantum number. These levels are of two sorts, the first being a finite number n of negative levels or bound states, $E_{n,l}^-$, which can be directly summed, the second being an infinite number of positive levels very closely spaced and approximating a continuum. For the ideal gas, there are never any bound states; but it is also possible that there are none even for the real gas, depending on the properties of the potential and the mass of the particles. On the other hand, the positive levels occur for both cases and the relative density of these states is the quantity we must find. Gropper (^{25}) and Beth and Uhlenbeck (^{26}) applied the method of the phase shift to determine the solution of this problem.

In quantum-mechanical scattering processes, the effect of the interparticle potential upon the wave function of the scattered particles may be given in terms of the phase shift $\eta_l(q)$, which is a function of the energy parameter q of the colliding particles and their angular momentum l. [In future notation, we use η_l for $\eta_l(q)$.] Equation (3.37) can be transformed to a dimensionless expression using the following substitutions:

$$R = r/\rho \qquad (3.38)$$

$$U(R) = (2\mu/\hbar^2)\rho^2 \Phi(r) \qquad (3.39)$$

$$q^2 = (2\mu/\hbar^2)\rho^2 E \tag{3.40}$$

$$R\Psi(R) = r\Psi(r) \tag{3.41}$$

Then, the solutions at large R, where the centrifugal and potential terms are negligible, become

$$R\Psi = \sin[qR - \tfrac{1}{2}\pi l + \eta_l] \tag{3.42}$$

For the ideal case in which $U(R)$ is everywhere zero, the particles suffer no phase shift as a result of the collision. Hence, comparing the solutions for the real and ideal cases, we see that the wave functions differ only in the presence or absence of η_l in the argument of the sine. From these considerations, it can be shown that the evaluation of $[Z_{2q}(\text{rel}) - Z_{2q}^0(\text{rel})]$ is determined by $d\eta_l/dq$, the manner in which the phase shift changes with the energy parameter.

In the calculation of B, particular care must be exercised in properly weighting the energy levels entering into the summations for $Z_{2q}(\text{rel})$ and $Z_{2q}^0(\text{rel})$. Taking into account both the nuclear spin and spatial degeneracies (involving l) the weighting factors g are given in Table 3.II. Using these factors, we may arrive at a final form convenient

Table 3.II. Statistical Weighting Factors for the Second Virial Coefficient

Value of g	Parity of l	Statistics of the particle pair
$(\sigma + 1)(2\sigma + 1)(2l + 1)$	odd	FD
	even	BE
$\sigma(2\sigma + 1)(2l + 1)$	even	FD
	odd	BE
$(2l + 1)$	immaterial	mixed

for computing the second virial coefficient for a pair of FD atoms, such as He^3–He^3:

$$
\begin{aligned}
B_{(FD)} = {} & \frac{N_A \pi^{1/2} \rho^3}{q_0^3} \\
& \times \Bigg[\frac{\pi}{2(2\sigma + 1)} - 8\pi \sum_n \Bigg\{ \frac{\sigma + 1}{2\sigma + 1} \sum_{l\,\text{odd}} (2l + 1)[\exp(-\beta E_{n,l}^-) - 1] \\
& + \frac{\sigma}{2\sigma + 1} \sum_{l\,\text{even}} (2l + 1)[\exp(-\beta E_{n,l}^-) - 1] \Bigg\} \\
& - \frac{16}{q_0^2} \int_0^\infty (\textstyle\sum) \exp(-q^2/q_0^2)\, q\, dq \Bigg]
\end{aligned}
\tag{3.43}
$$

where

$$q_0^2 = 2\mu\rho^2 k_B T/\hbar^2 = 2\pi\rho^2 \lambda_T^{-2} \qquad (3.44)$$

and

$$\left(\sum\right) = \frac{\sigma + 1}{2\sigma + 1} \sum_{l \text{ odd}} (2l + 1)\eta_l + \frac{\sigma}{2\sigma + 1} \sum_{l \text{ even}} (2l + 1)\eta_l \qquad (3.45)$$

For a pair of He^4 atoms, equation (3.43) is modified only to the extent of an interchange of the factors σ and $(\sigma + 1)$.

If we have a gaseous mixture of particles of different symmetry types, such as He^3 and He^4, the expression for the second virial coefficient of the mixture becomes

$$B_{\text{mix}} = N_3^2 B_{33} + 2N_3 N_4 B_{34} + N_4^2 B_{44} \qquad (3.46)$$

B_{33} and B_{44} are the second virial coefficients of pure He^3 and pure He^4 with mole fractions N_3 and N_4 in the mixture; B_{34} is the cross second virial coefficient and is determined by the partition functions for a system of an He^3 and an He^4 atom. In this case, B^0 is identically zero, since the two particles are now distinguishable, and the weighting factors for the problem are given in the last line of Table 3.II.

In the use of equation (3.43) to obtain values of B, although the expression appears quite formidable, the only real difficulty is presented by the calculation of the phase shifts. To calculate $\eta_l(q)$ from equation (3.42) would require integration of the wave equation to prohibitively large values of R. However, at much smaller R, a valid solution can be obtained using half-integral Bessel functions, $J_{\pm l \pm \frac{1}{2}}(qR)$,

$$R\Psi = A_1 R^{1/2} J_{l+\frac{1}{2}}(qR) + A_2 R^{1/2} J_{-l-\frac{1}{2}}(qR) \qquad (3.47)$$

$$\eta_l = \tan^{-1}[(-)^l A_2/A_1] \qquad (3.48)$$

A solution of the form (3.47) is first found at two values of R. The two resulting equations are then solved simultaneously in order to determine the ratio A_2/A_1 which appears in equation (3.48).

3.2.2. Results of Calculations of B

Early calculations of the second virial coefficient of He^4 employing the above formalism were made by Massey and Buckingham [27] and by Buckingham, Hamilton, and Massey [28] using variations of the Buckingham potential, and by de Boer and Michels [16] using the Lennard-Jones (12-6) potential LJ-1. Somewhat later, de Boer, van Kranendonk, and Compaan [29] also obtained B for He^3 from the LJ-1 potential. These studies were all accomplished through very laborious hand calculations of numerical integration to arrive at values of the phase shifts, and the results were necessarily confined to fairly low temperatures, since as T increases, the number of phase shifts required to give accurate values of B increases quite rapidly. Even so, the work, especially of de Boer *et al.*, produced remarkably good sets of B values in the range below 6°K, which of course is the region in which quantum effects are most dramatically displayed.

Capitalizing on the availability of a high-speed electronic computer, Kilpatrick *et al.* ([30]) were able to calculate the phase shifts with sufficient accuracy to extend the LJ-1 results to 60°K. In this work, η_l was calculated for a given value of q starting at $l = 0$ and progressing to higher l until $(2l + 1)\eta_l$, the contribution to (Σ), became less than 1×10^{-5} rad. This procedure was repeated for successive values of q at close intervals. Figure 3.3 shows the behavior of the He^3 and He^4 phase shifts for small l and q as a function of q. For He^4, $\sigma = 0$, so only the even l phase shifts are needed; for He^3, both the even and odd l sums must be calculated.

It is an interesting property of the $l = 0$ phase shift that its value at $q = 0$ divided by $\pi/2$ indicates the number of negative discrete levels $E_{n,l}^-$ of the system. Accordingly, Fig. 3.3 convincingly displays the absence of such levels for He^3 and in addition suggests that He^4, when described by the LJ-1 potential, just barely fails to have one bound state. A more quantitative way of determining the criteria for the occurrence of negative energy levels for particles interacting according to a Lennard-Jones (12-6) potential has been given by Kilpatrick and Kilpatrick ([31]). When this potential is written in the reduced form,

$$\Phi(R) = p^2(R^{-12} - R^{-6}) \tag{3.49}$$

with $\rho = r_0$ and $p^2 = 8\mu\epsilon r_0^2/\hbar^2$, they found that p^2 must exceed the critical value of 22.37 for the existence of at least one bound level. For He^4 and LJ-1, $p^2 = 22.049$; for He^3, p^2 is less by a factor 3/4, the mass ratio. Similarly, the numerical differences in the phase shifts between those for He^3 and those for He^4 depend only on the mass differences. Although no bound level is associated with LJ-1 for He^4, of the potentials listed in Table 3.I, both MR-1 and the hybrid each have one very weak bound state.

The quantities B_{33} and B_{44} calculated from LJ-1 are thus determined solely by the phase shift sums. Final results for the virial coefficients calculated by Kilpatrick *et al.* are plotted as a function of T in Fig. 3.4. At low temperature, the values obtained by de Boer *et al.* were essentially confirmed, and the minor discrepancies that do appear between the two sets of data should probably be resolved in favor of the machine calculations. The Boyle points, i.e., the temperature T_B for which $B = 0$, for He^3 and He^4 are found to be 19.64°K and 23.18°K, respectively; below T_B, B_{33} and B_{44} remain negative, becoming quite

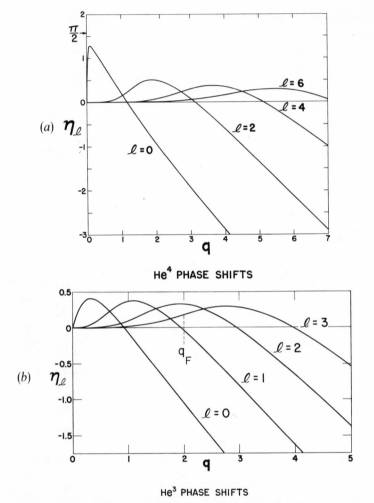

Fig. 3.3. Phase shifts calculated for (a) He^4 and (b) He^3 using the LJ-1 potential [from Kilpatrick et al. ([30])]. In (b) q_F represents the Fermi energy for liquid He^3 (see Section 6.1.3).

large. Only at the lowest temperatures calculated, about 0.1°K, does the repulsive FD ideal-gas term begin to dominate and suggest a rise in B_{33} toward positive values.

Also shown in Fig. 3.4 is the classical second virial coefficient, $B_{(cl)}$, calculated from LJ-1, which is the same for He^3 and He^4. The important general features of these results which interest us include

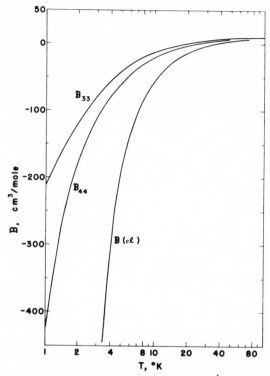

Fig. 3.4. Second virial coefficients of He³ and He⁴ as a function of temperature calculated quantum-mechanically compared with the classical values (same for both He³ and He⁴). The LJ-1 potential is used for all cases.

not only the differences between B_{33} and B_{44}, especially at low temperature, but also their deviations at high temperature from the classically calculated values. Both of these effects have been subjects of recent studies, and it turns out, curiously enough, that their quantitative verification is much more difficult to come by than one might anticipate.

We have already observed that quantum effects should arise from three sources: differences in mass, statistics, and nuclear spin weighting factors. The question now is to ascertain the temperature regions in which each of these contribute importantly. The first hint as to the correct answer came from the calculations by Kilpatrick et al. [30] of B for a hypothetical gas of particles with zero spin, BE statistics, and mass of He³. The results when compared with B_{33} showed only minor differences between the two cases except at very low temperature.

From this, it was concluded that the effects of statistics and spin are suppressed above about 4°K and that for higher temperatures, differences in mass account for the entire discrepancy between B_{33} and B_{44}, which even at 60°K amounts to about 10%. That the cutoff of the exchange effects should be so drastic and at so low a temperature was rather unexpected.

The phase-shift formalism is not the optimum way, especially at high T, of displaying the separate contributions to B. A method more adaptable to the high-temperature limit has been introduced by Lee and Yang ([32]) and developed by Larsen, Kilpatrick, and co-workers ([33–35]). Here, B is decomposed, not as in equation (3.29) but as

$$B = B_E + B_D \qquad (3.50)$$

where B_E includes all of the quantum (exchange) effects. Although B_D is essentially the second virial coefficient of a Boltzmann gas, it is nevertheless to be evaluated by quantum mechanics, not a trivial matter. The components of B can be written as

$$B_D = -\frac{N_A}{2} \int d\mathbf{r}[2^{3/2}\lambda_T^3\langle\mathbf{r}|\exp(-\beta\mathscr{H}_{\text{rel}})|\mathbf{r}\rangle - 1] \qquad (3.51)$$

and

$$B_E = \mp \frac{N_A}{2}(2\sigma + 1)^{-1} \int d\mathbf{r}[2^{3/2}\lambda_T^3\langle\mathbf{r}|\exp(-\beta\mathscr{H}_{\text{rel}})|\mathbf{r}\rangle] \qquad (3.52)$$

[(−) for BE, (+) for FD statistics], where the matrix elements are given as

$$\langle\mathbf{r}|\exp(-\beta\mathscr{H}_{\text{rel}})|\mp \mathbf{r}\rangle = \sum_n \Psi_n(\mathbf{r})\Psi_n(\mp \mathbf{r})^* \exp(-\beta E_n) \qquad (3.53)$$

$\mathscr{H}_{\text{rel}}$ is the Hamiltonian operator for the relative motion of two particles separated by a distance $\mathbf{r}$, and the $\Psi_n(\mathbf{r})$ form a complete set of eigenfunctions of $\mathscr{H}_{\text{rel}}$.

Larsen et al. ([33]) have solved equation (3.52) for the case of hard spheres with a core diameter a_0. The limiting low-temperature value of the integral is just the free-particle result, but at higher temperatures, B_E can rigorously ([36]) be expressed as an asymptotic series in λ_T/a_0. The upper bound to this series for $a_0 \approx 2$ Å, and m appropriate for He^4 has a principal temperature dependence $\sim e^{-T/2}$. This exponential falloff, which is much more rapid than the λ_T^3 falloff for the ideal gas, can be ascribed to the repulsive core: the exchange term is important only if $r < \lambda_T$; but since this condition cannot be fulfilled when λ_T is less than the core diameter, the exchange term becomes strongly suppressed with rising temperature (decreasing λ_T). Thus any potential with a steep repulsive core should similarly reduce the importance of the exchange terms, in support of the conclusions reached earlier by Kilpatrick *et al.* ([30]).

Quantum corrections to properties such as B at high temperature have often been expressed as a power series in $\hbar^2$ [see, for example, Hirschfelder *et al.* ([1]), Chapter 6]. On the other hand, De Witt ([37]) has shown that this type of series is not possible when $d\Phi(r)/dr$ is large (it is infinite for hard spheres), but should be replaced by an asymptotic series in λ_T/a_0 (a_0 is the collision diameter). Actually, Uhlenbeck and Beth ([26, 38]) had many years earlier predicted the coefficients of the zeroth and first-order terms of (λ_T/a_0) in the series applied to B for hard spheres. Later, Mohling ([39]) attempted to obtain the coefficient of $(\lambda_T/a_0)^2$ in order to evaluate B_D at high temperatures. He concluded that not only do quantum effects associated with the repulsive core persist up to very high temperature, but also the differences between B_{33} and B_{44} ought to amount to $\sim 5\%$ even at 1200°K. By solving equations (3.51) and (3.52) numerically, Boyd *et al.* ([35]) have recently made an accurate recalculation of both B_D and B_E for hard spheres over a wide temperature range; for B_D, they found the first six coefficients of the series in λ_T/a_0. Their work confirmed the two values obtained by Uhlenbeck and Beth but indicated that Mohling's estimate of the second-order term was too low by a factor of two. Finally, Handelsman and Keller ([40]) have derived the first four terms of the series by an analytic method and found agreement with the values given by Boyd *et al.*

Table 3.III samples several values of the direct and exchange second virial coefficients for hard spheres over a wide range of λ_T/a_0, or temperature, as adapted from the results of Boyd *et al.* ([35]). Here, the reduced values B_D^* and B_E^* are the ratios of B_D and B_E to the classical hard-sphere value, $B_{HS} = \frac{2}{3}\pi N_A a_0^3$. While the numbers given in

Table 3.III. Reduced Direct and Exchange Second Virial Coefficients for a Hard-Sphere Spinless Boson Gas as a Function of λ_T/a_0

λ_T/a_0	B_D^*	B_E^*	λ_T/a_0	B_D^*	B_E^*
0.125	1.14	—	1.5	3.35	-5.69×10^{-6}
0.5	1.61	—	1.75	3.90	-9.83×10^{-5}
0.75	1.98	—	2.0	4.49	-7.33×10^{-4}
0.8125	2.08	-2×10^{-15}	3.0	7.37	-5.74×10^{-2}
0.875	2.18	-1.16×10^{-13}	5.0	15.60	-1.77
1.0[a]	2.39	-4.48×10^{-11}	10.0	51.95	-40.71
1.125	2.62	-3.11×10^{-9}	20.0	195.40	-488.63
1.25	2.85	-7.31×10^{-8}	30.0	434.18	-1853.65

[a] For m and a_0 appropriate for He^4, $\lambda_T/a_0 = 1$ for $T \approx 16$°K.

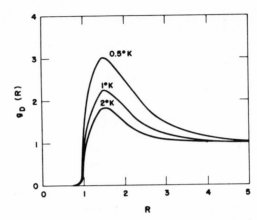

Fig. 3.5. The direct correlation function in reduced
units, $R = r/r_0$, for the LJ-1 potential at several
temperatures [after Larsen et al. ([34])].

Table 3.III hardly do justice to the accuracy of the calculations, they do
illustrate the relative importance of B_D and B_E and in particular show
how B_E becomes insignificant as λ_T/a_0 decreases (temperature increases)
below ~ 3.0.

The evaluation of B_D and B_E using more realistic potentials is
considerably more complex than the already difficult calculations for
the hard-sphere model. Larsen et al. ([34]) have shown that one way of
doing this is to obtain the volume-independent parts of the direct
and exchange correlation functions, $g_D(r, \beta)$ and $g_E(r, \beta)$, respectively.†
These can be shown to have the same matrix elements as required for
B_D and B_E, so that equations (3.51) and (3.52) become for He^4

$$B_D = -2\pi N_A \int_0^\infty (g_D - 1)r^2 \, dr \qquad (3.54)$$

and

$$B_E = -2\pi N_A \int_0^\infty g_E r^2 \, dr \qquad (3.55)$$

For the LJ-1 potential for He^4, Larsen et al. have solved the radial
Schrödinger equation (3.37) by numerical integration to obtain the
wave functions entering into the matrix elements (3.53). The resulting

† For a fluid, the *pair correlation function* g(r)—also known as the *radial distribution
function*—has the property that $\rho^{(2)}(\mathbf{r}_1, \mathbf{r}_2) = (N/\Omega)^2 g(r)$, where $\rho^{(2)}(\mathbf{r}_1, \mathbf{r}_2) \, d\mathbf{r}_1 d\mathbf{r}_2$, the
pair distribution function, represents the probability of finding any one of the N particles
at $\mathbf{r}_1$ (within $d\mathbf{r}_1$) and another at $\mathbf{r}_2$ (within $d\mathbf{r}_2$). g(r) can be measured by X-ray or neutron
scattering; at small r, $g(r) \to 0$, and at large r, $g(r) \to 1$. An excellent exposition of
probability and correlation functions appears in Hill's book ([41]) on statistical
mechanics.

values for g_D, shown in graphical form in Fig. 3.5, demonstrate the classical behavior of $g(r)$; however, the exchange correlation function (Fig. 3.6) approaches zero for large r. For comparison, the exchange for free particles is also given in Fig. 3.6. Calculations of B below 2°K using these correlation functions for He⁴ agree with the phase shift values (also using LJ-1) to within 1 or 2%.

3.2.3. Experimental Results for B

Measurements of the pressure–volume isotherms of He⁴ gas below 5°K were first made at the Kamerlingh Onnes Laboratory at Leiden, the most recent investigations being those of Keesom and co-workers ([42–44]). When gaseous He³ became available in practical quantities, Keller began a study of the equation of state of this substance, but first "checked" his apparatus with He⁴. Discrepancies appeared between his data ([45]) on He⁴ and those of the Leiden workers, which could be traced to errors in the analysis of the Leiden data. When these deficiencies were corrected, considerably better agreement was found among the various B_{44} results.

In determining P–V isotherms experimentally, the measurement subject to the largest percent error is that of the pressure. Kistemaker

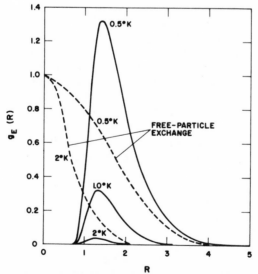

Fig. 3.6. Exchange correlation function in reduced units, $R = r/r_0$, for the LJ-1 potential at several temperatures. Dotted lines give the free-particle exchange correlation function [after Larsen *et al.* ([34])].

and Keesom ([44]), who worked with rather low pressures, used the ingenious method of determining levels of a mercury manometer by making x-ray shadowgraphs of the menisci followed by precise measurement of the photographic plates. On the other hand, Keller ([45]) used for pressures less than 40 mm Hg a manometer filled with dibutyl sebacate, which had been completely outgassed prior to filling and the density of which had been carefully calibrated as a function of temperature. This oil gives a magnification factor of about 13 over mercury. In addition, Keller eliminated "dead" volume corrections by placing a valve directly at the cell containing the experimental gas, and as well measured the number of moles of gas contained in the cell at room temperature (rather than at low temperatures, as done previously) where the appropriate corrections can be more accurately determined. These precautions are mentioned since they have significance for determining precise values of A and B, both being of considerable importance for establishing the temperature scale in the liquid helium region (see Chapter 4).

The analysis of the isotherms can be made according to either equation (3.13) or (3.14), from which B is obtained, respectively, as either

$$\left[\frac{d(P\Omega/N)}{d(N/\Omega)}\right]_{P=0} \quad \text{or} \quad \left[\frac{d(P\Omega/N)}{dP}\right]_{P=0}$$

where N is the number of moles of gas in the experimental cell of volume Ω. However, it has been established empirically for most gases below their Boyle points that the isotherms in the inverse-volume representation are more linear at low pressure, and thus more reliably extrapolated to $P = 0$, than the corresponding power series in pressure. The reverse is true above the Boyle temperature. Consequently, at low temperature, B_{44} is determined as the limiting slope of $(P\Omega/N)$ vs. (N/Ω) plots of the data, and A is obtained from the $(P\Omega/N)$ value of the intercept. A fit to the B_{44} results of Keller is given by the equation

$$B_{44} = (23.05 - 421.17/T) \quad \text{cm}^3/\text{mole} \tag{3.56}$$

The measured values of B_{44} are shown in Fig. 3.7 plotted against $1/T$.

Any curvature found in the isotherm plots is due to contributions from C_{44} and perhaps higher virial coefficients, but from all the data obtained so far it has not been possible to extract values of C_{44} which are statistically meaningful. About all one can say about C_{44} is that at $4.2°K$ it is small and negative, and that as the temperature is lowered it remains negative but increases in magnitude, apparently rather rapidly.

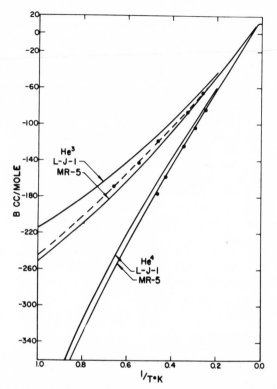

Fig. 3.7. Experimental values of B_{44} and B_{33} compared with calculations using LJ-1 and MR-5 [from Keller ([46])].

Five P–V isotherms between 1.5 and 3.8°K for pure He^3 have been measured by Keller ([46]) using the same apparatus as in the case of He^4. Values of B_{33} obtained from these are also plotted in Fig. 3.7, and it is seen that the differences between B_{33} and B_{44} are significant. Only two isotherms for He^3, those at 3.786°K and 2.991°K, displayed distinct curvature requiring for their description positive values of C_{44}, which evidently have real significance. The virial-coefficient data may be used to calculate the density of the gas at saturated vapor pressure, and if this is done at 2.991°K using only B_{33} in the inverse-volume expansion, one arrives at an imaginary solution for the density. However, if the term in C_{33} is added, a real solution results in good agreement with the saturated density measured directly by Kerr ([47]). Peshkov ([48]) has used an optical method to measure the equation of state of He^3 between 1.6°K and 3.4°K. While there is rather more scatter in these data than in Keller's, the results for B_{33} from the two investigations are compatible.

In the process of arriving at the 1962 Scale of Temperatures, Roberts, Sherman, and Sydoriak ([49]) reanalyzed Keller's isotherm data by more powerful statistical methods than originally used. With the exception of one isotherm, the reanalysis produced changes of considerably less than 1 % in values of B_{33} and B_{44}. Empirical fits to the He^3 data were given for B_{33} and C_{33} as

$$B_{33} = (4.942 - 270.976/T) \quad \text{cm}^3/\text{mole} \qquad (3.57)$$

and

$$C_{33} = 2866T^{-1/2} \quad \text{cm}^6/\text{mole}^2 \qquad (3.58)$$

Finally, Keller ([50]) has measured B_{mix} at 2.146°K and at 3.944°K for a gaseous solution containing 54.75 atomic percent He^3, 45.25% He^4. The experimental values of B_{mix} at these two temperatures are respectively -144.5 and -70.0 cm^3/mole, and may be compared with the figures -145.2 and -73.0 cm^3/mole obtained from equation (3.46) in the following way. We first rewrite this equation as

$$B_{\text{mix}} = N_3^2 B_{33} + N_4^2 B_{44} + 2N_3 N_4 \Delta \qquad (3.59)$$

with

$$\Delta = B_{34} = \tfrac{1}{2}(B_{33} + B_{44}) \qquad (3.60)$$

If $\Delta = 0$, the solution is ideal. Values of Δ have been calculated ([30]) and found to be small, -1.73 and -0.98 cm^3/mole at the two temperatures in question, indicating a small solution nonideality. When these values of Δ are combined with B_{44} and B_{33} as obtained from the interpolation formulas (3.56) and (3.57), the above results are calculated. The reasonable agreement between the calculated and observed B_{mix} is interpreted to mean that the gaseous solutions of He^3 and He^4 are indeed nearly ideal and that B_{mix} may be reliably calculated for all concentrations and for temperatures between 2°K and 4°K.

3.2.4. Comparison of Experimental and Calculated Values of B

When the calculations of B_{44} made using LJ-1 ([30]) were compared with the experimental low-temperature values, considerable divergence appeared between the two sets of results, as is evident from Fig. 3.7. At that time, parameters for the Exp-6 (MR-1) potential became available ([18]), but B_{44} calculated from this function offered an even poorer fit to the experiments than did LJ-1. Consequently, the parameters r_m and ϵ were varied, keeping α constant, until a good fit with experimental B_{44} was obtained. The resulting potential was

MR-5. The low-temperature B_{44} calculated ([19]) from it are drawn in Fig. 3.7, indicating that MR-5 provides an excellent interpolation scheme for B_{44} in the low-temperature region. On the other hand, neither LJ-1 nor MR-5 is a good fit to B_{33}, and while the superiority of MR-5 over LJ-1 is clearly evident, a still unresolved question centers about why MR-5 represents B_{33} no better than it does.

3.2.5. The Third Virial Coefficient

For the hard-sphere and square-well potentials, equation (3.34) for the third virial coefficient can be calculated in closed form, the results for the former case being

$$C_{HS} = (5/8)[B_{HS}]^2 \tag{3.61}$$

where $B_{HS} = \frac{2}{3}\pi N_A a_0^3$ is the classical hard-sphere second virial coefficient. When more realistic potentials are considered, exact analytical procedures are not available for solving the three-body problem for Z_3 and it becomes necessary to resort to data-fitting approximations. Even at high temperatures there are limitations upon these procedures, since the potentials used are derived from second virial coefficient data, whereas C depends differently on the shape of the potential than does B.

The situation for He³ and He⁴ at low temperature is far more complicated still, since quantum effects must be considered. A description of the progress made toward the solution of this problem is contained in the work of Pais and Uhlenbeck ([51]). Their investigation shows the extent to which the scattering phase shifts are relevant to C and indicates that the evaluation of C differs according to the type of intermolecular pair forces present. In the case of purely repulsive forces where no two- or three-body bound states exist, the development depends on the results of Lee and Yang ([32]), who showed how many-body interactions may be expressed in terms of two-body interactions (binary collision expansion for evaluating Z_N). For temperatures sufficiently low that only S-wave ($\eta_{l=0}$) contributions need be considered, Pais and Uhlenbeck found for the BE case (in cm⁶/mole²):

$$C_{BE} = N_A^2 \lambda_T^6 \left[\left(\frac{1}{8} - \frac{2}{3^{5/2}} - \frac{4a^2}{\lambda_T^2} + \frac{2^{1/2}\pi}{12\lambda_T^3}(226a^3 - 33a^2 r_0 - 16d^3) \right) \right] \tag{3.62}$$

where a and r_0 are, respectively, the scattering length and the effective range of the potential, and d is a length not derivable from scattering data (for hard spheres of diameter a_0, $a = a_0$, $r = 2a_0/3$, and $\eta_{l=0} = -\mathbf{q}a_0$ with $\mathbf{q}$ in nonreduced units of cm⁻¹).

For the FD gas, the authors indicated that the expression

$$C_{FD} = \frac{N_A^2 \lambda_T^6}{(2\sigma + 1)^2}\left[\left(\frac{1}{8} - \frac{2}{3^{5/2}} + \frac{4\sigma a_0^2}{\lambda_T^2} + \cdots\right]\right. \tag{3.63}$$

derived in the S-wave approximation for hard spheres by Huang, Yang, and Luttinger ([52]) is also appropriate for the general repulsive case. Pais and Uhlenbeck have suggested that He³ at low temperatures might be an example of this case, since it clearly has no bound level. They found that from equation (3.63), C_{33} should be positive and proportional to T^{-2}. Numerically, the experimental values of C_{33} ([46]) at 3.0°K and 3.8°K are in rough accordance with the predictions, though the temperature dependence is quite different [see equation (3.58)]. On the other hand, relation (3.63) should probably not be considered valid at such high temperatures.

Equation (3.62) is not applicable to He⁴, since this isotope may very well have either a bound two-body or three-body level, or both. The appropriate formalism for this situation, called the case of "weak binding," has been shown by Pais and Uhlenbeck to lead to

$$C_{BE} = N_A^2 \lambda_T^6 \left[\frac{81}{8} - \frac{77}{9\sqrt{3}} + \frac{8}{\pi}\right]$$

$$= \frac{9.4 \times 10^5}{T^3} \quad \text{cm}^6/\text{mole}^2 \tag{3.64}$$

We should therefore expect C_{44} to be large and positive for $T < 1°K$, contrary to the indications of experiments thus far.

Larsen ([53]) has calculated C_{44} at low temperatures by evaluating the terms in the Lee and Yang binary collision expansion for forces described by an attractive square well with a finite, though large, repulsive core. The constants for this potential were determined by a fit to low-temperature values of B_{44}—a process with dangers as indicated earlier—under the condition that there should be no two-body bound levels. These calculations gave for $1.7° < T < 8°K$ large positive values of C_{44} similar to the predictions of equation (3.64), even though this equation was derived on the basis of a two-body level. When Larsen introduced the effect of a three-body bound state and evaluated the binary-collision expansion, the results were qualitatively altered to conform roughly to the experimental C_{44} behavior.

3.3. TRANSPORT COEFFICIENTS FOR GASEOUS He³ AND He⁴ AT LOW TEMPERATURES

3.3.1. Formulation of the Transport Coefficients

The derivation of the formalism describing the transport properties of light gases at low temperatures takes into account the same type of quantum effects as were considered for the equation of state. In the latter, for the limit of low densities, it was necessary only to obtain the relative energy levels for the two-body scattering process expressible in terms of the phase shifts. For the transport coefficients, we are interested in how the collisions between particles bring about the transfer of momentum, energy, and matter from one part of the system to another. Consequently, we must investigate the history of the particles before and after the collision. Classically, this can be done in terms of the initial relative energy of the particles, g, and of the angle of deflection, χ, which the trajectory of the center of mass suffers due to the interaction. But in quantum mechanics, if we know g prior to the collision we cannot specify simultaneously the position and the energy of the particles afterwards. It can be shown, however, that it is possible to describe the effects of an encounter by a suitable averaging technique which determines the "total scattering cross section." This in turn becomes expressible as a function of the phase shifts.

A complete account of the theory of the quantum-mechanically determined transport coefficients is given in Chapter 10 of Hirschfelder et al. ([1]), as well as in ([54]). Here we shall give an essentially descriptive resume of the principles involved together with the important equations that result.

The starting point is the classical Boltzmann integrodifferential equation which relates the fluxes of the dynamical variables (e.g., mass flux, momentum flux, and energy flux) of the particles to the external forces acting on the particles. Symbolically, we may write this equation

$$\frac{\partial f}{\partial t} = -\mathbf{p}\frac{\partial f}{\partial \mathbf{r}} + J(ff) \tag{3.65}$$

which has as solutions the single-particle distribution functions $f(t, \mathbf{p}, \mathbf{r})$, describing the nonequilibrium system in terms of the time and the momentum and position vectors of the particles. The time rate of change of f is given as the sum of two terms, the first of which is the streaming term. The second is the collision term, and, as denoted by the appearance of (ff), this depends on the dynamics of the particles undergoing binary collisions only.

In seeking a connection between equation (3.65) and the transport coefficients, we pass through three conceptual steps. The Boltzmann equation describes the behavior of a system not in equilibrium, and though physical reasoning assures us that the system will tend to equilibrium, an additional statement is required to tell us *why* equation (3.65) correctly describes this tendency. The adjunct that provides this is the Boltzmann *H*-theorem. Next we need to know *how* equilibrium is reached, and this is contained in the hydrodynamic equations derived from the Boltzmann equation. And finally, the transport coefficients, such as those of viscosity η, heat conductivity λ, diffusion D, etc., describe *how rapidly* equilibrium is approached.

Some 50 years ago, work with the Boltzmann equation by Hilbert, Chapman, and Enskog resulted in a special solution for f as a power series:

$$f = f_0 + \alpha f_1 + \alpha^2 f_2 + \cdots \tag{3.66}$$

Here the term f_0 is the local Maxwell–Boltzmann distribution and leads to Euler's equations of hydrodynamics for ideal fluids. When $(f_0 + \alpha f_1)$ is considered, the Navier–Stokes equations result, and this is as far as we find it practical to go in the series for our purposes. In order for the series (3.66) to be valid, the ratio (mean time between particle collisions) : (mean time for the particle to traverse the container), expressed through the coefficient α, must be considerably less than unity. The function f_1 embodies the gradients of such quantities as the temperature and the velocities, and these must be small; furthermore, f_1 contains the effects of the interparticle potential and is independent of density. Within these limitations of the Navier–Stokes approximation for a dilute gas, f can be expressed in terms of the expansion coefficients of a certain class of functions known as the Sonine polynomials, which are at the same time related to the transport coefficients.

In establishing the interrelation between these quantities, Chapman and Cowling [55] have deduced the following temperature-dependent integral expressions which describe the dynamics of the collision between two particles of types i and j:

$$\Omega_{ij}^{(n,s)} = \left(\frac{2\pi k_B T}{\mu_{ij}}\right)^{1/2} \int_0^\infty \int_0^\infty \exp(-\gamma_{ij}^2)\, \gamma_{ij}^{2s+3}(1-\cos^n \chi)b\, db\, d\gamma_{ij} \tag{3.67}$$

$\mu_{ij} = m_i m_j/(m_i + m_j)$ is the reduced mass of the particles; γ_{ij} is their reduced relative velocity prior to collision such that $\gamma_{ij}^2 = \frac{1}{2}\mu_{ij}g_{ij}^2/k_B T$; χ is the angle of deflection after collision; and b is an "impact parameter" indicating the distance of closest approach that the two particles would have in the absence of an interparticle potential. The effects of the potential are contained in χ, given by

$$\chi(g, b) = \pi - 2b \int_{r_0}^{\infty} \left(1 - \frac{b^2}{r^2} - \frac{\Phi(r)}{\frac{1}{2}\mu g^2} \right)^{-1/2} r^{-2} \, dr \qquad (3.68)$$

and the cross sections for the collision are defined by

$$Q^{(n)}(g) = 2\pi \int_0^{\infty} (1 - \cos^n \chi) b \, db \qquad (3.69)$$

so that equation (3.67) may be rewritten for a single component as a weighted average over the cross sections,

$$\Omega^{(n,s)} = \left(\frac{k_B T}{2\pi\mu} \right)^{1/2} \int_0^{\infty} \exp(-\gamma^2) \gamma^{2s+3} Q^{(n)}(g) \, d\gamma \qquad (3.70)$$

In terms of the integrals $\Omega^{(n,s)}$, the viscosity and thermal conductivity coefficients for a pure gas are expressed as

$$\eta_{(1)} = 5k_B T / 8\Omega^{(2,2)} \qquad (3.71)$$

$$\lambda_{(1)} = 25c_V k_B T / 16\Omega^{(2,2)} \qquad (3.72)$$

where $c_V = 3k_B/2m$ is the specific heat at constant volume. The diffusion coefficient for a gaseous mixture of two species i and j is

$$[D_{ij}]_{(1)} = 3k_B T / 16\mu_{ij}\Omega_{ij}^{(1,1)} \qquad (3.73)$$

In the case where $i = j$, $\mu_{ij} = m_i/2$, and relation (3.73) describes the self-diffusion coefficient. The subscript (1) in the last three equations indicates that the transport coefficients here are given in the first approximation—that is, using only the first term in the Sonine expansion. Even in this degree of refinement, the formulas provide a rather good account of the transport coefficients, so that the second approximations, which include additional Sonine polynomials, produce corrections that are generally small. $\eta_{(2)}$ and $\lambda_{(2)}$ are given in terms of $\Omega^{(2,s)}$ with $s = 2, 3, 4$, and the $[D_{ij}]_{(2)}$ are given in terms of $\Omega_{ij}^{(2,2)}$ and $\Omega_{ij}^{(1,s)}$ with $s = 1, 2, 3$.

The quantum-mechanical transport coefficients are derived from the classical ones by correspondence, starting with the quantum-mechanical analog of the Boltzmann equation. The latter was first obtained by Uehling and Uhlenbeck[56] who introduced the diffraction and symmetry effects and arrived at solutions for the transport coefficients in terms of the phase shifts. In this treatment, equations (3.70)–(3.73) remain the same. However, since in quantum mechanics the trajectories of the particles after collision are not well-defined, $Q^{(n)}(g)$ can no longer be given directly by equation (3.69), but must be replaced by the corresponding quantum-mechanical versions of the collision cross-sections. For $n = 1$ and 2, these are

$$Q^{(1)} = \frac{8\pi}{q^2} \sum_l (2l + 1) \sin^2 \eta_l \tag{3.74}$$

and

$$Q^{(2)} = \frac{4\pi}{q^2} \sum_l \frac{(l + 1)(l + 2)}{(l + \frac{3}{2})} \sin^2[\eta_{l+2} - \eta_l] \tag{3.75}$$

where $\mathbf{q}$ is in nonreduced units of cm^{-1} but l and η_l have the same significance as discussed earlier in connection with the second virial coefficient. The summations are to be taken over odd l for FD statistics to arrive at $Q_{FD}^{(n)}$ and over even l for BE statistics to obtain $Q_{BE}^{(n)}$.

The above cross sections are for spinless particles; but when $\sigma \neq 0$, they may be combined in the following manner to yield the appropriate total cross sections:

$$[Q_{FD}^{(n)}]^\sigma = \left(\frac{\sigma + 1}{2\sigma + 1}\right) Q_{FD}^{(n)} + \left(\frac{\sigma}{2\sigma + 1}\right) Q_{BE}^{(n)} \tag{3.76}$$

$$[Q_{BE}^{(n)}]^\sigma = \left(\frac{\sigma + 1}{2\sigma + 1}\right) Q_{BE}^{(n)} + \left(\frac{\sigma}{2\sigma + 1}\right) Q_{FD}^{(n)} \tag{3.77}$$

Finally, for the quantum-mechanical case, γ^2 becomes $\hbar^2 q^2/\mu k_B T$. Then, using relations (3.74)–(3.77), the integrals (3.70) may be evaluated for determining the transport coefficients.

For some time after the original derivation of these equations, there were doubts as to whether the method possessed sufficient rigor, since it did not begin from first principles. Subsequently, several groups of authors deduced the quantum-mechanical Boltzmann equation using more sophisticated techniques but achieved essentially the same results. Confidence concerning these increased with each new derivation, although the starting points were still not from first principles. A review of some of these advances has been presented by Mori *et al.*[57]. Recently, however, Hoffman *et al.*[58] have obtained the Boltzmann equation from the N-particle Schrödinger equation and have indeed demonstrated that in the approximation of small gradients, the classical and quantum-mechanical equations are analogous and differ only in the cross sections as indicated above. These authors doubt, nevertheless, that the collision integrals can be expressed in terms of the simple phase-shift representation when higher-order gradients appear. Furthermore, the results are valid only to the extent that the two-particle distribution function can be written as a functional of f. It is still not clear what would be the effect of two-body bound levels on the transport coefficients, but, fortunately, for all practical purposes in the case of helium, this question may be evaded.

3.3.2. Calculation of the Transport Coefficients of He³ and He⁴ at Low Temperature

Quite naturally, the same groups of workers which calculated phase shifts for determining second virial coefficients have also calculated the collision cross sections (3.74) and (3.75) for use in obtaining the transport coefficients. Using the LJ-1 potential, de Boer and co-workers determined the low-temperature (below 5°K) viscosity and thermal conductivity coefficients for He⁴ [59] and He³ [60], while Buckingham's group [28,61] reported these coefficients determined from the Buckingham-type potentials. From the phase shifts obtained by Kilpatrick et al.[19,30], Keller [62] extended the transport calculations to 40°K for both the LJ-1 and MR-5 potentials; more recently, Monchick et al.[63] have carried the LJ-1 results to 300°K. For the temperature regions in which these various calculations overlap, there is general agreement as to the major characteristics of the results. The details of the minor differences will be discussed in the next section, where the calculations are compared with experiment.

For η and λ, the pertinent cross section is $Q^{(2)}$, and it is of interest to inquire how this quantity varies for He⁴ and He³ and depends upon the statistics. These effects were first clearly demonstrated by de Boer and Cohen [60]. Figure 3.8 is based on their results. Here we show the reduced cross section, $Q^{(2)*} = Q^{(2)}/r_0^2$, plotted against reduced energy parameter q for the He⁴ cross section $Q_4^{(2)}$ given by equation (3.77)

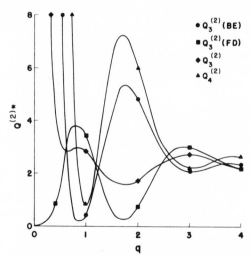

Fig. 3.8. Reduced collision cross sections as a function of reduced energy parameter [from de Boer and Cohen [60] and Keller [62]].

with $\sigma = 0$, the He^3 cross section $Q_3^{(2)}$ given by equation (3.76) with $\sigma = \frac{1}{2}$, and the cross sections $Q_3^{(2)}$ (BE) and $Q_3^{(2)}$ (FD) for hypothetical spinless gases with the mass of He^3 obeying, respectively, BE and FD statistics. At low q, the effect of mass becomes apparent in the different behavior of $Q_4^{(2)}$ and $Q_3^{(2)}$ (BE). Because of the existence of a nearly bound state for two He^4 atoms, the former approaches infinity, while the latter goes to a constant value at $q = 0$, since the smaller mass definitely removes the possibility of a bound state. At higher q, the differences due to mass effects appear to become damped out. The symmetry effects as illustrated by the $Q_3^{(2)}(BE)$–$Q_3^{(2)}(FD)$ pair remain rather dramatic in the interval shown in the figure, but disappear at higher q.

Results for the quantum-mechanically calculated viscosity coefficients are compared in Fig. 3.9 with the classical counterparts for both He^3 and He^4 as a function of temperature. The LJ-1 potential is used as a basis for comparison throughout. As indicated by equations (3.70)

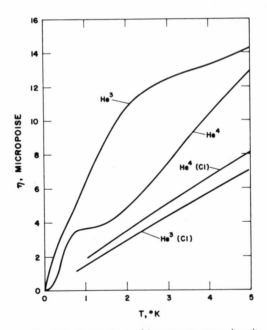

Fig. 3.9. Comparison of low-temperature viscosity coefficients calculated quantum-mechanically (upper curves) and classically (lower curves) from the LJ-1 potential.

and (3.71), at a given temperature, η should depend upon $m^{1/2}$, so we should expect $\eta(\text{He}^3)$ to be smaller than $\eta(\text{He}^4)$ by the factor $\sqrt{3/2}$. In the classical case, this accounts for all the differences observed for the two isotopes; but at low temperatures, symmetry effects dominate the quantum-mechanically determined η and even cause $\eta(\text{He}^3)$ to become larger than $\eta(\text{He}^4)$. As with the case of the second virial coefficient, the exchange contribution dies out rapidly with increasing T, and the differences between $\eta(\text{He}^3)$ and $\eta(\text{He}^4)$ become due entirely to the mass differences. Nevertheless, diffraction effects persist to higher temperatures such that at 40°K the quantum-mechanical value of η for a given isotope is about 4% larger than the corresponding classical value.

The principles involved in the calculation of $Q^{(1)}$, and thus also of the diffusion coefficient, are similar to those indicated above for $Q^{(2)}$, η and λ, with one exception. In the calculations of the cross sections $Q^{(2)}$ for a single-component gas according to equation (3.75), we have assumed that the particles are indistinguishable. If we have a binary mixture of two symmetry types, it makes no difference in the calculation what is assumed about the distinguishability, since the interference terms between even and odd angular momentum states cancel out. However, as Emery [64] has pointed out, in the case of diffusion for such a mixture, these terms for $Q_{ij}^{(1)}$ do not cancel; instead, it is necessary to use nonsymmetrized cross sections, summed over all l, in order to obtain values of $[D_{ij}]_{(1)}$ which may be appropriately compared with experimental results. This point was not appreciated by earlier workers [61,65] who calculated transport properties of mixtures; but the physical reasonableness of Emery's conclusion is evident since the experimental determination of D_{ij} depends entirely upon the two molecular types being distinguishable. Furthermore, collisions between the same species have no effect upon the diffusion flux of one species with respect to the other, so that the important collisions for this process are those involving different kinds of molecules. Symmetry effects do appear in the calculation of $[D_{ij}]_{(2)}$ but contribute minimally to the total coefficient. Remarks similar to these about D_{ij} should apply as well to the thermal diffusion factor α_T, since it also depends upon the integrals $\Omega_{ij}^{(1,s)}$.

3.3.3. Comparison between Experimental and Calculated Transport Coefficients

Measurements of the thermal conductivity of gaseous He^4 between 1.6°K and 90°K have been made by Ubbink and De Haas [66] and of both He^3 and He^4 more recently by Fokkens et al. [67]. In the latter experiments, the temperature range was confined to 0.5°K to 3.0°K for He^3 and 0.9°K to 3.0°K for He^4, the lower limit for He^4 having been determined by the appearance of Knudsen effects due to the low vapor density. Both investigations used the "plate method," in which the gas to be measured is contained between two closely spaced horizontal parallel plates made of copper. The lower plate is held at constant temperature while heat is applied to the upper plate to establish a temperature gradient in a direction to minimize convection effects. In each apparatus, a device was incorporated for varying the distance between the plates. This permitted the determination of corrections associated with the effective thermal resistance due to the small temperature discontinuities which occurred at the gas–metal interfaces. Also, guard plates were added to minimize energy losses from the heated plates to the surroundings. From measurements of the heat inputs and of the resultant temperature gradients, together with appropriate geometrical factors of the apparatus, the thermal conductivity coefficients could be obtained [cf. equation (1.6)].

Results from these experiments are plotted in Fig. 3.10 in comparison with several calculations made using different types of potentials. The agreement between the various investigations is

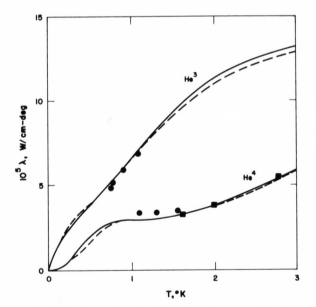

Fig. 3.10. Comparison of calculated and experimental values of thermal conductivity. Calculations: solid lines, Keller ([62]) and Monchick et al. ([63]); dashed lines, Buckingham and Scriven ([61]). Experiments: circles, Fokkens et al. ([67]); squares, Ubbink and De Haas ([66]).

considered quite satisfactory, and it is difficult to assign any significance to the slight differences that do appear.

van Itterbeek et al. ([68]) measured the He⁴ viscosity from 1.3° to 4.2°K by observing the damping of the oscillations of a thin disk suspended in the gas and centered between two fixed disks. Results were obtained which were about 10% larger than the calculations of de Boer ([59]). More recent experiments ([69]) on He⁴ with a similar apparatus but operating in the temperature range 20° to 80°K disclosed a correction that should have been taken into account in the earlier work, but was not. This correction arose from the added damping caused by the mirror attached to the disk suspension and used for measuring the oscillation characteristics. It amounts to about 5% and has the effect of bringing the experimental and theoretical results into closer agreement. Becker and Misenta ([70]) and Becker et al. ([71]) have developed a sensitive technique for measuring η by employing an oscillating cylinder and appropriate electronic circuitry to detect changes in capacitance associated with changes in the amplitudes of oscillation. An accuracy of better than $\sim 1\%$ in η (at 5 μP) was claimed by the authors. Measurements were made on both He³ and He⁴ gas in the liquid He range ([71]) and in the liquid H₂ range ([70]). The results are quite well represented by the LJ-1 calculations of Keller ([62]) below 40°K and the calculations of Buckingham and Scriven ([61]) below 5°K. Above 40°K, the data of Coremans et al. ([69]) are also well fitted by a LJ-1 potential, calculations for which have been made by Monchick et al. ([63]). When the LJ-1 and MR-5 potentials are compared, it is found that although MR-5 gives a superior fit to the low-temperature second virial coefficients, it provides a particularly poor representation for the experimental viscosity data.

Diffusion measurements of He³ in He⁴ at twelve temperatures between 1.7°K to 296°K have been obtained by Bendt ([72]) using a "diffusion bridge." Two reservoirs of gas with different isotopic concentrations were connected to opposite ends of a 5-cm-long tube. The resulting concentration gradient along the tube under steady-state flow conditions was measured by sampling the gas at the tube ends and subsequently analyzing the samples with a mass spectrometer. This, together with a knowledge of flow rates of gas from the reservoirs, allowed determination of the mutual-diffusion coefficient D_{34} which relates the concentration gradient dN_3/dz to the isotopic diffusion velocity v_3. Thus

$$N_3 v_3 = D_{34} \, dN_3/dz \qquad (3.78)$$

where N_3 is the mole fraction of He³. Bendt measured D_{34} for mixtures of He³ and He⁴ starting with pure He⁴ in one reservoir and He⁴ containing 15.88 mole-% He³ in the other. His results of $nD_{34}\mu$

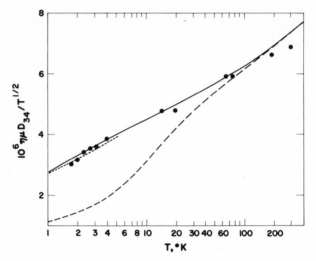

Fig. 3.11. He³–He⁴ diffusion coefficient plotted as $nD_{34}\mu/T^{1/2}$ *vs.* T [after Monchick *et al.* [63]]. Circles are experimental points of Bendt [72]. Dashed curve is classical theory; solid and dotted curves are quantum calculations by Monchick *et al.* [63] and by Bucking-ham and Scriven [61].

(n is the atomic density and μ the reduced mass) are presented in Fig. 3.11 along with calculations by Monchick *et al.* [63] based on the LJ-1 potential. Here again, the usefulness of this potential is demonstrated for describing the actual properties of helium. While in the first approximation, the calculated D_{34} is independent of concentration, this is not true for the second approximation. However, Monchick *et al.* found that for Bendt's case of an average He³ concentration of 7.94 mole-%, the correction is at most 1%. Since, as we have already seen, symmetry effects are negligible here, all of the differences between the quantum calculation of D_{34} and the classical one, also plotted in Fig. 3.11, arise from diffraction effects.

Monchick *et al.* [63] have also discussed the self-diffusion coefficients D_{33} and D_{44} as well as the thermal diffusion factor α_T. Since He³ has a nuclear spin, two orientations are possible in a magnetic field, and therefore the particles can be considered as distinguishable. Using the spin-echo technique, Luszczynski *et al.* [73] have measured the spin-diffusion coefficient of He³ between 1°K and 4.2°K. According to Emery's prescription [64], this is equivalent to self-diffusion, and on this basis the calculations are in good accord with the observations.

D_{44} has not as yet been observed experimentally, since no way has been demonstrated for "tagging" these spinless particles. The thermal diffusion factor is strongly dependent upon the mixture concentration and is more sensitive than the other transport coefficients to the details of the potential function chosen for calculation. Watson *et al.* ([74]) have determined α_T experimentally for mixtures containing equal parts of He^3 and He^4 for temperatures above 100°K, and van der Valk ([75]) has measured α_T for a 10% He^3 mixture between 14°K and room temperature. There is good agreement between the results of these two investigations in the region of overlap, but at all temperatures, there are serious discrepancies between the calculations and observations, which Monchick *et al.* ascribe to excessive steepness in the repulsive part of the LJ-1 potential.

REFERENCES

1. J. O. Hirschfelder, C. F. Curtiss, and R. B. Bird, *Molecular Theory of Gases and Liquids,* John Wiley, New York (1954). See especially Chapters 6 and 10.
2. J. O. Hirschfelder, *J. Chem. Phys.*, **43**, S199 (1965).
3. J. C. Slater, *Phys. Rev.*, **91**, 528 (1953).
4. C. W. Scherr and R. E. Knight, *Rev. Mod. Phys.*, **35**, 436 (1963).
5. E. Hylleraas, *Z. Physik*, **65**, 209 (1930).
6. C. L. Pekeris, *Phys. Rev.*, **126**, 1470 (1962).
7. P. Rosen, *J. Chem. Phys.*, **18**, 1182 (1950).
8. P. E. Phillipson, *Phys. Rev.*, **125**, 1981 (1962).
9. H. Margenau, *Phys. Rev.*, **56**, 1000 (1939).
10. Y. M. Chan and A. Dalgarno, *Proc. Phys. Soc. (London)*, **86**, 777 (1965).
11. C. H. Page, *Phys. Rev.*, **53**, 426 (1938).
12. N. R. Kestner and O. Sinanoglu, *J. Chem. Phys.*, **45**, 194 (1966).
13. L. W. Bruch and I. J. McGee, *J. Chem. Phys.*, **46**, 2959 (1967).
14. A. Dalgarno, *Rev. Mod. Phys.*, **35**, 611 (1963).
15. R. A. Buckingham, *Planetary and Space Science*, **2**, 205 (1961).
16. J. de Boer and A. Michels, *Physica*, **5**, 945 (1938).
17. J. de Boer and R. J. Lunbeck, *Physica*, **14**, 510 (1948).
18. E. A. Mason and W. E. Rice, *J. Chem. Phys.*, **22**, 522, 843 (1954).
19. J. E. Kilpatrick, W. E. Keller, and E. F. Hammel, *Phys. Rev.*, **97**, 9 (1955).
20. R. A. Buckingham, A. E. Davies, and A. R. Davies, reported at Conference on Thermodynamic and Transport Properties of Fluids, London, 1957.
21. J. L. Yntema and W. G. Schneider, *J. Chem. Phys.*, **18**, 646 (1950).
22. H. L. Johnston and E. R. Grilly, *J. Phys. Chem.*, **46**, 938 (1942).
23. A Michels and W. Wouters, *Physica*, **8**, 923 (1941).
24. B. Khan, Thesis, Utrecht (1938); also reprinted in *Studies in Statistical Mechanics* (J. de Boer and G. E. Uhlenbeck, eds.), Vol. III, North Holland, Amsterdam (1965).
25. L. Gropper, *Phys. Rev.*, **51**, 1108 (1937).
26. E. Beth and G. E. Uhlenbeck, *Physica*, **4**, 915 (1937).
27. H. S. W. Massey and R. A. Buckingham, *Proc. Roy. Soc. (London)*, **A168**, 378 (1938); **A169**, 205 (1939).
28. R. A. Buckingham, J. Hamilton, and H. S. W. Massey, *Proc. Roy. Soc. (London)*, **A179**, 103 (1941).
29. J. de Boer, J. van Kranendonk, and K. Compaan, *Physica*, **16**, 545 (1950).

30. J. E. Kilpatrick, W. E. Keller, E. F. Hammel, and N. Metropolis, *Phys. Rev.*, **94**, 1003 (1954).
31. J. E. Kilpatrick and M. F. Kilpatrick, *J. Chem. Phys.*, **19**, 930 (1951).
32. T. D. Lee and C. N. Yang, *Phys. Rev.*, **105**, 1119 (1957); **113**, 1165 (1959).
33. S. Y. Larsen, J. E. Kilpatrick, E. H. Lieb, and H. F. Jordan, *Phys. Rev.*, **140**, A129 (1965).
34. S. Y. Larsen, K. Witte, and J. E. Kilpatrick, *J. Chem. Phys.*, **44**, 213 (1966).
35. M. E. Boyd, S. Y. Larsen, and J. E. Kilpatrick, *J. Chem. Phys.*, **45**, 499 (1966); **46**, 1224 (1967).
36. E. H. Lieb, *J. Math. Phys.*, **7**, 1016 (1966).
37. H. E. DeWitt, *J. Math. Phys.*, **3**, 1003 (1962).
38. G. E. Uhlenbeck and E. Beth, *Physica*, **3**, 729 (1936).
39. F. Mohling, *Phys. Fluids*, **6**, 1097 (1963).
40. R. A. Handelsman and J. B. Keller, *Phys. Rev.*, **148**, 94 (1966).
41. T. L. Hill, *Statistical Mechanics*, Chapter 6, McGraw-Hill, New York (1956).
42. W. H. Keesom and H. H. Kraak, *Physica*, **2**, 37 (1935).
43. W. H. Keesom and W. K. Walstra, *Physica*, **7**, 985 (1940).
44. J. Kistemaker and W. H. Keesom, *Physica*, **12**, 227 (1946).
45. W. E. Keller, *Phys. Rev.*, **97**, 1 (1955); *Phys. Rev.*, **100**, 1790 (1955).
46. W. E. Keller, *Phys. Rev.*, **98**, 1571 (1955).
47. E. C. Kerr, *Phys. Rev.*, **96**, 551 (1954).
48. V. P. Peshkov, *Zh. Eksperim. i Teor. Fiz.*, **33**, 833 (1957) [English translation, *Soviet Phys.—JETP*, **6**, 645 (1957)].
49. T. R. Roberts, R. H. Sherman, and S. G. Sydoriak, *J. Res. Natl. Bur. Std.*, **68A**, 567 (1964).
50. W. E. Keller, *Phys. Rev.*, **100**, 1021 (1955).
51. A. Pais and G. E. Uhlenbeck, *Phys. Rev.*, **116**, 250 (1959).
52. K. Huang and C. N. Yang, *Phys. Rev.*, **105**, 767 (1957); K. Huang, C. N. Yang, and J. M. Luttinger, *ibid*, 776.
53. S. Y. Larsen, *Phys. Rev.*, **130**, 1426 (1963).
54. J. de Boer, in *Advances in Low Temperature Physics* (C. J. Gorter, ed.), Vol. I, p. 381, North Holland, Amsterdam (1955).
55. S. Chapman and T. G. Cowling, *The Mathematical Theory of Non-Uniform Gases*, Cambridge University Press (1939).
56. E. A. Uehling and G. E. Uhlenbeck, *Phys. Rev.*, **43**, 552 (1933).
57. H. Mori, I. Oppenheim, and J. Ross, in *Studies in Statistical Mechanics* (J. de Boer and G. E. Uhlenbeck, eds.), Vol. I, p. 217, North Holland, Amsterdam (1962).
58. D. K. Hoffman, J. J. Mueller, and C. F. Curtiss, *J. Chem. Phys.*, **43**, 2878 (1965).
59. J. de Boer, *Physica*, **10**, 348 (1943).
60. J. de Boer and E. G. D. Cohen, *Physica*, **17**, 993 (1951).
61. R. A. Buckingham and R. A. Scriven, *Proc. Phys. Soc.* (*London*), **B65**, 376 (1952).
62. W. E. Keller, *Phys. Rev.*, **105**, 41 (1957).
63. L. Monchick, E. A. Mason, R. J. Munn, and F. J. Smith, *Phys. Rev.*, **139**, A1076 (1965).
64. V. J. Emery, *Phys. Rev.*, **133**, A661 (1964).
65. E. G. D. Cohen, M. J. Offerhaus, and J. de Boer, *Physica*, **20**, 501 (1954).
66. J. B. Ubbink and W. J. De Haas, *Physica*, **10**, 465 (1943).
67. K. Fokkens, W. Vermeer, K. W. Taconis, and R. De Bruyn Ouboter, *Physica*, **30**, 2153 (1964).
68. A. van Itterbeek, F. W. Schapink, G. J. van den Berg, and H. J. M. van Beek, *Physica*, **19**, 1158 (1953).
69. J. M. J. Coremans, A. van Itterbeek, J. J. M. Beenakker, H. F. P. Knaap, and P. Zandbergen, *Physica*, **24**, 557 (1958).

70. E. W. Becker and R. Misenta, *Z. Physik*, **140**, 535 (1955).
71. E. W. Becker, R. Misenta, and F. Schmeissner, *Phys. Rev.*, **93**, 244 (1954); *Z. Physik*, **137**, 126 (1954).
72. P. J. Bendt, *Phys. Rev.*, **110**, 85 (1958).
73. K. Luszczynski, R. E. Norberg, and J. E. Opfer, *Phys. Rev.*, **128**, 186 (1962).
74. W. W. Watson, A. J. Howard, N. E. Miller, and R. M. Shiffrin, *Z. Naturforsch.*, **18A**, 242 (1963).
75. F. van der Valk, Thesis, University of Amsterdam (1963).

Chapter 4

The Transition from the Gas to the Liquid

In this chapter, we bridge our discussions of the gas and the liquid by considering several aspects of the vapor pressures, P_{sat}, of the two helium isotopes. The P_{sat} vs. T relations for He^3 and He^4 relative to some fixed absolute temperatures establish convenient and practical temperature scales. Indeed, these scales have become the temperature standards for work in the liquid helium region. By itself, this fact is of considerable importance; in addition, the thermodynamic formulation of the vapor pressure function embodies all of the essential thermal and state data for the two phases in equilibrium and thereby serves as a criterion for consistency between the temperature scale and the various experimentally measured thermodynamic quantities. The liquid–vapor equilibria will be discussed from this viewpoint.

4.1. ABSOLUTE THERMOMETRY IN THE LIQUID HELIUM REGION

The absolute thermodynamic scale of temperature is generally derived from the second law of thermodynamics by considering the efficiency of an ideal Carnot cycle operating between two temperatures t_1 and t_2. If Q_1 is the heat isothermally and reversibly absorbed by a reservoir at t_1 and Q_2 the heat similarly extracted from a reservoir at t_2, then the scale is determined by

$$Q_1/Q_2 = f(t_1)/f(t_2) = T_1/T_2 \qquad (4.1)$$

The equality on the right is made arbitrarily, a condition which is removed when the size of the scale interval, or degree, is agreed upon. Presently, this is done by fixing the number of degrees between the zero of the scale and the triple point of water to be 273.16. The result is the "Kelvin scale," with temperatures T given in degrees Kelvin. This scale is independent of the properties of a particular substance and in practice may be established by measuring the quantities that appear in any formulation of the second law of thermodynamics. Since the vapor-pressure–temperature relation is not one of these, it can function only as a secondary standard and must be based on more fundamental determinations. Two of the latter type that have been used for the scale in the liquid helium region are the gas thermometer and the acoustic interferometer.

The basis for gas thermometry is that given a constant number of moles of gas maintained successively at two temperatures T_1 and T_2, then the ratio of the products P_1V_1 and P_2V_2 is equal to the ratio of T_1 and T_2. This relation holds for an ideal gas; but for a real gas, the PV products must be corrected through the equation of state, usually written in the convenient virial form according to either equation (3.13) or (3.14). A common experimental arrangement for a gas thermometer is shown schematically in Fig. 4.1 where the bulb A communicates with a pressure-measuring device C (in this case, a constant-volume manometer) via the line B. The system is charged with a fixed amount of gas determined at some reference temperature T_0 by measuring the PV product and applying the appropriate nonideality corrections.

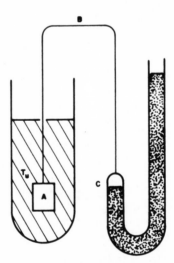

Fig. 4.1. Gas thermometer, schematic. The pressure of gas in bulb A at the unknown temperature T_u is measured by constant-volume manometer C. B is dead space connecting A and C.

To establish the unknown temperature T_u at which the bulb may be subsequently maintained, it is then merely necessary tó measure the corresponding pressure. Though simple in principle, the gas thermometer must be carefully designed and operated for it to yield accurate results, since the method is subject to a variety of more or less insidious errors. Some of the more important sources of error are:

1. Since the environment of A changes from T_0 to T_u, the coefficient of volume expansion must be accurately known for A.

2. The amount of gas in the system is distributed between A and C, which are at different temperatures, and also in the co-called "dead" space of B, along which a temperature gradient exists. Since the reliability of the results from the thermometer depends intimately upon knowledge of the precise amount of gas in A, it is necessary to: (a) keep the volume ratio of A to C large; (b) know the absorption properties of the gas in A at T_u and T_0; and (c) maintain the volume of B small and as well determine the temperature distribution along it.

3. The initial pressure at T_0 is usually kept low in order to minimize uncertainties due to nonideality corrections. Hence, when T_u is at helium temperatures, P_u is likely to be very small and consequently difficult to measure accurately. This difficulty is enhanced by a thermomolecular pressure correction which must be made when both P_u and the cross section of B are small and $T_u \ll T_0$.

Several of these difficulties can be avoided by extracting absolute temperatures from PV isotherm measurements, as described in Section 3.2.3. This method becomes in principle equivalent to the gas thermometer once the value of the gas constant, $R = N_A k_B$, is established. For the low-temperature He^4 isotherms obtained at Leiden ([1]), the amounts of gas involved were ultimately determined relative to the boiling point temperature of normal-H_2. This was necessary in order to avoid large "dead" space corrections; but it also entailed some drawbacks. Possible errors are magnified since the temperatures in the liquid helium range are obtained in two gas thermometer steps instead of one; and, in addition, the boiling point of a given sample of n-H_2 may be uncertain due to the occurrence of ortho–para conversion in the sample, the boiling point of $20°K$ equilibrium H_2 being about $0.12°K$ lower than that of n-H_2. On the other hand, Keller's method ([2]) of placing a valve directly on the gas cell eliminated corrections for the "dead" space and as well permitted the amounts of gas to be measured directly at room temperature relative to an accurately known fixed temperature point. These results at 10 temperatures below $4°K$ remain the only gas thermometer points in the helium region which are independent of low-temperature fixed-point determinations.

More recently, workers at the National Bureau of Standards in Washington, D.C., have adopted an intriguing approach to low-temperature absolute thermometry which bypasses some of the above-indicated difficulties associated with gas thermometer techniques. The method involves the measurement of the speed of sound, u_1, in gaseous helium as a function of pressure at constant temperature. The absolute temperature is obtained through the relation

$$u_1^2 = (C_P/C_V)_{P=0}(RT/M)(1 + \alpha P + \beta P^2 + \cdots) \qquad (4.2)$$

The derivation of equation (4.2) follows from the definition of u_1^2 as the product of the density and the adiabatic bulk modulus of the gas, $\rho^{-1}(\partial \rho/\partial P)_s$, plus the assumption of the virial form for the equation of state. $(C_P/C_V)_{P=0}$ for He gas is taken to be 5/3; M is the molecular weight of the sample gas; the coefficient α is given as

$$\alpha = \frac{1}{RT}\left[2B + \frac{4T}{3}\left(\frac{dB}{dT}\right) + \frac{4}{15}T^2\frac{d^2B}{dT^2}\right] \qquad (4.3)$$

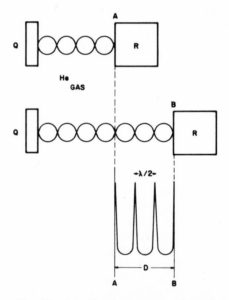

Fig. 4.2. Acoustic thermometer, schematic [after Plumb and Cataland [3]]. Q is the quartz resonator and R the reflector. When R is displaced from A to B, the number of half-wavelengths is counted by the voltage peaks. Measurement of D then gives λ.

and β is a similar but much more complicated function involving both the second and third virial coefficients together with their temperature derivatives. A plot of u_1^2 vs. P for an isotherm when extrapolated to $P = 0$ gives the absolute temperature of the isotherm.

Plumb and Cataland ([3]) have described an ultrasonic interferometer designed to measure the wavelength λ of a constant-frequency ($\nu \approx 10^6$ c/sec) sound signal which is generated by a quartz crystal driven in its resonant mode (Fig. 4.2). The signal is transmitted through the gas sample and reflected back to the crystal from a plane surface, the position of which is variable with respect to the source. Monitoring of the voltage across the piezoelectric crystal discloses sharp peaks when standing waves are established between the crystal and the reflecting plate, so that as the plate is displaced, successive peaks are spaced at $\lambda/2$. The speed is then obtained from the usual relation $u_1 = \lambda\nu$. Hence the measurement of T depends most sensitively upon the exact spatial relationship between the crystal and the plate. Since in practice the pressure of the sample gas is sufficiently low that the higher terms in P occurring in equation (4.2) are negligible, the demands for precise manometry are not nearly so exacting as in the case of gas thermometry. Five isotherms of u_1^2 vs. P for He^4 gas in the range 2° to 5°K have been analyzed by Cataland and Plum ([4]). Grimsrud and Werntz ([31]) have more recently measured u_1 in He^4 gas between 2.130° and 3.816°K and in He^3 gas between 1.232° and 3.598°K using a similar apparatus. The results will be considered in Section 4.4 with respect to the presently accepted temperature scale.

4.2. THE SATURATED VAPOR PRESSURE OF LIQUID He^4

Beginning with the first liquefaction of helium in 1908 and continuing until about 15 years ago, definitive measurements of the vapor pressure of He^4 had been almost exclusively the province of the Leiden laboratory. During that period, extensive and careful investigations were made upon various aspects of the problem. These have been chronicled in Keesom's book ([5]) and in the review article by van Dijk and Durieux ([6]). We wish here to comment briefly on two of the outstanding results of this early work which have been incorporated in the most recent temperature scale.

In 1911, Kamerlingh Onnes ([7]), during the course of vapor pressure measurements above the boiling point, determined the critical temperature and critical pressure of the gas (listed in Table 1.I) using a gas thermometer filled to a pressure of 300 mm Hg at the ice-point of water. To date, there has not been another fundamental investigation of this pair of critical properties. However, Berman and Swenson ([8]) have reexamined the vapor pressure above the boiling point and, by assuming

Kamerlingh Onnes' value for the critical pressure, find the corresponding temperature in accord with the 1911 results. See, however, Section 7.2.1.

The other set of data which has so far stood the test of time is a determination of the normal boiling point of liquid He^4 made in 1937 by Schmidt and Keesom ([9]). Results were obtained in the form of a ratio of the He^4 and n-H_2 boiling points. The accepted value of the latter has wandered slightly with time but is now fixed such that the Schmidt and Keesom original results are changed by only $-0.0006°K$. A considerable amount of confidence has been placed on this determination, especially by subsequent Leiden workers ([10–12]) who based all He^4 vapor pressure measurements on this one point. Fortunately, this confidence has proved well founded, the Leiden He^4 boiling point value of $4.215°K$ having been confirmed by Berman and Swenson ([8]) and indirectly by Keller ([2]) so that it remains a "tie-down" point for the He^4 temperature scale presently in use. As will be more fully discussed in Section 4.4, the acoustical-thermometer results presently challenge the accuracy of this point, but a serious proposal for a replacement value has not yet been made.

In addition to the acceptance of the normal boiling point and the critical point of He^4, as indicated above, the following more modern vapor pressure determinations are presently regarded as being the most accurate: 14 points between $4.2°$ and $5.2°K$ by Berman and Swenson ([8]), with amounts of gas measured relative to the n-H_2 boiling point; 10 points between $1.5°$ and $4.0°K$ by Keller ([2]) in which the He^4 vapor pressure was compared with five isotherms of He^4 and five isotherms of He^3, the amounts of gas being determined relative to the transition temperature of $Na_2SO_4 \cdot 10\,H_2O$ at $305.54°K$; and 14 gas thermometer points between $1.3°$ and $2.15°K$ by Kistemaker ([12]) and 14 He^4 isotherm extrapolations by Kistemaker and Keesom ([11,12]) between $1.84°$ and $2.1°K$, both sets of data being referred to the normal boiling point of He^4.

It can readily be appreciated that the derivation of an accurate P_{sat}–T relation by using an absolute thermometer is an onerous task and one which cannot practicably be accomplished at temperature intervals sufficiently close-spaced to define the entire range. Hence it is necessary to supplement the absolute measurements using interpolation devices which may be calibrated at appropriate fixed points. These devices should involve physical properties which are smooth monotonic functions of the temperature and which have large enough temperature coefficients to enable small temperature changes to be easily distinguishable. Two convenient methods satisfying these requirements involve the use of a resistance thermometer, which may be made of phosphor bronze, germanium, or an ordinary radio carbon resistor,* and the

* See, for example, Clement et al. ([13]).

magnetic thermometer [14], which depends upon the temperature variation of the susceptibility of a paramagnetic sample. Both of these methods are considerably more sensitive at low temperatures than the gas thermometer and have been effective in establishing the $P_{sat}-T$ relation for He^4. A survey of absolute thermometry at liquid helium temperatures, together with a discussion of interpolation devices and the experimental difficulties encountered in making accurate vapor pressure measurements, has been given by Durieux [15].

4.3. THE SATURATED VAPOR PRESSURE OF LIQUID He^3

Measurements of the vapor pressure of pure He^3 were first obtained by Sydoriak et al. [16] and subsequently refined in 1950 by Abraham et al. [17] and in 1964 by Sydoriak and Sherman [18]. All of these investigators arrived at the He^3 $P_{sat}-T$ relation by intercomparison with that of He^4. In the 1950 work, the authors calculated from their data the thermodynamic properties along the saturation curve (see Section 4.5) and concluded that the liquid displayed some sort of anomaly at about 1°K. Since further studies on the properties of He^3 failed to disclose any anomaly and since additional thermodynamic inconsistencies appeared in the interval 1° to 2°K, Sydoriak and Sherman were led to repeat the intercomparison of the vapor pressures, designated (P_3, P_4).

The 1950 (P_3, P_4) measurements were made with the two vapor pressure bulbs side by side and drilled out from a common copper block, with the expectation that thereby good thermal contact would be ensured. However, the 1964 work demonstrated that below the λ-point of He^4, the P_{sat} measured in a He^4 vapor pressure bulb does not properly reflect the temperature of either an object or a refrigerating bath with which the bulb is in contact. Errors in using a bulb are considered to arise from two sources. The first is due to the He^4 film which at some height in the tube evaporates and then recondenses in some colder portion of the system, presumably at the surface of the liquid; the return flow of the vapor is accompanied by a pressure drop, ΔP_F, which contributes to the apparent observation of the vapor pressure. The second phenomenon affecting the measurements is associated with a temperature jump across a liquid–solid boundary whenever there is heat flow, $\dot{Q}$, across the boundary. This effect was first studied in He^4 by Kapitza [19] and the temperature jump ΔT_K has therefore come to be known as the "Kapitza resistance." He found the relation $\Delta T_K = 5.9 \, \dot{Q}/AT^3$, when the boundary of area A was between He II and polished copper. Subsequent investigators [20] have found higher values for the numerical coefficient, depending somewhat upon the condition of the surface, and a temperature behavior more like $T^{-2.5}$. Since the Kapitza resistance increases rapidly as the temperature decreases, the heat flux, due largely to the recondensing film, causes ΔT_K to increase by a factor of about 10 between the λ-point and 1°K. In experimental arrangements incorporating a vapor pressure bulb near 1°K and below, an intolerably large correction to the temperature measurement is introduced just when high accuracy is required. To avoid ΔT_K, Sydoriak and Sherman ([18]) measured He⁴ vapor pressures from the liquid bath, and although corrections for ΔP_F were required, these could be determined by careful ancillary experiments.

Thermal transpiration is another effect for which corrections must be made if vapor pressures are to be accurately measured at very low temperatures. When a steady-state temperature gradient is established in a tube containing a gas, the pressure at the warm end and cold end

Table 4.I. A Comparison of Vapor Pressures, Molar Volumes of the Saturated Liquids, and Latent Heats of He³ and He⁴ at Selected Temperatures

T,	$P_{sat}(3)$ [a]	$P_{sat}(4)$ [b]	$V(3)$ [a]	$V(4)$ [c]	$H_v(3)$ [a]	$H_v(4)$ [d]
°K	(mm Hg)	(mm Hg)	(cm³/mole)	(cm³/mole)	(J/mole)	(J/mole)
0	—	—	36.83	27.57	20.56	59.62
0.2	1.21×10^{-5}	—	36.78	27.58	24.39	—
0.4	2.81×10^{-2}	—	36.72	27.58	27.97	—
0.6	0.544	2.81×10^{-4}	36.72	27.58	31.42	—
0.8	2.893	1.14×10^{-2}	36.78	27.58	34.61	—
1.0	8.842	0.120	36.91	27.59	37.51	80.22
1.2	20.163	0.625	37.09	27.59	40.08	84.17
1.4	38.516	2.155	37.35	27.58	42.29	87.76
1.6	65.467	5.690	37.72	27.57	44.07	90.74
1.8	102.516	12.466	38.20	27.53	45.34	92.72
2.0	151.112	23.767	38.85	27.48	45.99	93.13
2.2	212.673	40.466	39.68	27.39	45.91	90.75
2.4	288.613	63.304	40.73	27.53	44.94	91.73
2.6	380.383	93.733	42.12	27.73	42.84	92.80
2.8	489.549	132.952	44.05	28.00	39.11	93.58
3.0	617.907	182.073	46.82	28.32	32.25	93.91
3.2	—	242.266	—	28.73	—	93.75
3.4	—	314.697	—	29.21	—	92.99
3.6	—	400.471	—	29.77	—	91.64
3.8	—	500.688	—	30.41	—	89.53
4.0	—	616.537	—	31.14	—	86.56
4.2	—	749.328	—	31.97	—	82.34

[a] From T_{62} and thermodynamic properties consistent with the scale ([32]).
[b] From T_{58}.
[c] From E. C. Kerr and R. D. Taylor, *Ann. Phys. (N.Y.)*, **26**, 292 (1964).
[d] H_v^0 from T_{58}; remaining values of H_v from T_{L55} ([6]).

will differ by an amount ΔP_{tm}, the thermomolecular pressure difference. The magnitude of ΔP_{tm} depends upon the temperatures T_w and T_c of the warm and cold ends, respectively, upon the mean pressure, and upon the tube radius. At low pressure and when T_c is small, the corrections can become very large and troublesome. Sydoriak and Sherman [18] have described graphical means for making the corrections. Quite recently, Watkins et al. [21] have carefully determined ΔP_{tm} for both He³ and He⁴ gas over a wide range of conditions. They found the same ΔP_{tm} for the two isotopes, other things being equal, except for He⁴ below the λ-point where effects due to the film complicate matters. However, the corrections apparently do not conform too well with theoretical predictions, suggesting that further work is necessary to ensure the accuracy in P_{sat} measurements required for international temperature scales.

Table 4.I presents an abbreviated listing of the vapor pressure intercomparisons for He³ and He⁴. The data given here are smoothed as finally obtained for the temperature scales T_{58} and T_{62}.

4.4. THE T_{58} SCALE OF TEMPERATURES—He⁴

The establishment of a temperature scale involves considerably more than just the publication of good data; it requires actual acceptance of those data by the scientific community after critical consideration of all the available information. Historically, this has resulted in continual changes and refinements in the numbers. From 1908 to 1939, these processes were effected by the single laboratory at Leiden which produced a succession of scales—the 1924, 1929, 1932, 1937, and 1939 scales [5,6]. All were based solely on gas thermometer measurements fitted numerically by interpolation formulas—with the exception of the 1939 scale, which, from 1.6°K downward, was given by a thermodynamic P_{sat}–T relation later confirmed by magnetic measurements [22]. The scale became more international in 1948 when groups at Leiden and Cambridge collaborated in publishing a detailed P_{sat}–T table based essentially on the 1939 scale. Even at the time of its issuance, the 1948 scale aroused some misgivings, for the work of Kistemaker [12] two years earlier suggested errors in the scale amounting to nearly 15 mdeg in the region near the λ-point. The 1950 (P_3, P_4) work [17] gave support to Kistemaker's corrections, as did several subsequent investigations [2,13,23], including a series of magnetic measurements made at Leiden begun in 1949 but not reported until 1953 [6]. Nevertheless, differences on the two sides of the Atlantic Ocean as to precisely what the corrections to the 1948 scale ought to be were sufficient that the participants at the Fifth International Conference on Low Temperature Physics (Paris, 1955) were offered two separate scales. To distinguish the two, the scale arrived at by van Dijk and Durieux from Leiden was referred to as T_{L55}, while that proposed by Clement from the U.S. Naval Research Laboratory came to be known as T_{55E}.

Below the boiling point, the maximum differences between T_{L55} and T_{55E} amounted to only four millidegrees; but the divergences increased at higher T, being nearly $0.012°K$ at the critical point. Derivation of the two scales rested on quite different principles, with T_{L55} determined from the standpoint of thermodynamic consistency and T_{55E} from what was judged to be the best experimental vapor pressure data. Although "a few millidegrees" may not have seemed terribly significant at first sight, the differences represented larger errors than the proponents of either scale were willing to concede. Furthermore, since many of the same fundamental data were used in determining both T_{L55} and T_{55E}, the fact that such large differences could appear emphasized the compliancy available in treating the data and served to point out the deficiencies of the experimental evidence. The situation at that time was summarized in an article by Keller ([24]).

A compromise, which might have been reached before the Paris conference, was finally achieved three years later. The resultant scale is presently in use and is referred to as T_{58}. To a large extent it is based on information that was available for constructing the 1955 scales. However, new thermodynamic data which appeared during the intervening years, while not materially altering the conclusions of previous investigations, were nevertheless of superior quality and therefore gave additional confidence to the final temperature scale that emerged. The awkwardness and inconvenience of having two scales was not without its compensations, since T_{58} is certainly a better-founded scale than either T_{55E} or T_{L55}. T_{58} takes the best features from both of its immediate predecessors, and, in effect, splits the numerical differences that did exist by achieving thermodynamic consistency without sacrificing the integrity of the gas thermometer data. An abbreviated listing of P_{sat} vs. T_{58} is given in Table 4.I.

Figure 4.3 shows, for various values of T_{58}, the differences between T_{58} and the presently acceptable absolute temperature determinations mentioned in the previous section. The scatter that is evident attests to the difficulties in making such measurements.

By equating the statistical-mechanical formula for the Gibbs free energy of the saturated vapor to its thermodynamic counterpart for the liquid, it is possible to derive the following expression for the vapor pressure of a real monatomic substance:

$$\ln P_{sat} = i_0 - \frac{H_v^0}{RT} + \frac{5}{2}\ln T - \frac{1}{RT}\int_0^T S_l\,dT + \frac{1}{RT}\int_0^{P_{sat}} V_l\,dP + \epsilon \quad (4.4)$$

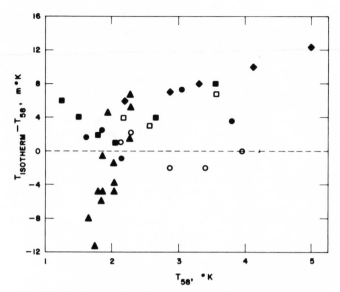

Fig. 4.3. Deviations from the T_{58} scale as determined by isotherm measurements. P–V isotherms: ▲ He⁴, Kistemaker ([12]); ● He³, ○ He⁴, Keller ([2]). Acoustic isotherms: ◆ He⁴, Plumb and Cataland; ■ He³, □ He⁴, Grimsrud and Werntz ([31]).

where H_v^0 is the molar latent heat of vaporization at absolute zero and the subscript l for the usual molar thermodynamic symbols indicates a property of the liquid phase; i_0 is the chemical constant given by

$$i_0 = \ln[g_\sigma(2\pi m)^{3/2}k_B^{5/2}h^{-3}] = 12.2440 \quad \text{(cgs units)} \quad (4.5)$$

in which g_σ is the degeneracy due to nuclear spin; and the term ϵ accounts for the gas imperfection usually expressed in one of the virial expansions. When the series in V_g^{-1} is used (V_g is the molar volume of the gas), ϵ may be written as

$$\epsilon = \ln\frac{P_{\text{sat}}}{RT}V_g - \frac{2B}{V_g} - \frac{3C}{2V_g^2} \quad (4.6)$$

Also, as is well known, the Clapeyron equation (1.5) expresses the vapor–liquid equilibrium through the latent heat H_v at temperature T. Equations (4.4) and (1.5) may be combined into a third relation

$$H_v = H_v^0 + \frac{5}{2}RT - \int_0^T C_{\text{sat}}\,dT - \int_0^{P_{\text{sat}}} V_l\,dP$$

$$+ \frac{RT}{V_g}\left(B - T\frac{dB}{dT}\right) + \frac{RT}{V_g^2}\left(C - \frac{T}{2}\frac{dC}{dT}\right) \quad (4.7)$$

and these three expressions, taken separately or together, have been used to test the thermodynamic consistency of the empirical $P_{sat}-T$ determinations for the helium isotopes.

We may begin a discussion of the thermodynamic consistency for T_{58} by referring to equation (4.4). An assumption implicit in this analysis is that the thermodynamic variables occurring in this relation have been measured on the absolute thermodynamic scale. Clearly, such a requirement can only be approximated, since this is the scale we seek and also since the measurements have been made relative to an empirical scale. Below 1.5°K, it is sufficient to take only the first three terms on the right-hand side of equation (4.4) to define the scale to better than 0.0005°K. Since i_0 can be calculated with considerable precision, the only empirical quantity required for establishing the scale in this region, within the accuracy presently obtainable for vapor pressure measurements, is H_v^0. This may be determined by using experimental data for H_v together with gas thermometer data in equation (4.7), as discussed by van Dijk and Durieux ([6, 15]). Three sets of latent heat data exist: one series of measurements between 1.5° and 4.2°K by Dana and Kamerlingh Onnes ([25]); a second between 2.9° and 4.5°K by Berman and Poulter ([26]); and a third between 2.2° and 5.0°K by ter Harmsel ([27]). In the region of overlap, all three investigations give compatible results; however, near the λ-point, there

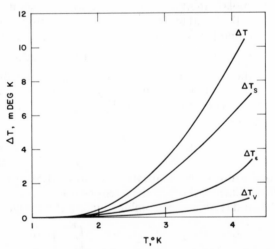

Fig. 4.4. Error in temperature scale determination, ΔT, as a function of T, due to 1 % errors in the terms in equation (4.4), assuming component errors ΔT_S, ΔT_V, and ΔT_ϵ are of the same sign.

is still need for better data. For H_v^0, 59.62 J/mole has been obtained as the most consistent value.

Above 1.5°K, the three terms of equation (4.4) neglected in the foregoing discussion begin to contribute importantly. Their collective effect may be appreciated from a consideration of the net temperature difference ΔT resulting from a 1 % error in each term ([15,24]). If ΔT_S represents the temperature difference due to such an error in the entropy term, ΔT_V in the liquid volume term, and ΔT_ϵ in the gas imperfection term, then for the most unfavorable case, $\Delta T = \Delta T_S + \Delta T_V + \Delta T_\epsilon$. Figure 4.4 illustrates the sensitivity of the scale to these various possible errors and emphasizes the necessity for accurate heat capacity measurements.

Durieux ([15]) has reported a private communication from Clement of a recent thermodynamically calculated scale between 1.5° and 4.5°K. The basic data entering this calculation, in addition to those already mentioned for H_v^0 and i_0, are: for the entropy term, the specific-heat measurements of Hill and Lounasmaa ([28]) which are considered by the authors to be accurate to 1 % or better; for the liquid volume term, the density determinations of Kerr ([29]); and for the nonideality term, a reanalysis by Clement of Keller's isotherm data ([2]). The results of this calculation are consistent with T_{58} within a maximum deviation of 0.002°K, and thus, for $T < 4.5$°K, it may be argued that T_{58} represents the true thermodynamic temperature within these limits.

For $T > 4.5$°K, it is not feasible to calculate the scale from relation (4.4) since the necessary experimental data are lacking. In this region, T_{58} is based on the Berman and Swenson ([8]) gas thermometer measurements which are made to join smoothly to the scale below 4.5°K. The possible errors are somewhat greater here than for the rest of the scale.

The 1958 He^4 Vapor Pressure Scale of Temperatures was accepted as an international standard for thermometry from 1° to 5.2°K by the International Committee on Weights and Measures on October 3, 1958. A discussion of the scale and tables for it are given by Brickwedde et al. ([30]).

Since the acceptance of the Scale T_{58}, several new pieces of data have been offered which are at odds with T_{58} and which pose serious questions as to its accuracy. We have already mentioned the work of Plumb and Cataland ([3,4]), which indicates that above ~ 2°K, the scale is low by from 5 to 10 mdeg. It should be noted that the acoustical isotherms in this work were analyzed retaining only the linear term αP in equation (4.2) (two-constant fit). But inclusion of the term in βP^2 (three-constant fit) appears to be statistically meaningful and results in temperatures in excellent agreement with T_{58} (T. R. Roberts, private communication). Second virial coefficients calculated from equation

(4.3) for either the two-constant or three-constant fit are consistent with the PV isotherm results of Keller ([2]). The more recent measurements of sound velocities in gaseous He^3 and He^4 by Grimsrud and Werntz ([31]) have provided additional evidence damaging to T_{58}. A three-constant analysis of these data gives corrections to T_{58} of the same sign but slightly smaller than the two-constant fit of Plumb and Cataland; and calculations of B derived using three constants are again consistent with the P–V isotherms.

Several constant-volume gas thermometer investigations in the helium region have also been reported recently. One, by Osborne et al. ([32]), fully supports the He^4 boiling point as given by T_{58}; another, by Rogers et al. ([33]) carried out at the National Standards Laboratory, Australia, suggests that the boiling point may be in error by 8 ± 3 mdeg in the direction indicated by the acoustical work.

While it is clear that these challenges to T_{58} must be seriously considered, it is also clear that T_{58}, because it is smooth and consistent with a large body of relevant thermodynamic data, will not easily be amended. Nevertheless, uncertainties in the Scale of the order of millidegrees do persist; and since temperature differences of the order of microdegrees are now measured without too much difficulty in low-temperature experiments, considerable motivation exists for further refinements in the absolute measurements of temperature.

4.5. THE T_{62} SCALE OF TEMPERATURES—He^3

Below $2°K$, thermometry based upon the vapor pressure of liquid He^3 has several obvious advantages over that using He^4. At a given temperature, $P_{sat}(He^3)$ is considerably larger than $P_{sat}(He^4)$—by a factor of seven at $2°K$, a factor of 73 at $1°K$, and a factor of 10,000 at $0.5°K$—allowing precise temperature measurements to be made with He^3 at much lower temperatures than with He^4. Furthermore, the use of He^3 avoids the complications associated with the refluxing He^4 film. These desirable features have led to the establishment of an He^3 vapor pressure scale of temperatures, the most recent representation of which is T_{62}.

A complete discussion of the derivation of T_{62} as well as a critique of the scale has been given by Roberts et al. ([34]), and tables for T_{62} have been published by Sherman et al. ([35]). We can give here only a brief summary of some of the salient characteristics of the scale. Table 4.I also compares T_{62} with T_{58}.

Based on the (P_3, P_4) intercomparisons by Sydoriak and Sherman ([18]) above $0.9°K$, on T_{58}, and on the empirical thermodynamic properties of He^3 between $0.2°$ and $2.0°K$, an Experimental Thermodynamic Equation (ETE) has been derived for He^3 in this latter interval.

Unlike the case for He^4, when equation (4.4) is applied to He^3, the entropy term cannot be ignored at reasonably low temperatures. To treat this more complicated problem, a scheme was devised ([34,36]) for recasting equation (4.4) in a form which separated the entropy integral from $0°K$ to T into two parts, one between the limits of $0°K$ and an arbitrary temperature T_m, the other between T_m and T. In this way, two constants, a and b, were introduced into the problem, allowing equation (4.4) to be rigorously written as

$$RF(P_{sat}, T) = \left(H_v^0 - \int_0^{T_m} C_{sat}\, dT \right) + S_l(T_m) \cdot T$$

$$= a + bT \tag{4.8}$$

where

$$F(P_{sat}, T) = T[\tfrac{5}{2} \ln T - \ln P_{sat} + i_0 + f(V_l) - f(C_{sat}) + \epsilon] \tag{4.9}$$

The terms $f(V_l)$ and $f(C_{sat})$ represent, respectively, the liquid volume integral over the range $0°K$ to T and the integral of the entropy as a function of temperature from T_m to T. When experimental data are substituted into relation (4.9) and when T_m is conveniently chosen to be $1°K$, these integrals may be approximated by separate power series fitting the data. The resulting evaluation of the true function $F(P_{sat}, T)$ is designated $F_x(P_{sat}, T)$ to indicate its empirical nature. It forms the basis for ETE. From $F_x(P_{sat}, T)$, it becomes possible to determine a and b by a least-squares analysis:

$$a = H_v^0 - \int_0^1 C_{sat}\, dT = 17.4459 \pm 0.0058 \quad \text{J/mole} \tag{4.10}$$

and

$$b = S_l(1.0°) = 9.0098 \pm 0.0038 \quad \text{J/mole-deg} \tag{4.11}$$

In addition to T_{58} and (P_3, P_4), the following information has been used to develop the thermodynamic consistency of ETE: latent heat of vaporization measurements in the range $1.2°$ to $2.1°$ by Weinstock, Abraham, and Osborne ([37]); a new reanalysis of Keller's gaseous isotherm data ([2,34,38]); the values of saturated liquid molar volumes given by Kerr and Taylor ([39]); and specific heat determinations by Strongin et al. ([40]) and by Anderson et al. ([41]). In connection with the specific-heat data, it should be appreciated that the uncertainties in the low-temperature values to be discussed in Chapter 6 do not seriously impair the accuracy of the result for b given in equation (4.11), though resolution of these difficulties would certainly enhance confidence in the scale. We also note that as yet reliable values for C_{sat} of He^3 are not available in the temperature range above about $2°K$.

The authors of T_{62} believe the scale is consistent with T_{58} to better than $0.0003°K$ over the range $0.9° < T < 3.324°K$. They consider it useful to $0.25°K$ as a lower limit practical for vapor pressure thermometry and point out that should improvements to T_{58} be conclusively established, T_{62} can be readily adjusted consistent with these refinements.

REFERENCES

1. W. H. Keesom and H. H. Kraak, *Physica*, **2**, 37 (1935); W. H. Keesom and W. K. Walstra, *Physica*, **7**, 985 (1940); J. Kistemaker and W. H. Keesom, *Physica*, **12**, 227 (1946).
2. W. E. Keller, *Phys. Rev.* **97**, 1 (1955); **98**, 1571 (1955); **100**, 1790 (1955).
3. H. H. Plumb and G. Cataland, *Science*, **150**, No. 3693, 155 (1965); *Metrologia* **2**, 6 (1966).
4. G. Cataland and H. H. Plumb, *J. Res. Natl. Bur. Std.*, **69A**, 531 (1965).
5. W. H. Keesom, *Helium*, p. 186ff, Elsevier, Amsterdam (1942).
6. H. van Dijk and M. Durieux, in *Progress in Low Temperature Physics* (C. J. Gorter, ed.), Vol. II, p. 431ff, North Holland, Amsterdam (1957).
7. H. Kamerlingh Onnes, *Commun. Leiden*, No. 124b; *Proc. Roy. Acad. Amsterdam*, **14**, 678 (1911).
8. R. Berman and C. A. Swenson, *Phys. Rev.* **95**, 311 (1954).
9. G. Schmidt and W. H. Keesom, *Commun. Leiden*, No. 250b; *Physica*, **4**, 963 (1937).
10. G. Schmidt and W. H. Keesom, *Commun. Leiden*, No. 250c; *Physica*, **4**, 971 (1937).
11. J. Kistemaker and W. H. Keesom, *Commun. Leiden*, No. 269b; *Physica* **12**, 227 (1946).
12. J. Kistemaker, *Commun. Leiden*, No. 269c; *Physica*, **12**, 272 (1946).
13. J. R. Clement, J. K. Logan, and J. Gaffney, Naval Research Laboratory Report 4542, Washington, D.C. (1955).
14. See, for example, E. Ambler and R. P. Hudson, *J. Res. Natl. Bur. Std.*, **56**, 99 (1956); **57**, 23 (1956).
15. M. Durieux, Thesis, Leiden (1960); see also H. van Dijk, *Physica*, **32**, 945 (1966).
16. S. G. Sydoriak, E. R. Grilly, and E. F. Hammel, *Phys. Rev.*, **75**, 303 (1949).
17. B. M. Abraham, D. W. Osborne, and B. Weinstock, *Phys. Rev.*, **80**, 366 (1950).
18. S. G. Sydoriak and R. H. Sherman, *J. Res. Natl. Bur. Std.*, **68A**, 547 (1964).
19. P. L. Kapitza, *J. Phys. (USSR)*, **4**, 181 (1941).
20. H. A. Fairbank and J. Wilks, *Proc. Roy. Soc. (London)*, **A231**, 545 (1955); L. J. Challis, K. Dransfeld, and J. Wilks, *Proc. Roy. Soc. (London)* **A260**, 31 (1961; Kuang Wey-Yen, *Zh. Eksperim. i Teor. Fiz.*, **42**, 921 (1962) [English translation, *Soviet Phys.—JETP*, **15**, 635 (1962)].
21. R. A. Watkins, W. L. Taylor, and W. J. Haubach, *J. Chem. Phys.*, **46**, 1007 (1967).
22. B. Bleaney and F. Simon, *Trans. Faraday Soc.*, **35**, 1205 (1939); B. Bleaney and R. A. Hull, *Proc. Roy. Soc. (London)*, **A178**, 74 (1941); H. B. G. Casimir, D. de Klerk, and D. Polder, *Commun. Leiden*, No. 261a; *Physica*, **7**, 737 (1940).
23. R. A. Erickson and L. D. Roberts, *Phys. Rev.*, **93**, 957 (1954).
24. W. E. Keller, *Nature*, **178**, 883 (1956).
25. L. I. Dana and H. Kamerlingh Onnes, *Commun. Leiden*, No. 179c (1926).
26. R. Berman and J. Poulter, *Phil. Mag.*, **43**, 1047 (1952).
27. H. ter Harmsel, Thesis, Leiden (1966).
28. R. W. Hill and O. V. Lounasmaa, *Phil. Mag.*, **2**, 143 (1957).

29. E. C. Kerr, *J. Chem. Phys.* **26**, 511 (1957).
30. F. G. Brickwedde, H. van Dijk, M. Durieux, J. R. Clement, and J. K. Logan, *J. Res. Natl. Bur. Std.*, **64A**, 1 (1960).
31. D. T. Grimsrud and J. H. Werntz, Jr., *Phys. Rev.*, **157**, 181 (1967).
32. D. W. Osborne, H. E. Flotow, and F. Schriener, *Rev. Sci. Instr.*, **38**, 159 (1967).
33. J. S. Rogers, R. J. Tainsh, M. S. Anderson, and C. A. Swenson (to be published).
34. T. R. Roberts, R. H. Sherman, S. G. Sydoriak, and F. G. Brickwedde, in *Progress in Low Temperature Physics* (C. J. Gorter, ed.), Vol. IV, p. 480ff, North Holland, Amsterdam (1964); S. G. Sydoriak, T. R. Roberts, and R. H. Sherman, *J. Res. Natl. Bur. Std.* **68A**, 559 (1964); T. R. Roberts, R. H. Sherman, and S. G. Sydoriak, *J. Res. Natl. Bur. Std.* **68A**, 567 (1964).
35. R. H. Sherman, S. G. Sydoriak, and T. R. Roberts, *J. Res. Natl. Bur. Std.* **68A**, 579 (1964).
36. E. F. Hammel, in *Progress in Low Temperature Physics* (C. J. Gorter, ed.), Vol. I, p. 78, North Holland, Amsterdam (1955).
37. B. Weinstock, B. M. Abraham, and D. Osborne, *Suppl. Nuovo Cimento*, **9**, 310 (1958).
38. T. R. Roberts, S. G. Sydoriak, and R. H. Sherman, in *Temperature, Its Measurement and Control in Science and Industry*, Vol. 3, Part 1, p. 75 (F. G. Brickwedde, ed.), Reinhold, New York (1962).
39. E. C. Kerr and R. D. Taylor, *Ann. Phys. (N.Y.)*, **20**, 450 (1962).
40. M. Strongin, G. O. Zimmerman, and H. A. Fairbank, *Phys. Rev.*, **128**, 1983 (1962).
41. A. C. Anderson, W. Reese, and J. C. Wheatley, *Phys. Rev.*, **130**, 495 (1963).

Chapter 5

Excitation Spectrum and Thermodynamic Properties of Liquid He^4

Hohenberg and Martin ([1]) have pointed out that the theory of liquid helium has been developed on three different levels. We have already discussed two of these levels, the first being the phenomenological theory of London and Tisza. Here, a comparison with the condensation of a free BE gas leads to a two-fluid model and predicts a macroscopic occupation of a single quantum state, the ground state, which is identified with the superfluid particles. Through this analogy, the unusual transport properties of He II as well as the transition at the λ-point find an appealing approximation. The second level is the semiphenomenological excitation picture due to Landau, in which a two-fluid description for He II follows from an examination of the energy states permissible for the liquid and the subsequent calculation of the thermal properties in terms of these states.

The third level attempts to explain liquid helium on a "first principles" or microscopic basis. One begins with an ensemble of 10^{23} helium atoms interacting via an appropriate potential function and then proceeds to explore the extent to which realistic results may be obtained through quantum-statistical mechanics. Obviously, the rigorous treatment of 10^{23} particles is impossible, and Feynman ([2]) has succinctly sounded the limitations of the method: "The quantum mechanics will not supplant the phenomenological theories. It turns out to support them." Despite the difficulties of this imponderable task, measurable progress has been achieved toward deducing the energy level scheme of the He^4 liquid system, calculating the thermal properties from the spectrum, and finally predicting the transport properties. The ground gained in treating the many-body problem in quantum-statistical mechanics has been made possible largely through the recent invention of rather powerful and ingenious mathematical techniques. Still, it must be emphasized that the treatments are approximate, with "answers" known in advance, and therefore Feynman's dictum remains substantiated.

Since knowledge of the elementary excitations in liquid helium is essential for both the thermodynamic properties of the liquid and the nature of superfluidity, the theoretical and experimental determination of the spectrum has been given high priority. The first part of this chapter will indicate some of the attempts at developing a microscopic theory for liquid He^4, and following that we shall describe the theory and the results of neutron scattering experiments which have so beautifully confirmed Landau's and Feynman's earlier predictions of the excitation spectrum. Then a comparison will be made between the thermodynamic quantities calculated from the neutron data and those measured directly.

5.1. THE NONIDEAL BE GAS AS A MODEL FOR LIQUID He^4

5.1.1. Preliminary Ideas Concerning the Excitation Spectrum

The most significant advances in the microscopic theory of He II have been made following the original ideas of London and Tisza. However, as we have indicated earlier, the BEC concept for an ideal gas is in many ways unrealistic. One particularly nonphysical result is the character of the isotherms as discussed in Section 2.3. Because of the volume collapse below the condensation pressure, if a real system obeyed the ideal BEC, all of the particles would be concentrated in the center of the container. To correct this defect, repulsive forces of some kind are required. Schematically, the distribution of particles over the container is given in Fig. 5.1 for (a) the ideal case and (b) the case when a weakly repulsive interparticle force is introduced.

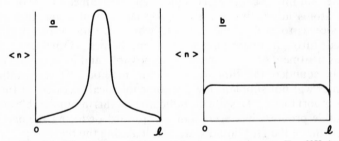

Fig. 5.1. Distribution of BE particles in a container at $T = 0°K$ (one dimension of length l shown schematically): (a) the ideal BE gas; (b) for weakly repulsive particles.

Another result of the ideal BE gas that does not conform to experimental evidence for He II is the temperature dependence of the specific heat, which goes at low T as $T^{3/2}$ rather than the empirically observed T^3. An early attempt was made by Bijl et al. [3] to modify the thermal properties of the ideal BE gas by requiring all nonzero momentum states to be elevated above the ground state by an additional amount of energy Δ. This single-particle spectrum with an energy gap is essentially the same as proposed initially by Landau [4] for rotons, and it does indeed provide a better representation of the thermal properties of He II than does the unaltered spectrum. However, it has become clear that a single-particle type spectrum alone cannot properly describe the superfluidity of He II, and that collective excitations, such as phonons, must somehow be introduced. In addition, since the λ-transition is observed to be higher than first order, the ideal BEC is again a poor approximation and special considerations are required.

5.1.2. Bogoliubov's Treatment of the Ground State

Bogoliubov's [5] microscopic approach to the nonideal BE gas gave the first indication of how the above-mentioned deficiencies of the ideal-gas model might be overcome and as well directed attention to the special role played by the zero momentum state in superfluidity. His paper and most others on the N-body problem are written in the language of "second quantization," which is used to describe the quantal changes in the population of the various momentum states in response to forces acting on or in the system. The mathematical formalism will not be presented here; instead, we shall attempt to translate this formalism into physical terms which will allow the basic assumptions and conclusions of the various treatments to be appreciated.

The main contribution of Bogoliubov was the preparation for the nonideal BE system at $T = 0°K$ of a tractable Hamiltonian, $\mathscr{H}_B$, the eigenvalues of which have characteristics satisfying Landau's criterion for superfluidity. $\mathscr{H}_B$ includes a potential energy, $\Phi(|\mathbf{r}_i - \mathbf{r}_j|) = \Phi(r)$, which describes the two-body interparticle forces when the particles are considered as points; it is upon this term that we focus our attention.

At $T = 0$ for the ideal BE case, $\langle n_0 \rangle / N = 1$; it is shown for the nonideal case that through $\Phi(r)$ a large number of the particles is raised from the zero momentum, or $\mathbf{p} = 0$, state. Bogoliubov assumed that even in the presence of interparticle forces, $\rho_0 = \langle n_0 \rangle / N$ should be a finite fraction. Thus, while for the ground state of the system the total momentum $\mathbf{P}$ remains zero with $\mathbf{p} = 0$ the most populated single level, many other momentum states are also occupied, but in pairs, $\mathbf{p}$ and $-\mathbf{p}$ (or in other more complicated combinations contributing zero net momentum). These we refer to as "virtual states." The particles

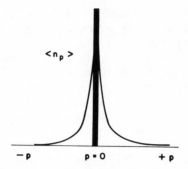

Fig. 5.2. Distribution of occupation numbers at $T = 0°\text{K}$. For the ideal case, all particles occupy the $\mathbf{p} = 0$ state (heavy line); in the presence of interactions, the $\mathbf{p} = 0$ state is depleted as shown by light lines.

macroscopically occupying the $\mathbf{p} = 0$ level contributing to ρ_0 are labeled the "condensate" or "condensed mode," and those particles removed from the $\mathbf{p} = 0$ state through the many-body forces, the "depletion." Figure 5.2 shows schematically the distribution of occupation numbers, $\langle n_{\mathbf{p}} \rangle$, as a function of $\mathbf{p}$ in a system with and without interactions at $T = 0$.

It was next *assumed* that the ground-state wave function $\Psi(n_0)$ with n_0 particles in the condensed mode is insignificantly different from $\Psi(n_0 + 1)$ or $\Psi(n_0 - 1)$. That is, the properties of the system are negligibly affected when a particle is added to or removed from the condensate. This assumption allows considerable simplification of $\Phi(r)$, but at the same time restricts the amount of information that can be learned about the properties of the condensate. It also brings with it the difficulty that the Hamiltonian no longer conserves particles; but fortunately a trick is available for correcting this.

With these assumptions $\mathcal{H}_B$ becomes the kinetic energy in terms of $p^2/2m$ plus the potential energy, which is considered a perturbation. The terms that remain in $\Phi(r)$ are equivalent to those obtained in the usual Rayleigh–Schrödinger perturbation theory truncated after the third term, where the energy change of the ground state, ΔE_0, due to the many-body interactions is given by the series

$$\Delta E_0 = E_0^{(1)} + E_0^{(2)} + \cdots = \Phi_{00} + \sum_{k \neq 0} \Phi_{0k} \left(\frac{1}{E_0 - E_k} \right) \Phi_{k0} + \cdots \quad (5.1)$$

The matrix element Φ_{ij} is defined as

$$\Phi_{ij} \equiv \langle i|\Phi|j \rangle \equiv \int \Psi_i \Phi \Psi_j \, d\tau \tag{5.2}$$

Ψ_i being the wave function of the state i and Φ the interaction energy. In this way, we may associate with Φ_{00} the process of two particles of the condensate interacting via the potential and then falling back to the condensate; with Φ_{0k}, two $\mathbf{p} = 0$ particles interacting via Φ to form two particles with $\mathbf{p} = \pm\mathbf{k}$; with Φ_{k0} these excited particles returning to the $\mathbf{p} = 0$ level; and so on.

In second quantization language, $\Phi(r)$ is expressed as a sum of interactions over the various momentum states, with the coefficient for each term the Fourier transform of the potential. For the kth momentum state, this is

$$\phi_{\mathbf{k}} = \int e^{i\mathbf{k}\cdot\mathbf{r}}\Phi(r) \, dr^3 \tag{5.3}$$

Since the unperturbed Hamiltonian places all the particles in the zero momentum state, the first-order correction to the energy is due almost entirely to the processes associated with Φ_{00} and hence can be described in terms of $\phi_{\mathbf{k}=0} = \phi_0$. To a good approximation, $E_0^{(1)}$ becomes

$$E_0^{(1)} = \phi_0 N^2/2\Omega = \phi_0 N/2v \tag{5.4}$$

The Bogoliubov Hamiltonian treats those parts of the interactions which cannot be considered small and includes the following processes: interaction of ground-state particles in lowest order as just mentioned; pair creation; pair annihilation; interaction of an excited particle directly with a ground-state particle; and exchange of an excited particle with a ground-state particle. It should be noted that interactions between pairs of excited particles are omitted. The form directly describing these processes is not diagonalized, but by a suitable canonical transformation which bears his name, Bogoliubov was able to make $\mathscr{H}_B$ diagonal under the important restrictive approximation that the coupling between particles is weakly repulsive. The transformed $\mathscr{H}_B$ describes an ensemble of noninteracting excitations with an energy spectrum $\epsilon_{\mathbf{k}} = \hbar\omega_{\mathbf{k}}$, for which the frequencies are given by

$$\omega_{\mathbf{k}} = \left\{ \frac{k^2 n_0 \Phi}{m} + \frac{k^4}{4m^2} \right\}^{1/2} \tag{5.5}$$

Relation (5.5) is obtained under the conditions that the particle density $\rho = N/\Omega$ is dilute and remains fixed as N and Ω each approaches infinity.

In the limit of $k \to 0$ (long wavelength), the k^4 term of equation (5.5) becomes negligible compared with the k^2 term, and we find the spectrum reduces to $\omega_\mathbf{k} = ck$. This form, linear in k, is typical for a phonon spectrum with the velocity

$$c = (n_0 \Phi / m)^{1/2} \tag{5.6}$$

and establishes the basis for the superfluid character of the system in accordance with Landau's notions. Note that c depends explicitly upon the extent of the zero-momentum state occupation. At large k (short wavelength), where the term in k^4 dominates, the spectrum exhibits free-particle behavior but does not resemble the Landau rotons. The total increase found in the ground-state energy E_0 due to the weakly repulsive interactions between particles is listed in Table 5.I.

In considering equation (5.5) we can no longer speak in terms of "particle excitations" as in the ideal BE gas, but instead must consider "quasiparticles," or excitations of the whole system. Indeed, the physical meaning of the Bogoliubov transformation represents this change from particle to quasiparticle language. Corresponding to the assumptions made for the energy levels of an ideal gas, any energy level of the interacting gas can be considered as a sum of a certain number of quasiparticles. Through $\mathcal{H}_B$, the system becomes an ideal quasiparticle gas, though the number of quasiparticles does not represent the actual number of particles in the ensemble. The quasiparticle concept is quite flexible and for different situations assumes, as we shall see later in connection with Fermi fluids, somewhat different meanings.

In the initial proposal by London and Tisza indicating the similarities between BEC and liquid He II, the condensed fraction ρ_0 of the gas was identified with the superfluid fraction ρ_s of the liquid. We have just seen, however, that the Bogoliubov assumptions for the nonideal BE gas lead to a depletion of the ground state so that $\rho_0 < \rho_s$, suggesting that these two quantities are quite different. This raises the question of whether BEC is indeed meaningful for a nonideal BE system, and, if so, whether there is any connection between ρ_0 and ρ_s in liquid helium.

5.1.3. BEC in Nonideal Systems

Convincing arguments that BEC is possible in the general case of interacting bosons, and therefore that the condensation should be exhibited in real liquid He[4], were first produced by Penrose and Onsager [6]. For the stationary system at equilibrium, the relations for describing BEC are given as (valid for $T < T_c$):

$$\lim_{N \to \infty} \langle n_0 \rangle / N = \alpha \qquad \alpha \text{ finite} \tag{5.7}$$

$$\lim_{N \to \infty} \langle n_\mathbf{p} \rangle / N = 0 \qquad \mathbf{p} \neq 0 \tag{5.8}$$

Table 5.I. Some Results of Approximate Microscopic Theories for Liquid He⁴ near $T = 0°K$ [a]

Degree of approximation (Investigators)	Ground-state energy $\Delta E_0/N$	Low-lying excitation spectrum ω_k	Ground-state depletion $\langle n' \rangle = N - \langle n_0 \rangle$
Ideal gas Point repulsive potentials $\Phi(r) = \Phi\delta(r)$	0	$k^2/2m$	0
Bogoliubov [5]	$\dfrac{\Phi}{2}\left[1 + \dfrac{16}{15\pi^2} n_0^{1/2}(m\Phi)^{3/2}\right]$	$\left[\left(\dfrac{k^2}{2m}\right)^2 + \dfrac{n_0\Phi k^2}{m}\right]^{1/2}$	$\dfrac{(n_0 m\Phi)^{3/2}}{3\pi^2}$
Girardeau and Arnowitt [23]	Same as Bogoliubov	Energy gap	Same as Bogoliubov
Beliaev [8] and Hugenholtz and Pines [9]	$\dfrac{\Phi}{2}\left[1 + \dfrac{16}{15\pi^2} n_0^{1/2}(m\Phi)^{3/2}\right.$ $\left. + b\{n_0(m\Phi)^3 \ln[n_0(m\Phi)^3] + \cdots\}\right]$ [b]	$\left(\dfrac{n_0\Phi k^2}{m}\right)^{1/2}\left\{1 + \dfrac{7}{6\pi^2}[n_0(m\Phi)^3]^{1/2}\right\}$ $+ ik^5[(3/640)\pi m n_0]$	$\dfrac{(n_0 m\Phi)^{3/2}}{3\pi^2}$ $\times [1 + dn_0^{1/2}(m\Phi)^{3/2} + \cdots]$ [d]
Hard sphere LYH [10-15] and Brueckner and Sawada [19]	$\dfrac{2\pi a_0}{mv}\left[1 + \dfrac{128}{15}\left(\dfrac{a_0^3}{\pi v}\right)^{1/2}\right]$ [c]	$\dfrac{k}{2m}\left(k^2 + \dfrac{16\pi a_0}{v}\right)^{1/2}$	$\dfrac{8N}{3}\left(\dfrac{a_0^3}{\pi v}\right)^{1/2}$

[a] Throughout, Φ represents the interaction energy, and $\hbar = 1$.
[b] Here, b is a constant.
[c] Here, a_0 is the hard-sphere diameter.
[d] Here, d is a constant.

where $\langle n_{\mathbf{p}} \rangle$ represents the average number of particles with momentum $\mathbf{p}$.

As a suitable formalism for evaluating these expressions, Penrose and Onsager considered the density matrix in the momentum representation for a homogeneous system:

$$\rho(\mathbf{r}, \mathbf{r}') = \sum_{\mathbf{p}=0}^{\infty} \langle n_{\mathbf{p}} \rangle \exp[i\mathbf{p} \cdot (\mathbf{r} - \mathbf{r}')] \qquad (5.9)$$

In an ordinary system, there are a great many momentum states very closely spaced, so that equation (5.8) holds for *all* $\mathbf{p}$ and no single term in the sum (5.9) contributes substantially. Physically, this means that since the momentum correlations of the particles have a short range, the average value of $\rho(\mathbf{r}, \mathbf{r}') \to 0$ as $(\mathbf{r} - \mathbf{r}') \to \infty$. On the other hand, in BEC, the $\mathbf{p} = 0$ term is expected to make a considerable contribution to the sum; accordingly, it can be separated out to give

$$\rho(\mathbf{r}, \mathbf{r}') = n_0 + \sum_{\mathbf{p}=1}^{\infty} \langle n_{\mathbf{p}} \rangle \exp[i\mathbf{p} \cdot (\mathbf{r} - \mathbf{r}')]$$

$$= n_0 + \tilde{\rho}(\mathbf{r}, \mathbf{r}') \qquad (5.10)$$

where the part $\tilde{\rho}(\mathbf{r}, \mathbf{r}')$ behaves as in ordinary systems; but the condensate particles n_0 experience correlations over very large distances and thereby prevent $\rho(\mathbf{r}, \mathbf{r}')$ from vanishing. When $\rho(\mathbf{r}, \mathbf{r}')$ is expressed as an operator in the coordinate representation, it can be shown that its eigenvalues are just the occupation numbers of the momentum states $\mathbf{p}$. Thus, since these results are applicable to interacting as well as ideal BE systems, once we are given the wave function for the system it is possible to calculate $\langle n_{\mathbf{p}} \rangle / N$ to determine whether the conditions (5.7) and (5.8) are satisfied and whether the separation made in equation (5.10) is justified. For a FD gas, since $0 \leqslant n_{\mathbf{p}} \leqslant 1$, these conditions for condensation are not met.

For liquid He^4, Penrose and Onsager chose a crude but plausible ground-state wave function, Ψ_0, to arrive at an estimate of $\langle n_0 \rangle / N$. They considered Ψ_0 to be

$$\Psi_0(\mathbf{r}_1, \mathbf{r}_2, \ldots, \mathbf{r}_N) = Z_N^{-1/2} F_N(\mathbf{r}_1, \mathbf{r}_2, \ldots, \mathbf{r}_N) \qquad (5.11)$$

with

$$F_N(\mathbf{r}_1, \mathbf{r}_2, \ldots, \mathbf{r}_N) = \prod_{i,j=1}^{N} f(\mathbf{r}_{ij}) \quad \begin{cases} f(\mathbf{r}) = 0, & |\mathbf{r}| < a \\ f(\mathbf{r}) = 1, & |\mathbf{r}| > a \end{cases} \qquad (5.12)$$

which describes a system of hard spheres with two-body interactions. Z_N is a normalization constant, the configurational partition function for a classical hard-sphere gas. With a taken as 2.56 Å, the "diameter" of the He atom, the calculations showed that $\langle n_0 \rangle / N$ is approximately

0.08, i.e., 8 % of the He atoms are condensed, with the remaining 92 % forming the depletion.

Penrose and Onsager, by extending the density-matrix treatment, were able to indicate that BEC should also occur for interacting bosons under the separate conditions when the system is not homogeneous, when the system is in uniform translation, when the temperature is finite but below T_c, and when some single momentum state other than the $\mathbf{p} = 0$ state is macroscopically occupied. Furthermore, they showed why BEC should not be expected in a solid.

Despite the considerable care with which Penrose and Onsager constructed their arguments, their conclusions do not constitute a *proof* that the mathematical formalism of BEC describes liquid He II because the results depend upon certain *a priori* assumptions. The most important of these is that the system, for which it is desired to show momentum correlations, must not exhibit long-range configurational order; for if there were such order, the amplitude of the density matrix would drop off too rapidly for all values of $\mathbf{p}$, thereby preventing macroscopic occupation of any momentum state. Also, it has not been shown what the effect upon BEC might be if weakly attractive forces were included in the potential.

If, despite this lack of rigor, we allow that BEC is a meaningful concept for liquid He^4, we may then seek the answer to the second part of our question—namely, what is the relationship between ρ_0, the condensate density, and ρ_s, the phenomenological superfluid density. Although the Penrose and Onsager treatment sheds no light on this problem, we may initially declare that the two quantities are not the same, $\rho_s \neq \rho_0$! While there is a definable distinction between ρ_s and ρ_0 which may be found from the microscopic theories, unfortunately, this distinction cannot be put easily into a few words. A discussion has been given in a recent article by Martin ([7]). The important point is that the microscopic theories do not destroy the validity of our operational conception of ρ_s. At $T = 0°K$ it is still proper to consider $\rho_s = \rho$, and at finite temperatures, $\rho_s = \rho - \rho_n$, where ρ_n represents the *thermal* excitations of the liquid. As yet no experiment has been devised which measures ρ_0.

5.1.4. Recent Refinements for the Ground State

Largely as a result of the confidence in the BE model engendered by the Penrose–Onsager treatment of the condensation, there have been numerous subsequent treatments of the nonideal BE gas. Most of them, like that of Bogoliubov, have started with the unperturbed wave functions and Hamiltonian for the ideal gas and have incorporated the interparticle forces as a perturbation; others have begun with a pair-product function similar to equation (5.11) as a trial wave function for use in a variation treatment.

The successively more refined perturbation results have generally embodied more sophisticated ways of handling the perturbation series—and thereby allowing higher terms to be evaluated—or more realistic potentials. However, the results in most cases have been surprisingly similar in the estimates of the change in the ground-state energy as the interactions are "turned on" and in the prescriptions for determining the permissible low-lying excited states. One problem common to the perturbation calculations but often avoided in the variational treatment is the divergent terms which arise from the macroscopic occupation of the zero momentum state. These terms are a consequence of the considerable energy necessary to excite particles from the ground state, and describe the so-called "self-energy" of the system by a sequence of processes in which *one* particle of momentum $\mathbf{p} = 0$ interacts with the system to produce *two* particles of momenta $\mathbf{p}_1$ and $\mathbf{p}_1'$, which in turn interact to produce two more particles of $\mathbf{p}_2$ and $\mathbf{p}_2'$, etc., and ending with $\mathbf{p}_i$ and $\mathbf{p}_i'$ producing again *one* particle of $\mathbf{p} = 0$ (under the condition that each process conserves momentum). When the integrals corresponding to these processes are summed for a system of finite density in which the $\mathbf{p} = 0$ state is macroscopically occupied, the result is infinite. This distressing divergence is not foreign to those who work in quantum field theory and is generally surmounted by the invention of a physically justifiable mathematical trick. For the case of BE systems, this has been done in several ways, which, however, will not be detailed here. Nevertheless, we do emphasize that considerable care is required to correct properly for the self-energy, and often, the making of this correction provides the principal obstacle to achieving a satisfactory solution to the problem, especially for high-order perturbation calculations.

Table 5.I summarizes the results of some of the more important $T = 0$ theoretical investigations with respect to: the ground-state energy, $\Delta E_0/N$; the spectrum of low-lying excitations, $\omega_{\mathbf{k}}$; and the depletion, $\langle n' \rangle = N - \langle n_0 \rangle$. These calculations are for the low-density limit and therefore are not strictly applicable to liquid He^4.

5.1.4a. Perturbation Treatment for Repulsive Point Particles. The works of Beliaev ([8]) and of Hugenholtz and Pines ([9]) independently extended the Bogoliubov treatment to higher order approximations by applying the Green's function formalism of quantum field theory to the many-body interacting BE system. This method is equivalent to perturbation theory but allows the important terms of the series to be more easily identified and calculated. Divergences associated with the zero momentum state are made to disappear through the introduction of an undetermined multiplier, $n'\mu$ (n' is the depletion) into the Hamiltonian; μ is then identified as the chemical potential per particle of the ground state, representing the change in E_0 due to the addition of one particle to the condensate, i.e.,

$$\mu = E_0^{N+1} - E_0^N \approx \partial E_0^N / \partial N \tag{5.13}$$

In lowest order, these authors recovered the results of Bogoliubov, and in higher orders, they found that corrections to E_0 are not, as was expected at first, in the form of a power series in the parameter $[n_0(m\Phi)^3]^{1/2}$, but rather in a logarithmic series. Table 5.I shows the Beliaev–Hugenholtz and Pines dispersion relation to include an imaginary term, which arises from processes in which a phonon of momentum $\mathbf{p}$ decays into two phonons of momenta $\mathbf{q}$ and $\mathbf{p} - \mathbf{q}$.

From Beliaev's treatment ([8]), the chemical potential as defined by equation (5.13) assumes an additional interesting role in relation to the condensate n_0 appearing in equation (5.10). Here, n_0 may be expressed as

$$n_0 = \langle \psi^*(\mathbf{r})\psi(\mathbf{r}') \rangle \tag{5.14}$$

where $\langle \psi(\mathbf{r}) \rangle$ is an off-diagonal matrix element between two states differing only in that one state has an additional particle in the condensate compared with the other. Beliaev deduced that $\langle \psi(\mathbf{r}) \rangle$ could be written as the product of an amplitude and a time-dependent phase factor involving the chemical potential; thus

$$\langle \psi(\mathbf{r}) \rangle = n_0^{1/2} e^{-i\mu t/\hbar} \tag{5.15}$$

$\langle \psi(\mathbf{r}) \rangle$ has come to be known by several names, such as the "superfluid order parameter" or the "condensate wave function." The fact that for liquid He II, n_0, as given by equation (5.14), is finite and that the off-diagonal long-range ordering implied by this relation can be explicitly expressed by equation (5.15) forms the important basis for our current thinking on superfluid dynamics. This will be reconsidered in Chapter 8.

Two other significant features emerge from the Hugenholtz and Pines paper ([9]), the first being a proof, subject to the Bogoliubov assumptions, that any boson system at $T = 0$ with weak repulsive forces will exhibit a phonon spectrum without a gap. The second is a reasonable demonstration that the velocity c calculated for the phonon spectrum as in equation (5.6) should be identified with the sound velocity u_1 obtained from macroscopic considerations.

5.1.4b. Perturbation Treatment for Hard Spheres. Although the hard-sphere model might seem limited in its representation of liquid He⁴, this approximation possesses several eminent points of merit. Among these is the simplification it allows in the calculations compared with those involving more complicated potentials, thereby making $T \neq 0$ information more accessible. The objective is to determine the thermodynamic properties of the system (as $N \to \infty$, $\Omega \to \infty$, N/Ω

constant) once the energy spectrum is given; the central problem is to express the grand partition function (GPF), embodying the spectrum, in a form which can be evaluated. Although the early calculations could be made only for the dilute gas, which is quite unlike the actual liquid, more recently it has become possible to study densities corresponding to liquid He^4 with surprisingly realistic results.

The most extensive investigations of the hard-sphere boson gas have been made in an elegant series of papers by Lee, Yang, and Huang (LYH) ([10-15]). These are summarized in some detail in Huang's review article ([16]). Here we will be content to give the essentials of the methods used and the consequences of the calculations.

For the hard-sphere problem, the important parameters of the system are the thermal wavelength λ_T, the mean interparticle distance $v^{1/3}$, and the sphere diameter a_0. However, a difficulty arises due to the all-or-nothing character of the two-body potential [for such a potential, the Fourier transform, equation (5.3), does not exist]. Another mathematical trick is required to remove the effects of the singularity, and for this, LYH in the first series of their papers ([10-14]) used the method of the pseudopotential. This artifact, borrowed from electrostatic theory, allows an analytic continuation of the effective potential to be made for $r < a_0$ so that the scattering phase shifts may be determined. Then it becomes possible to express the spectrum of the system in terms of the phase shifts. Thus, $\mathcal{H}$ for the system is $\mathcal{H}_0$, the unperturbed Hamiltonian, plus the pseudopotential expressed as a series of terms corresponding to successively higher values of angular momentum l. The eigenvalues of $\mathcal{H}$ are the same as those of $\mathcal{H}_0$, and the eigenfunctions of $\mathcal{H}$ outside the sphere approach those of the original Hamiltonian. For low values of energy (k), only S-waves $(l = 0)$ are important, and in terms of the phase shift, $\eta_{l=0}(k) = \eta_0$, the S-wave pseudopotential for hard spheres is given by

$$-\frac{4\pi}{k \cot \eta_0} \delta(r_i - r_j) \frac{\partial}{\partial r_{ij}} r_{ij} \qquad (5.16)$$

Even in the treatment of the pseudopotential as a perturbation to first order, significant differences emerge for the nonideal BE gas as opposed to the ideal gas. The results, valid only for low density and low momentum, show an increase of E_0, a depletion of the zero momentum state at $T = 0$, and a quasiparticle spectrum with a gap—this is not a phonon spectrum (but the gap does disappear in higher orders). The partition function incorporating this spectrum can be easily evaluated to yield the thermodynamic properties at nonzero temperatures, and in particular, it is found that at T_c, there is a jump in C_V. The isotherms of the hard-sphere gas in this approximation also differ qualitatively from the ideal gas in that they show a discontinuity of slope at the transition line with both branches concave upward (cf. Fig. 2.2f); and the phase transition line in the $P–T$ plane, given in Fig. 2.2d, now does represent the separation of two real phases, the upper one being a degenerate phase, the lower one nondegenerate.

To obtain the above results, LYH used a pseudopotential Hamiltonian which included only diagonal matrix elements between unperturbed states. For the next approximation, off-diagonal elements were added to describe the processes of pair creation and destruction with respect to the ground state. The resulting Hamiltonian was diagonalized by a Bogoliubov transformation to yield the energies for the ground state and excited states as given in Table 5.I. The excitation spectrum for small k, i.e., $k^2 \ll 16\pi a_0/v$, reduces to a phononlike dispersion relation. If we introduce a value of a_0 and v appropriate for helium, the speed of sound may be calculated as ~ 200 m/sec, which is quite realistic despite the crudity of the model.

In this same degree of approximation, LYH obtained the ground-state wave function Ψ_0 in form somewhat similar to relations (5.11) and (5.12). From this, they were able to determine $g_0(r)$, the pair correlation function, i.e., the probability of finding two particles in the ground state at a distance r apart. For $r > r_0$, $g_0(r)$, as graphed in Fig. 5.3, approaches unity as $(1 - r^{-4})$, and for $r < r_0$, goes to zero at a_0 parabolically. Here, $r_0 = (v/8\pi a_0)^{1/2}$ has the significance of a "correlation length," or the average maximum distance over which two particles may be spatially correlated. The r^{-4} behavior of $g_0(r)$ for large r originates from the phonon spectrum and does not depend upon perturbation theory. Finally, from Ψ_0, it is possible to calculate the depletion (shown in Table 5.I) which for parameters corresponding to liquid He⁴ implies that 4% of the particles occupy the zero momentum state.

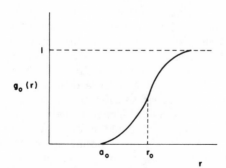

Fig. 5.3. The pair correlation function for the ground state of the hard-sphere BE gas.

Higher order terms in the expression for the ground-state energy have been calculated by Wu ([17]). Again contrary to expectation, the continuation of the expression for E_0 is not a power series in a_0^3/v, but instead contains terms in $\log(a_0^3/v)$ similar to those for repulsive point particles.

Huang ([18]) has extended the hard-sphere description to include a weakly attractive part in the potential in an attempt to improve the realism of the model. The results are of interest with respect to the BE system, but, unfortunately, the calculated thermodynamic properties bear less resemblance to the liquid they were intended to describe than do those derived from the purely repulsive hard spheres.

Coincident with the LYH development, Brueckner and Sawada (BS) ([19]) applied to the hard-sphere BE problem a formalism previously invented to deal with a high-density, strongly interacting system of bosons. To account for the divergent multiple scattering terms of the ground state, BS introduced a scattering matrix, or "T-matrix," which removed the difficulties arising from the singularity in the interparticle potential. An energy spectrum was obtained which at low $\mathbf{k}$ was in essential agreement with the results of LYH and at higher $\mathbf{k}$ displayed a dip reminiscent of the Landau roton spectrum. Subsequently, this latter characteristic was shown by Parry and ter Haar ([20]) to be due to an improper treatment by BS of the depletion of the $\mathbf{p} = 0$ state. Parry and ter Haar tried to regain the dip by proper accounting of the self-energy and by adding an attractive part to the potential, but these efforts netted no better results than those of Huang mentioned above. This failure led Parry and ter Haar to doubt whether the hard-sphere model would ever be a reasonable representation for liquid He^4. Subsequently, however, Liu and Wong ([21]) pointed out that the interaction used in the preceding work was not strictly descriptive of hard spheres, but rather of slightly penetrating spheres. Following this, Liu, Liu, and Wong ([22]) combined the T-matrix and pseudopotential techniques to treat the high-density boson hard-sphere problem, with the result that a rotonlike dip again appeared in the excitation spectrum. By suitable adjustment of a "screening factor" in the potential, close similarity to the He^4 spectrum can be achieved.

5.1.4c. Variational Calculations. In an early attempt at a variational treatment for the ground-state, Girardeau and Arnowitt ([23]) used as a trial wave function a generalization of Bogoliubov's function describing pair excitations. As can be seen from Table 5.I, the ground-state energy and the depletion are obtained in forms identical to the results of Bogoliubov. However, this variational procedure yields energy values which are shifted upward by a constant amount from the eigenvalues appropriate for the Bogoliubov pair Hamiltonian; i.e., there is an energy gap and the phonon spectrum, $\omega_{\mathbf{k}}$, does not go to zero at long wavelengths ($k = 0$). It should be noted that: (1) this gap does not preclude superfluid behavior; and (2) $\mathscr{H}_B$ would also give rise to a gap were it not for terms which describe the continuous exchange between the excited and $p = 0$ particles.

More recently, McMillan [24] has computed the ground-state energy of a BE system interacting via a Lennard-Jones potential (LJ-1) and for a range of densities corresponding to liquid and solid He⁴. A pair-product wave function with factors of the form $f(r_{ij}) = \exp[-(a/r_{ij})^5]$ was used as a trial function in a variational treatment in which the configurational integrals were evaluated by Monte Carlo computations for 32 and 108 particles. Essentially, this program involved the calculation of the single-particle density matrix when the LJ-1 interaction law is included in $\mathscr{H}$. For this case, $\langle n_0 \rangle / N$ is calculated to be about 11%, the normalized single-particle density matrix approaching this constant value when $(r - r')$ is greater than ~ 4 Å. In determining the ground-state energy for the liquid, a value of 2.6×10^{-8} cm was found optimum for the quantity a_0 in the trial function; the ground-state energy corresponding to this is about 20% above the experimental value. Some of the results calculated by McMillan are tabulated in Table 5.II. In addition, the theoretical curve

Table 5.II. Various Properties of Liquid He⁴ at $T = 0°K$

Property		Experiment	Variational calculation	
			McMillan [24]	Massey [28]
$\rho(P = 0)$	$(10^{22}$ atoms/cm³)	2.18	1.95	Fixed at experimental value
E_0 at $\rho = 2.18$	$(10^{-15}$ erg/atom)	-0.97	-0.78	
E_0 at $\rho = 2.59$	$(10^{-15}$ erg/atom)	-0.91	-0.62	-0.88
P at $\rho = 2.18$	(atm)	0	13	Fixed at 0
P at $\rho = 2.59$	(atm)	25	40	29
u_1 at $\rho = 2.18$	(m/sec)	238	267	242
u_1 at $\rho = 2.59$	(m/sec)	365	316	400

for the pair correlation function shows considerably more structure than does that for the hard-sphere BE gas (Fig. 5.3) and bears close resemblance to $g(r)$ for the actual liquid, as indicated by the comparisons in Table 5.III.

McMillan's calculation of E_0 is encouragingly realistic. Use of a better potential function should improve the agreement between theory and experiment, but the calculations would be extremely difficult. Nevertheless, the results gained so far, besides showing the

BE condensation for a reasonable He–He potential, give the first substantial microscopic indication that He^4 is a liquid at zero pressure and temperature. This study also presents good evidence that the pair-function form is correct for BE systems with weak interactions. [A calculation similar to McMillan's has been made by Levesque et al. [25].]

The general pair-product trial wave function

$$\Psi(\mathbf{r}_1, \mathbf{r}_2, \ldots, \mathbf{r}_N) = \prod_{i<j} \exp[\tfrac{1}{2}u(r_{ij})] \qquad (5.17)$$

known as the Bijl–Dingle–Jastrow type, has been investigated often, but principally of late by Feenberg and co-workers* and by Broyles and co-workers.† From this equation plus the expression for the two-particle distribution function, the expectation value of the ground-state Hamiltonian has been obtained by the former group as

$$\langle \mathcal{H} \rangle = \langle \mathcal{T} \rangle + \langle \mathcal{V} \rangle \qquad (5.18)$$

$$\langle \mathcal{T} \rangle = \frac{N^2}{\Omega} \left(\frac{\hbar^2}{8m} \right) \int \frac{dg(r)}{dr} \frac{du(r)}{dr} \, d\mathbf{r} \qquad (5.19)$$

$$\langle \mathcal{V} \rangle = \frac{N^2}{2\Omega} \int g(r)\Phi(r) \, d\mathbf{r} \qquad (5.20)$$

where $\Phi(r)$ is the pair potential, $g(r)$ is the pair correlation function, and $u(r)$ is another correlation function related to $g(r)$ but with the properties $u_{r=0} = -\infty$, $u_{r=\infty} = 0$ [at small r, $u(r) \sim \ln g(r)$]. Using this formalism with $\Phi(r)$ of the LJ(12-6) type, Massey [28] has recently included the three-particle distribution function to compute values of E_0, $g(r)$, pressure, and sound velocity as functions of the density $\rho = N/\Omega$. For these calculations, Massey first obtained the parameters r_m and ϵ/k_B for $\Phi(r)$ consistent with the experimental values of E_0 and $\rho(P = 0, T = 0°K)$, finding: $r_m = 2.974$ Å, $\epsilon/k_B = 10.21°K$ (cf. other values as given in Table 3.I). The resulting agreement between theory and experiment is quite good, some indication of this being given in Table 5.II. Also, the calculated $g(r)$ is quite similar to McMillan's curve. A comparison of the salient features of $g(r)$ as obtained from different sources is given in Table 5.III.

5.1.5. Calculations for $T \neq 0$

By introducing a variant form of GPF (the so-called "x-ensemble") which automatically takes into account the macroscopic occupation of the condensate, Lee and Yang [31] were able to investigate the

---

* See, for example, Wu and Feenberg [26].
† See, for example, Lee and Broyles [27].

Table 5.III. Comparison of the Salient Features of $g(r)$ from Various Sources

Investigation	T (°K)	Nearest-neighbor distance (Å)	Height of first maximum in $g(r)$	Distance of closest approach (Å)
X-ray scattering				
Goldstein and Reekie [29]	2.06	3.2	1.35	2.25
Neutron scattering				
Henshaw [30]	1.06	3.4	1.42	2.27
Theoretical				
McMillan [24]	0	3.4	1.28	2.00
Theoretical				
Massey [28]	0	3.48	1.31	2.18

consequences of the hard-sphere spectrum upon the BE condensation process. In this formalism, the GPF is expressed in terms of particle clusters which, the authors show, can be decomposed into two-body interactions (binary collision expansion, as mentioned in Section 3.2.5). The most important thermodynamic consequences of this calculation, which is still a dilute gas treatment, are the demonstration of BEC for the hard-sphere gas at $T \neq 0$ and a new-found shape of the specific heat curve. The plot of C_V/Nk_B vs. T in Fig. 5.4 shows the T^3 dependence at low T and as well a discontinuity at the transition point, which is shifted to slightly lower T as compared with T_c for the ideal gas. In further studies of this model, Lee and Yang deduced the kinetic

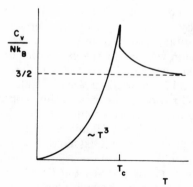

Fig. 5.4. Specific heat of hard-sphere BE gas in the approximation of Lee and Yang [31].

properties characteristic of a superfluid system. However, overall, the conclusions drawn from these hard-sphere studies provide a rather primitive representation for liquid He^4.

Further progress toward more realistic results for the hard-sphere model had been impeded by the difficult problems of (1) handling the self-energy terms when higher densities were considered and (2) reducing to calculable form the terms corresponding to very large clusters (of order N) which become physically important when T approaches T_c. Mohling ([32]) has to some extent been able to bypass these bottlenecks by using the Lee and Yang x-ensemble and binary collision expansion but beginning with the classical (high-temperature) gas and approaching T_c from above rather than from below. Upon entering the degeneracy region, a transformation is made, analogous to the Bogoliubov transformation, which changes the language from that of particle clusters to quasiparticle clusters. Then, calculation of the thermodynamic properties may be carried out for liquid He^4 densities immediately above T_c. For example, the curves for C_P bear considerable resemblance, including the singularity, to those of the actual liquid ([33]). Moreover, the speed of sound at these temperatures is calculated in excellent agreement with the experimental results. It should be emphasized that for these calculations, the only bits of input information are the empirically determined mass of the He atom and the density of the liquid, plus the assumption of 2.6 Å for the hard-sphere diameter. (Other calculations near the λ-point are considered in Section 7.4.)

Although the hard-sphere model can be juggled to give in some respects a satisfactory representation for liquid He^4, much motivation remains for investigations of more general nonideal BE systems at $T \neq 0$. Several starts have been made in this direction to extend various $T = 0$ formalisms (other than hard-sphere) to finite temperatures. In one of these, Parry and Turner ([34]) have modified the Hugenholtz and Pines method ([9]) by introducing a temperature-dependent chemical potential. Their results lead, for low k and for zero and nonzero T, to a phonon spectrum with an energy gap, which nevertheless can be removed under certain conditions. At higher k, the spectrum is exceedingly complicated and is not easily treated by statistical mechanics.

Luban ([35]) has provided a more rewarding approach to the problem by considering a directly diagonalizable Hamiltonian which is a generalization of the Bogoliubov Hamiltonian, $\mathscr{H}_B$. Groundwork for this study was established first by Glassgold et al. ([36]), who developed the statistical mechanics at $T \neq 0$ for $\mathscr{H}_B$ [these authors applied the method to low-density boson systems, but Parry and Turner ([34]) have indicated it is also appropriate for high-density systems] and by later developments, particularly due to Wentzel ([37]) and Zubarev and Tserkovnikov ([38]). In these studies, the Bogoliubov approximation was retained neglecting the differences between $\Phi(n_0)$ and $\Phi(n_0 \pm 1)$; however, the $\mathscr{H}$ which Luban works with avoids this approximation. Furthermore, while this new $\mathscr{H}$ is a pair Hamiltonian truncated similarly to $\mathscr{H}_B$, it includes the more general exchange terms between pairs of excited particles with momenta $\mathbf{p}$ and $\mathbf{q}$ when $\mathbf{p} \neq \pm\mathbf{q}$. The results of this treatment include: (1) a criterion for BEC obtained without the necessity of making special assumptions; (2) a conclusion that the existence of BEC is sufficient to ensure a phonon spectrum at low $\mathbf{k}$; (3) a spectrum exhibiting an energy gap; (4) a justification for the Bogoliubov approximation; (5) a BEC transition T lower than in the ideal gas; and (6) thermodynamic properties, such as the behavior of the C_V vs. T curve and the P–V isotherms, qualitatively similar to those deduced from the hard-sphere model.

Our purpose here is not to survey the spectrum of treatments given the finite-temperature interacting boson system; the literature is far too extensive and we would bog down in detail. Rather, we indicate the sort of progress typically being made toward a realistic microscopic description for this system, and our point is that such progress is painfully slow and exceedingly arduous. Some very novel approach or the development of considerably more powerful mathematical techniques than now available is needed to increase the tempo of the pace.

5.2. FEYNMAN'S THEORY OF LIQUID He⁴

In a series of five elegant papers, Feynman [39,40] and Feynman and Cohen [41] have combined powerful physical arguments within the framework of quantum mechanics to construct a highly practical and satisfying description of the excitation spectrum for liquid He⁴. Feynman first considered the requirements for preparing a ground-state function Ψ_0 depending only on the positions of the N boson atoms, namely: the particles must not touch one another, and, since curvature in the wave function implies kinetic energy, such curvature must be kept as small as possible. As a consequence, Ψ_0 should everywhere have the same sign varying slowly from particle to particle and having no nodes, and the density of particles should be uniformly distributed over the system. This suggests that the most likely configuration for the ground state is one in which the atoms are widely spaced, each atom being constrained to a cell created by its surrounding neighbors but with no preferred structure.

Excited states Ψ_E are required to be orthogonal to Ψ_0; again, there can be no overlap of particles, and since the curvature must be minimized, the introduction of nodes into Ψ_E must be done as gradually as possible. Feynman considered the effect of a particle wandering about through the liquid from cell to cell, with other particles moving out of the way to maintain the density roughly constant. Under the condition prescribed by BE statistics, that a mere permutation of the atoms cannot change the wave function, he concluded that the form of Ψ_E should be

$$\Psi_E = \sum_i f(\mathbf{r}_i)\Psi_0 \tag{5.21}$$

where the summation is taken over all particles and $f(\mathbf{r}_i)$ is a function of the coordinates given by

$$f(\mathbf{r}_i) = \exp(i\mathbf{k} \cdot \mathbf{r}_i) \tag{5.22}$$

The functions (5.22) are eigenfunctions of the momentum operator, which commutes with $\mathscr{H}$ such that $\Sigma_i f(\mathbf{r}_i)$ satisfies the orthogonality requirements, and it can be shown that these eigenfunctions are simply those for phonons in the system. The net important result is a plausible argument to show that the only possible low-lying excitations of the system are phonons.

A more rigorous treatment was also given, in which the functions $f(\mathbf{r}_i)$ were introduced into Schrödinger's equation and evaluated in a variational treatment. The Hamiltonian of the system was expressed in terms of the density function $|\Psi_0|^2$ for the ground state, which leads to integrals involving the pair correlation function $g(r)$. Feynman showed that equation (5.22) is indeed the solution which minimizes the energy of the system, and this energy is

$$\epsilon(k) = \hbar^2 k^2 / 2mS_0(k) \tag{5.23}$$

The function $S_0(k)$ is the Fourier transform of the ground-state function $g_0(r)$:

$$S_0(k) = \int g_0(r)e^{i\mathbf{k} \cdot \mathbf{r}}\, dr^3 \tag{5.24}$$

and is well known as the liquid structure factor (at $T = 0°\text{K}$).

We may make the definition, summing over all particles,

$$\rho_\mathbf{k} = \int \rho(\mathbf{r})\exp(i\mathbf{k} \cdot \mathbf{r})dr^3 = \sum_i \exp(i\mathbf{k} \cdot \mathbf{r}) \tag{5.25}$$

and identify $\rho_\mathbf{k}$ as the density fluctuation operator. This is just the Fourier transform of the density operator and describes the small fluctuations from the mean density. We also have the complex conjugate, $\rho_{-\mathbf{k}}$. In this notation, the excited-state wave function can be written as $\Psi_\mathbf{k} = \rho_\mathbf{k}\Psi_0$ and $S_0(k)$ as the expectation value of $|\rho_\mathbf{k}|^2$ in the ground state:

$$S_0(k) = \langle \Psi_0|\rho_{-\mathbf{k}}\rho_\mathbf{k}|\Psi_0 \rangle = \sum_{ij} \langle \exp[i\mathbf{k} \cdot (\mathbf{r}_i - \mathbf{r}_j)] \rangle \tag{5.26}$$

The analysis of $S_0(k)$ for low k shows that the density fluctuations represent sound waves and that ρ_k is the coordinate of the normal mode for a sound wave with velocity u_1. By treating the sound waves as harmonic oscillations, Feynman deduced that in the region of low k, where the medium can be treated as a continuum since the wavelength is over many atomic spacings, $S_0(k)$ changes linearly with k and may be evaluated as $\hbar k/2mu_1$. When substituted into equation (5.23), this gives the familiar linear dispersion relation $\epsilon(k) = u_1\hbar k = u_1 p$.

In scattering experiments of X-rays or neutrons from a classical monatomic liquid, the intensity of the scattered beam is found proportional to $S(k)$ (for $T \neq 0$) when k is considered as the momentum transfer suffered in elastic collisions. Thus, if we send a beam of, say, neutrons, with momentum q into a sample of liquid, then at an angle θ with respect to the incoming beam, the momentum transfer will be given by

$$\mathbf{k} = 2\mathbf{q}\,\sin(\theta/2) \tag{5.27}$$

It is well known that for $k \approx 2\pi/a$, where a is the average atomic separation distance, a maximum in the intensity, i.e., in $S(k)$, is observed. Feynman considered that liquid He^4 at $T = 0$ should in this respect be much like a classical liquid, so that a corresponding maximum in $S_0(k)$ should also be found for He. Therefore, there should be a minimum in $\epsilon(k)$ at approximately $2\pi/a$. In the variational treatment, the function (5.21) is still the solution for this range of k; but here, changes in the modulation factor (5.22) go from plus to minus over distances comparable to an atomic spacing, so that Ψ_E becomes representative of a highly localized excitation. These are just the properties we expect for rotons.

For increasing values of k, $S(k)$ from scattering experiments decreases, shows subsidiary maxima corresponding to the next-nearest-neighbor and higher correlations of $g(r)$, and finally approaches unity at very large k. These features were used by Feynman to indicate that past the minimum in $\epsilon(k)$ the spectrum should rise as $\hbar k^2/2m$.

For the numerical evaluation of $\epsilon(k)$, the X-ray scattering data of Reekie and Hutchison ([42]) and the corresponding neutron data of Henshaw and Hurst ([43]) were at the time found to give results in agreement for $g(r)$, from which $S_0(k)$, and thus also $\epsilon(k)$, could be obtained. Figure 5.5 shows the relationship between these three quantities and indicates that the Feynman calculation of the roton minimum is about a factor of two too high compared with the Landau spectrum as determined from specific-heat and second-sound data. As shown in Table 5.IV, several calculations have been made for the Landau parameters from experimental thermal data with slightly different results. A certain amount of compliance is available in these calculations, so that the

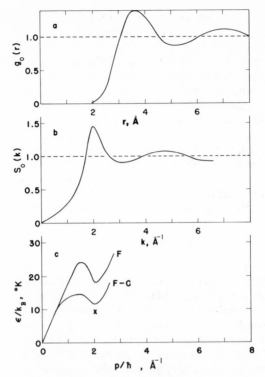

Fig. 5.5. Relationship among: (a) the pair correlation function, $g_0(r)$; (b) its Fourier transform, the structure factor $S_0(k)$; and (c) the excitation spectrum calculated as described in text. Curve F is Feynman's original calculation ([39]) and Curve F-C is that of Feynman and Cohen ([41]). The cross represents the coordinates of the roton minimum according to Khalatnikov ([44]).

variations in the parameters should not be regarded as very significant.

A wave packet constructed from the functions (5.22) may be localized to correspond to the situation in the vicinity of the roton dip. Such a packet has associated with it a current and a density of the particles, but it does not represent a stationary state of the system since it prescribes that all the particles move in the same direction and lacks the return flow required to conserve the current. The deficiency of relation (5.22) in this respect is enhanced as k increases. From an analog with classical hydrodynamics—that of a sphere moving through a fluid and the concomitant backward streaming of particles displaced

Table 5.IV. Experimental and Theoretical Values of the Landau Parameters

	Δ/k_B (°K)	$p_0/\hbar$ (Å⁻¹)	$\mu(m_{He})$
Khalatnikov ([44])[a]	8.9	1.99	0.26
Wiebes et al. ([45])[a]	8.8	1.96	0.23
Feynman ([39])[b]	19	1.8	—
Feynman and Cohen ([41])[b]	11.5	1.85	0.20
Yarnell et al. ([51])[c]	8.65	1.92	0.16
Henshaw and Woods ([52])[c]	8.65	1.91	0.16

[a] Thermal data.
[b] Calculated.
[c] Neutron data, $T = 1.1$°K.

by the sphere—Feynman and Cohen ([41]) were able to construct a trial wave function which does conserve current and has the form

$$\Psi_E = \Psi_0 \sum_i \exp(i\mathbf{k} \cdot \mathbf{r}_i)\left[1 + i \sum_{j \neq i} F(\mathbf{r}_{ji}) \right] \qquad (5.28)$$

with

$$F(\mathbf{r}) = A\mathbf{k} \cdot \mathbf{r}/r^3 \qquad (5.29)$$

This Ψ_E qualifies as a proper eigenfunction of the total momentum and gives a picture of the roton as a microscopic vortex ring of diameter comparable to the interatomic spacing of the liquid. We should not, however, take this picture too literally, since it cannot adequately include the appropriate quantum-mechanical effects. Use of equation (5.28) in a variational treatment also produced results describable in terms of the two-particle correlation function, and when the experimental scattering data were introduced, the upper bound to Δ/k_B was significantly lowered compared with the earlier calculations. Moreover, these calculations are in good agreement with the spectrum derived from thermal data. The Feynman–Cohen dispersion curve is given in Fig. 5.5c, and a comparison of the Landau parameters obtained here and by various other methods is given in Table 5.IV.

In concluding this section, we wish to point out several properties of ρ_k and $S_0(k)$. First, we note that for an ideal gas, the excitations are simply single-particle momentum states described by $\Psi_k = \Sigma \exp(i\mathbf{k} \cdot \mathbf{r}) = \rho_k$, so that ρ_k itself determines the density. However, in the liquid, $\Psi_k = \rho_k\Psi_0$, with Ψ_0 controlling the gross density modulated by ρ_k, thereby accounting for the collective phonon modes which are not possible in the gas.

Next, we should appreciate the differences between the ground-state structure factor and this function at temperatures other than zero. The principal temperature dependence of $S(k)$ is confined to the region of small k (long wavelength), and here there are important qualitative differences. We have already observed from equation (5.26) that $S_0(k)$ begins at zero for $k = 0$ and rises linearly with k. But for $T \neq 0$, $S(k)$ rises quadratically from a nonzero value given by the relation

$$\lim_{k \to 0} S(k) = (N/\Omega)k_B T \beta_T \qquad (5.30)$$

where β_T is the isothermal compressibility. This relation, which has been obtained both theoretically and experimentally for classical liquids clearly vanishes as $T = 0°K$. On the other hand, for a classical ideal gas, there are no correlations between particles, and the value of equation (5.30) is unity for all T.

5.3. DETERMINATION OF $\epsilon(k)$ BY NEUTRON SCATTERING

Although the theory had been worked out earlier [46] for determining the $\epsilon(k)$ relation for phonons in a solid by the inelastic scattering of slow neutrons,† it was not appreciated at the time that similar techniques might be applicable to liquid He⁴. Rather, it was generally expected that the continuous background at all scattering angles would completely overshadow any evidence of momentum transfers involving the creation or destruction of excitations in the helium. The fallacy in this belief was dramatically exposed in the study of the scattering processes made by Cohen and Feynman [47], who proposed in considerable detail an experiment for measuring $\epsilon(k)$.

Earlier investigations of liquid He⁴ with neutrons had been attempted, but not with the purpose of determining the spectrum. We have already mentioned the neutron diffraction experiments of Henshaw [30] and of Henshaw and Hurst [43], who elastically scattered monochromatic neutrons ($\lambda \approx 1$ Å) to obtain information on the atomic arrangement in the liquid by measuring $S(k)$ from the angular distribution of the scattered neutrons. At about the same time, other experiments [48] with long-wavelength neutrons ($3 < \lambda < 16$ Å) were attempted in order to detect, among other things, effects associated with BEC. Although negative results were obtained in this regard, the scattering cross sections were obtained as a function of T and λ, it being found that as λ is increased, the cross section decreases somewhat like a reversed S-curve. For a given λ, the cross section decreases with T, this dependence being more pronounced at longer wavelength.

---

† In the elastic scattering of neutrons, neither the neutrons nor the bombarded system suffers an energy change, whereas in inelastic scattering, such changes do occur subject to the conservation laws.

The conclusions reached by Cohen and Feynman ([47]) suggested that not only could the angular distribution of scattered neutrons be measured, but also the energy transfer resulting from the scattering. Thus it should be possible to measure the probability $S(k, \omega)$ that a neutron exits from the system with momentum k after suffering an energy transfer ω. For a system at $T = 0°K$, $S(k, \omega)$ is defined as

$$S(k, \omega) = \sum_f |\langle f|\rho_{\mathbf{k}}|0\rangle|^2 \, \delta(E_f - E_0 - \omega) \qquad (5.31)$$

Here the matrix element of $\rho_{\mathbf{k}}$ is taken between the ground state of the system with energy E_0 and the final state with energy E_f; the δ-function is unity when $E_f = E_0 + \omega$ and zero otherwise. Thus, neutrons of momentum $\mathbf{q}$ are sent into the liquid, and in being scattered give up amounts of energy ω which correspond to the excitation energies of the liquid when the collision processes are subject to the rules for the conservation of energy and momentum, given respectively as

$$E_{\mathbf{q}} - E_{\mathbf{k}} = \omega \qquad (5.32)$$

and

$$q^2 + k^2 - 2qk \cos \theta = (p/\hbar)^2 \qquad (5.33)$$

In equation (5.32), $E_{\mathbf{q}}$ refers to the energy of the incident neutron and $E_{\mathbf{k}}$ to that of the scattered neutron. Accordingly, $\mathbf{q}$ may be fixed and the scattering angle θ varied so that at the value of $\mathbf{q}$ for which the δ-function becomes unity, the scattered intensity is sharply enhanced; or we can fix θ and vary $\mathbf{q}$. Under the latter conditions, the total intensity is

$$NS(k) = \int_0^\infty S(k, \omega) \, d\omega \qquad (5.34)$$

and $S(k, \omega)$ plotted as a function of ω is found as schematically given by the solid curve of Fig. 5.6. Cohen and Feynman used the wave function (5.28) to calculate the angular variation of line strength for various $\mathbf{q}$, and although these are considered too large, the qualitative features are correct, namely: the line should be very sharp and the background from multiple scattering should be negligible if the incident neutrons have $\lambda \geqslant 4$ Å.

At $T \neq 0$, the possibility arises that the system can also give up energy to the neutron as well as receive it, so that ω can be either negative or positive. Expression (5.31) must also be modified in that E_0 becomes E_i for the more general initial state and a thermal distribution factor $\exp(-\beta E_i)/Z$ must be included. It is expected that at nonzero temperatures, the peak will be slightly smeared out, as shown by

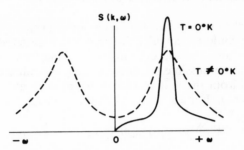

Fig. 5.6. Probability of energy transfer as a function
of energy transfer in inelastic neutron scattering.

the dotted curve in Fig. 5.6, and that a similar peak should occur for
$-\omega$. The background should remain low so long as the temperature
of the helium does not exceed about 2°K. Cohen and Feynman also
concluded that the kinematics of the scattering processes are such that
when λ of the incident neutrons is > 16.5 Å, no excitations can be produced in the liquid, and for $\lambda \gtrsim 10$ Å, only very-low-energy phonons
can be created. Finally, for $\lambda < 10$ Å (corresponding to $q = 0.6$ Å^{-1}),
the majority of excitations produced should have $k > 0.4$ Å^{-1}.

Announcement of the above predictions proved sufficiently stimu-
lating that three separate groups, at Chalk River ([49]), Stockholm ([50]),
and Los Alamos ([51]), endeavored to put the theory to test. All used
essentially the same method, and all succeeded in observing in inelastic
neutron scattering by liquid He^4 the small changes in momentum which
could be interpreted, using the Cohen–Feynman treatment, as the
production of discrete excitations in the liquid. The Stockholm
group ([50]) was able to obtain results which delineated the roton minimum of the spectrum between $p/\hbar$ values of 1.5 and 2.3 Å^{-1}, while
Henshaw ([49]) observed four points between 0.8 and 2.2 Å^{-1} which
could be similarly interpreted. At Los Alamos ([51]), the range 0.5 to
2.4 Å^{-1} was investigated at small momentum intervals with the
results clearly showing the phonon and roton portions. Thus the Landau spectrum was elegantly and directly verified.

Somewhat later, Henshaw and Woods ([52]) refined earlier measurements in a detailed study of the spectral parameters over the temperature range 1.1° to 4.2°K. Since these studies represent the more recent
methods and results, they will form the basis of our discussion, it being
understood that no new principle is involved *vis à vis* the earlier work.
A review of the latter has been given by Andronikashvili ([53]).

In the double-crystal neutron spectrometer used by Henshaw and
Woods, a beam of thermalized neutrons from the reactor enters the
collimator through a graphite plug and is filtered by a beryllium block
and quartz crystals. An aluminum single crystal is used to monochro-

matize the beam, which then impinges upon the liquid He⁴ sample.
The scattered beam is analyzed by reflecting it from the [111] planes of
a lead single crystal after which the intensity is detected by a BF_3
counter. The wavelength of the neutrons, after reflections from the Al
and Pb crystals, was determined to be 4.039 $\pm$ 0.005 Å. Scattering
angles between 10° and 140° were analyzed.

The results of the spectrum with liquid He⁴ at 1.12°K are shown in
Fig. 5.7, where the experimental data extend from 0.3 to 2.7 Å⁻¹. The
dotted straight line beginning at the origin is drawn with a slope determined by $u_1 = 237$ m/sec, and it is seen that the experiment strongly
supports the postulated linear dispersion relation at low k. At about
0.6 Å⁻¹, the spectrum begins to deviate from linearity and passes

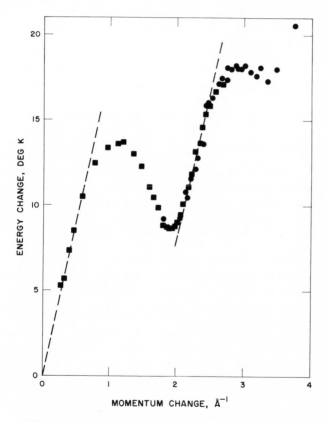

Fig. 5.7. Experimental dispersion curve of He II at P_{sat}: ■ Henshaw
and Woods, $\lambda = 4.039$ Å, $T = 1.12°K$; ● Woods, $\lambda = 2.48$ and
2.77 Å, $T = 1.6°K$.

through a maximum at 1.10 Å^{-1} and 13.7°K. The constants representing the dispersion in the vicinity of the roton minimum are listed in Table 5.IV. However, here the experimental curve is not truly parabolic, and outside the range ± 0.15 Å^{-1} from $p_0/\hbar$, the spectrum calculated using these parameters lies above the measured points. On the high wave number side of the roton minimum, the observed dispersion curve appears to rise slightly less steeply than the dotted curve representing the initial phonon slope, with the curve ending in a manner suggestive of another maximum at higher momenta.

Yarnell *et al.* [51] had earlier observed the temperature variation of the dispersion curve, and this has been subsequently investigated more extensively by Henshaw and Woods [52]. By studying the wavelength distribution of neutrons scattered at $\theta = 80°$, corresponding closely to the momentum at the roton minimum, Henshaw and Woods determined the changes in the gap energy Δ/k_B, in line width, and in the effective mass of an excitation as the temperature was increased from 1.78° to 4.21°K. (Here, the effective mass is not the roton parameter μ, but is defined as the number of He masses required to produce the same ω for neutron scattering by free particles as the measured scattering by the liquid.) The results of these observations are shown in Fig. 5.8, which illustrates the rapid variations in these quantities just below T_λ, with apparently sharp changes in slope at the transition followed by nearly constant values above this temperature. Of particular interest is the decrease in energy required to form an excitation as the temperature rises to the λ-point; in addition, the broadening of line width with T is believed to be associated, through the uncertainty principle, with the increasingly short lifetime of the excitations between collisions. Also represented in the figure are calculations of the excitation line widths based on the Landau–Khalatnikov theory but including the temperature dependence of Δ/k_B.

The continuous nature of the observed excitation curve as well at its temperature variation emphasizes once more that the original Landau approximation to the spectrum, of monoenergetic rotons plus the simple linear phonon dispersion relation, must be inadequate in accounting for the liquid properties above about 1.7°K. Similarly, the question arises as to whether phonons and rotons are really different types of thermal excitations. Lee and Mohling [54] have suggested a criterion for making this distinction in terms of the *helicity* of the excitation, defined as the projection of the angular momentum vector in the direction of the linear momentum vector. It is known that phonons have zero helicity, i.e., they have no angular momentum of their own; but it is not yet known whether the same holds true for rotons, though, in principle, this should be determinable from neutron scattering data. If it were to turn out that the helicity for rotons were

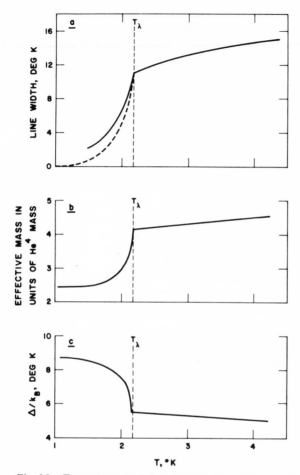

Fig. 5.8.   Temperature variation of (a) the line width at half-maximum of the observed scattering intensity of neutron peaks, (b) effective mass (see text), and (c) the gap energy Δ/k_B. Data were taken at $\theta = 80°$, which corresponds roughly to the roton minimum after Henshaw and Woods (^{52}). Dashed line in (a) is the Landau–Khalatnikov theory.

also zero (as seems probable), then there would be little justification for speaking of two distinct classes of excitations.

Subsequent to the work of Henshaw and Woods (^{52}), features of the spectrum outside the momentum range covered by them have attracted considerable interest. Miller et al. (^{55}) have analyzed the situation at long wavelengths, and have concluded, based upon the properties of certain sum rules for $S(k, \omega)$, that the excitation of single quasiparticles from the condensate accounts for all the small momentum transfer processes. This result, combined with the experimental data of Henshaw and Woods, introduces small changes in the liquid structure factor, primarily a previously unsuspected bump in the $S_0(k)$ curve corresponding to the region near $0.6 \, \text{Å}^{-1}$. The full significance of this bump is not clear, but has been the object of interest and conjecture [56].

Somewhat later, Hohenberg and Martin [57] suggested that the initial slope of the phonon branch of the dispersion curve should be given by u_1 (the hydrodynamic speed of ordinary sound) only when $\rho \approx \rho_s$. They predicted that for temperatures approaching the λ-point, the slope should decrease as $u_1(\rho_s/\rho)^{1/2}$ accompanied by a broadening in the dispersion relation. These effects should be observed for momentum transfers with $p/\hbar$ of the order of $0.1 \, \text{Å}^{-1}$. This is a very difficult region experimentally. Nevertheless, Woods [58] has succeeded in making a detailed study at $p/\hbar = 0.38 \, \text{Å}^{-1}$, which is probably a sufficiently long

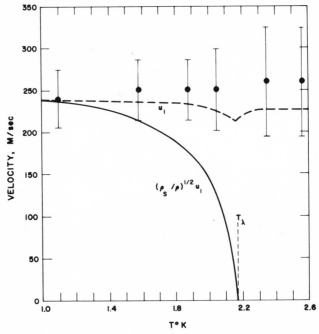

Fig. 5.9. Comparison of phonon velocities as obtained from neutron data, sound velocity (dashed curve), and predictions of Hohenberg and Martin [57] (solid curve). Vertical bars indicate linewidth at half-maximum of the neutron peaks. [After Woods [58].]

wavelength for the detection of the Hohenberg–Martin effect should it exist. The observed results are compared with the predictions in Fig. 5.9. It can be seen that there is neither a decrease in slope of the $\epsilon(k)$ curve nor a pronounced broadening of the line shape near the λ-point, indicating that the phonon spectrum is essentially independent of whether the liquid is superfluid or normal. In this latter respect, the phonon behavior differs considerably from that of the rotons (see Fig. 5.8).

For the region of large momentum transfers, i.e., $p/\hbar > 2.6 \text{ Å}^{-1}$, Pitaevskii [59] has speculated that at some limiting value of $p/\hbar = p^*/\hbar$, the spectrum should terminate. He suggested three probable ways in which it may come about through the decay of a high-energy roton. However, the theory gives no clues as to which of the decay schemes should be the actual one. The three choices are: (a) If the speed of the roton were greater than u_1, it should decay by emitting a phonon, which implies that the slope of the dispersion curve beyond the roton minimum should be greater than that of the initial phonon region; however, we have already mentioned that the data of Henshaw and Woods [52] indicate that the rise in question is not so steep as the phonon slope, so that this mode of decay is rather unlikely. (b) The high-energy roton might decay into two other rotons of longer wavelength, the minimum energy required for this process being 2Δ. Here, two decay modes are possible. In the first, the two product rotons acquire the same energy and travel in the same direction, in which case the dispersion curve should end abruptly at the threshold $p^*/\hbar$ with a finite slope. (c) The second type of degeneration into two rotons is characterized by the two product rotons having equal energies but with momenta directed at some nonzero angle. Then the termination should occur at $p^*/\hbar$ with zero slope.

The investigation of this region of the spectrum was undertaken by Woods [60] using neutrons of incident wavelength 2.48 Å and 2.77 Å. As expected [55], the efficiency of exciting single quasiparticles from the condensate decreases markedly at increasing values of momentum transfer. Nevertheless, Woods was able to secure meaningful data for $p/\hbar$ as large as 4 Å^{-1}. The results, shown in Fig. 5.7, indicate a broad plateau at $\epsilon/k_B = 17.9 \pm 0.6°\text{K}$, which, although slightly larger than $2\Delta/k_B = 17.3°\text{K}$, appears to substantiate the case (c) predictions of Pitaevskii.

5.4. CALCULATION OF THERMODYNAMIC PROPERTIES FROM THE EXCITATION SPECTRUM

The ultimate goal of all the "particle" theories and experiments we have considered so far for the thermal excitations of He II has been

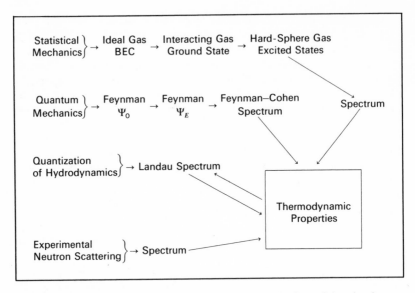

Fig. 5.10. Interrelations between theory and experiment in determining the thermodynamic properties of He II.

to reproduce the macroscopically observed thermal properties of the
liquid. The diagram in Fig. 5.10 is suggestive of the diverse paths
available for reaching this result, arranged from top to bottom in order
of increasing accuracy with which the thermal properties can be
determined. One step we have not as yet taken, but are about to take,
is that of joining the experimentally determined spectrum with the
macroscopic properties. The accuracy with which this can be done is
rather spectacular, providing us with a large measure of confidence in
the entire scheme, though the calculations are still not well defined
near the λ-point.

Bendt et al. [61] have introduced the Los Alamos $\epsilon(k)$ curve, along
with its temperature dependence, into the usual statistical thermodynamic formalism to calculate a variety of thermodynamic properties
of He II. Because the neutron measurements were made at $T = 1.1°$,
$1.6°$, and $1.8°$K, it was necessary to devise an interpolation formula
for $\epsilon(k)$ at intermediate temperatures. BE statistics were assumed to
apply to rotons as well as to phonons. To facilitate the calculations,
the dispersion curve was divided into four momentum intervals:
(1) the phonon section which makes the only contribution to the
thermodynamic quantities for temperatures up to $0.5°$K; (2) the
transition region between about 0.5 and 1.6 Å^{-1}, which includes the

maximum in the curve; (3) the roton region, which dominates the calculations above 1°K; and (4) momenta above 2.2 Å^{-1}, the effects of which must be included beginning at 1°K. Table 5.V lists the relative contribution, in percent, made by the four momentum intervals to the entropy of He II at several temperatures.

Table 5.V. Relative Contribution (in %) to Entropy Coming from the Four Momentum Intervals as a Function of Temperature

T (°K)	Interval 1 (Phonon region)	Interval 2 ($0.5 < p/\hbar < 1.6$ Å^{-1})	Interval 3 (Roton region)	Interval 4 ($p/\hbar > 2.2$ Å^{-1})
0.5	100	0	0	0
1.0	42	1	55	2
1.8	7	8	74	11
2.17	4	10	73	13

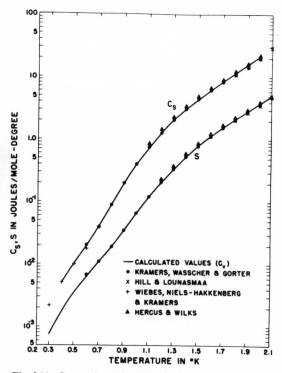

Fig. 5.11. Comparison of entropy and specific heat of He II as determined from thermal measurements and calculated from neutron data [from Bendt et al. ([61])].

The liquid He^4 thermodynamic properties calculated by Bendt *et al.* and the corresponding temperature ranges investigated were: entropy, 0.2 to 1.8°K; specific heat, 0.2 to 1.7°K; the velocity of second sound, 0.8 to 1.8°K; and the normal fluid density, 0.7 to 1.9°K. In general, the agreement between the calculated values and those determined empirically is well within the probable uncertainty of the measurements. Examples of this agreement are shown in Fig. 5.11, where the calculated entropy and specific heat are compared with experimental data ([45,62,63]), the deviations being no larger than $\pm 4\%$ over the whole range.

The statistical calculations of ρ_n/ρ were compared with experimental values determined in several ways, the data for ρ being those of Kerr ([64]) and of Atkins and Edwards ([65]). Andronikashvili ([66]) and Dash and Taylor ([67]) have measured the damping of stacks of oscillating disks to arrive at values of ρ_n/ρ, and these results are all lower than the

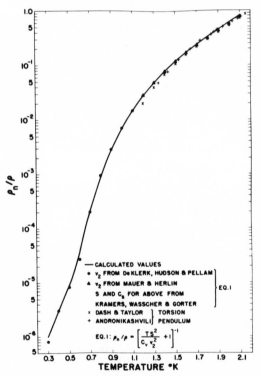

Fig. 5.12. Comparison of experimental values of ρ_n/ρ with calculations from the neutron data [from Bendt *et al.* ([61])].

calculated quantities, the largest discrepancy being 27% at 1.2°K. Considerably better agreement was obtained when ρ_n/ρ was derived from the relation for second sound

$$u_2^2 = \frac{\rho_s}{\rho_n} \frac{TS^2}{C_V} \tag{5.35}$$

These comparisons are shown in Fig. 5.12. When the calorimetric data ([45,62]) combined with second sound measurements ([68,69]) were inserted into equation (5.35), the maximum deviations from the calculated ρ_n/ρ were reduced to about 8%.

An additional test for consistency was made starting with relation (5.35) and using the statistical calculations for S, C_V, and ρ_n. In comparing the resulting values of u_2^2 with the experimental observations ([68,69]), we find that above 1.0°K, there is agreement to within $\pm 2\%$; below this temperature, the effects of dispersion of the heat pulses must be taken into account, making meaningful comparisons difficult.

REFERENCES

1. P. C. Hohenberg and P. C. Martin, *Ann. Phys. (N.Y.)*, **34**, 291 (1965).
2. R. P. Feynman, *Phys. Rev.*, **91**, 1291 (1953).
3. A. Bijl, J. de Boer, and A. Michels, *Physica*, **8**, 655 (1941).
4. L. Landau, *J. Phys. (USSR)*, **5**, 71 (1941).
5. N. N. Bogoliubov, *J. Phys. (USSR)*, **11**, 23 (1947).
6. O. Penrose and L. Onsager, *Phys. Rev.*, **104**, 576 (1956).
7. P. C. Martin, *J. Math. Phys.*, **4**, 208 (1963).
8. S. T. Beliaev, *Zh. Eksperim. i Teor. Fiz.*, **34**, 417 (1958); **34**, 433 (1958); [English translation, *Soviet Phys.—JETP*, 7, 289 (1958); 7, 299 (1958)].
9. N. M. Hugenholtz and D. Pines, *Phys. Rev.*, **116**, 489 (1959).
10. K. Huang and C. N. Yang, *Phys. Rev.*, **105**, 767 (1957).
11. K. Huang, C. N. Yang, and J. M. Luttinger, *Phys. Rev.*, **105**, 776 (1957).
12. T. D. Lee and C. N. Yang, *Phys. Rev.*, **106**, 1119 (1957).
13. T. D. Lee, K. Huang, and C. N. Yang, *Phys. Rev.*, **106**, 1135 (1957).
14. T. D. Lee and C. N. Yang, *Phys. Rev.*, **112**, 1419 (1958).
15. T. D. Lee and C. N. Yang, *Phys. Rev.*, **113**, 1165 (1959); **116**, 25 (1959); **117**, 12 (1960); **117**, 22 (1960); **117**, 897 (1960).
16. K. Huang, in *Studies in Statistical Mechanics* (J. de Boer and G. E. Uhlenbeck, eds.), pp. 3–105, North Holland, Amsterdam (1964); also see K. Huang, *Statistical Mechanics*, Chapter 19, John Wiley, New York (1963).
17. T. T. Wu, *Phys. Rev.*, **115**, 1390 (1959).
18. K. Huang, *Phys. Rev.*, **115**, 765 (1959); **119**, 1129 (1960).
19. K. A. Brueckner and K. Sawada, *Phys. Rev.*, **106**, 1117 (1957); **106**, 1128 (1957).
20. W. E. Parry and D. ter Haar, *Ann. Phys. (N.Y.)*, **19**, 496 (1962).
21. L. Liu and K. W. Wong, *Phys. Rev.*, **132**, 1349 (1963).
22. L. Liu, L. S. Liu, and K. W. Wong, *Phys. Rev.*, **135A**, 1166 (1964).
23. M. Girardeau and R. Arnowitt, *Phys. Rev.*, **133**, 755 (1959).
24. W. L. McMillan, *Phys. Rev.*, **138A**, 442 (1965).
25. D. Levesque, D. Schiff, T. Khiet, and L. Verlet (unpublished report); also see D. Schiff and L. Verlet, *Phys. Rev.*, **160**, 208 (1967).
26. F. Y. Wu and E. Feenberg, *Phys. Rev.*, **122**, 739 (1961); D. K. Lee and E. Feenberg, *Phys. Rev.*, **137**, A731 (1965).

27. J. C. Lee and A. A. Broyles, *Phys. Rev. Letters*, **17**, 424 (1966).
28. W. E. Massey, *Phys. Rev.*, **151**, 153 (1966).
29. L. Goldstein and J. Reekie, *Phys. Rev.*, **98**, 857 (1955).
30. D. G. Henshaw, *Phys. Rev.*, **119**, 9 (1960).
31. T. D. Lee and C. N. Yang, *Phys. Rev.*, **113**, 1406 (1959).
32. F. Mohling, *Phys. Rev.*, **135A**, 831, 855, 876 (1964).
33. P. T. Sikora and F. Mohling, Los Alamos Sci. Lab. Report LA-DC 8333 (1967).
34. W. E. Parry and R. E. Turner, *Phys. Rev.*, **128**, 929 (1962).
35. M. Luban, *Phys. Rev.*, **128**, 965 (1962).
36. A. E. Glassgold, A. N. Kaufman, and K. M. Watson, *Phys. Rev.*, **120**, 660 (1960).
37. G. Wentzel, *Phys. Rev.*, **120**, 1572 (1960).
38. D. N. Zubarev and Iu. A. Tserkovnikov, *Dok. Akad. Nauk. SSSR*, **120**, 991 (1958);
    [English translation. *Soviet Phys.—Doklady*, **3**, 603 (1958)].
39. R. P. Feynman, *Phys. Rev.*, **91**, 1291 (1953); **91**, 1301 (1953); **94**, 262 (1954).
40. R. P. Feynman, in *Progress in Low Temperature Physics* (C. J. Gorter, ed.), Vol. I,
    p. 17, North Holland, Amsterdam (1955).
41. R. P. Feynman and M. Cohen, *Phys. Rev.*, **102**, 1189 (1956).
42. J. Reekie and T. S. Hutchison, *Phys. Rev.*, **92**, 827 (1953).
43. D. G. Henshaw and D. G. Hurst, *Phys. Rev.*, **91**, 1223 (1953); D. G. Hurst and
    D. G. Henshaw, *Phys. Rev.*, **100**, 994 (1955).
44. I. M. Khalatnikov, *Usp. Fiz. Nauk.*, **59**, 673 (1956). [An English translation by
    M. G. Priestly has had limited circulation.]
45. J. Wiebes, C. G. Niels-Hakkenberg, and H. C. Kramers, *Physica*, **23**, 625 (1957).
46. G. Placzek and L. Van Hove, *Phys. Rev.*, **93**, 1207 (1954).
47. M. Cohen and R. P. Feynman, *Phys. Rev.*, **107**, 13 (1957).
48. H. S. Sommers, J. G. Dash, and L. Goldstein, *Phys. Rev.*, **97**, 855 (1955); P. A.
    Egelstaff and H. London, *Proc. Roy. Soc. (London)*, **A242**, 374 (1957).
49. D. G. Henshaw, *Phys. Rev. Letters*, **1**, 127 (1958).
50. H. Palevsky, K. Otnes, K. E. Larsson, R. Pauli, and R. Stedman, *Phys. Rev.*, **108**,
    1346 (1957); H. Palevsky, K. Otnes, and K. E. Larsson, *Phys. Rev.*, **112**, 11 (1958).
51. J. L. Yarnell, G. P. Arnold, P. J. Bendt, and E. C. Kerr, *Phys. Rev. Letters*, **1**, 9
    (1958); *Phys. Rev.*, **113**, 1379 (1959).
52. D. G. Henshaw and A. D. B. Woods, *Phys. Rev.*, **121**, 1266 (1961).
53. E. L. Andronikashvili, *Usp. Fiz. Nauk.*, **72**, 697 (1960 [English translation, *Soviet
    Phys.—Usp.*, **3**, 888 (1961)].
54. T. D. Lee and F. Mohling, *Phys. Rev. Letters*, **2**, 284 (1958).
55. A. Miller, D. Pines, and P. Nozières, *Phys. Rev.*, **127**, 1452 (1962).
56. *Quantum Fluids* (D. F. Brewer, ed.), p. 241, North Holland, Amsterdam (1966).
57. P. C. Hohenberg and P. C. Martin, *Phys. Rev. Letters*, **12**, 69 (1964).
58. A. D. B. Woods, *Phys. Rev. Letters*, **14**, 355 (1965).
59. L. P. Pitaevskii, *Zh. Eksperim i Teor. Fiz.*, **18**, 1168 (1959); [English translation,
    Soviet Phys.—JETP, **9**, 830 (1959)].
60. A. D. B. Woods, in *Inelastic Scattering of Neutrons*, Vol. II, p. 191, I.A.E.A.,
    Vienna (1965); *Quantum Fluids* (D. F. Brewer, ed.), p. 242, North Holland, Amster-
    dam (1966).
61. P. J. Bendt, R. D. Cowan, and J. L. Yarnell, *Phys. Rev.*, **113**, 1386 (1959).
62. H. C. Kramers, J. D. Wasscher, and C. J. Gorter, *Physica*, **18**, 329 (1952).
63. R. W. Hill and O. V. Lounasmaa, *Phil. Mag.*, **2**, 143 (1957).
64. E. C. Kerr, *J. Chem. Phys.*, **26**, 511 (1957).
65. K. R. Atkins and M. H. Edwards, *Phys. Rev.*, **97**, 1429 (1955).
66. E. L. Andronikashvili, *Zh. Eksperim. i Teor. Fiz.*, **18**, 424 (1948).
67. J. G. Dash and R. D. Taylor, *Phys. Rev.*, **105**, 7 (1957).
68. R. D. Mauer and M. A. Herlin, *Phys. Rev.*, **76**, 948 (1949); **81**, 444 (1951).
69. D. de Klerk, R. P. Hudson, and J. Pellam, *Phys. Rev.*, **93**, 28 (1954).

Chapter 6

Properties of Liquid He^3 at Low Temperatures

Just as liquid He^4 becomes more "interesting" as the temperature is lowered below the λ-point, so also does liquid He^3 begin to depart from rather classical behavior near its degeneration temperature. In this region and at lower temperatures, the nuclear spin and the antisymmetric statistics are the most notable characteristics of He^3 serving to distinguish this liquid from liquid He^4. In the present chapter, we propose to summarize some of the attempts that have been made at understanding the extent and nature of the roles played by these effects.

Again, as for liquid He^4, the He^3 problem has been attacked theoretically on essentially three different levels. A purely phenomenological description for liquid He^3 has been developed by Goldstein on the basis that the low-temperature equilibrium properties are dominated by the nuclear spin system. Through the assumption that the spin interactions are reflected by the measured nuclear paramagnetic susceptibility, he has combined these data with classical thermodynamics to describe quite accurately the thermal and state properties of condensed He^3. The kinetic properties of the liquid are not included in this treatment.

On the semiphenomenological level, Landau has considered how, beginning with an ideal Fermi gas, the transformation might occur to a Fermi liquid as the interparticle potential is gradually "turned on." The interactions are expressed through a function f which must be evaluated from experimental data. Various properties of the Fermi liquid have been expressed in terms of f in an extension of Landau's theory by Abrikosov and Khalatnikov. Of special interest among the features predicted by Landau for the Fermi liquid is a new type of sound propagation called "zero sound." It now appears that an experimental search for this phenomenon has been successful, and this

159

in itself provides much support for the validity of the Landau formalism. Whereas the theory was originally considered to hold only for temperatures below 0.05°K, some evidence has been offered indicating that this range may be extended.

The Landau theory has been fortified by investigations of the interrelations between the elementary excitations, the correlation functions, and the response of the system to external probes. In this way, such correlations as the dynamic form factor $S(k, \omega)$ have been calculated for liquid He^3. Unfortunately, the inelastic scattering of slow neutrons cannot be used as a probe to test the results experimentally as for the case of He^4 (He^3 has a prohibitively large capture cross section for slow neutrons). These theoretical studies nevertheless provide important clues concerning the extent of validity and the limitations of the Landau theory.

The first step in the microscopic theory of liquid He^3 is the calculation of the ground-state energy of the system. Efforts along this line have not met with notable success. Although the theory for a Fermi fluid does not have to deal with complications arising from depletion effects of a condensate, as for a boson system, the exceedingly strong interactions between particles at short distances makes the calculations very difficult. Some of the microscopic theories have predicted that the interparticle forces should produce through fermion pairing a correlated state for liquid He^3 at very low temperatures (such predictions come not from studies of the ground state, but rather from examinations of the regions of possible failure of the microscopic $T \neq 0$ formalism). At best, the physical evidence for this phase is ambiguous.

As discouraging as the foregoing may seem, the recent realization that studies of dilute solutions of He^3 in He^4 provide a significant tool for extending our knowledge of the Fermi liquid has brightened the hopes of theorists and experimentalists alike. Whereas it was once thought that He^3–He^4 solutions held the key to an understanding of superfluid He^4, it now appears that the door will open in the opposite direction. Work along these lines is currently receiving high priority.

The method of the present chapter will be first to describe briefly the principal elements of the Landau theory, since this pervades much of the He^3 work. Succeeding sections will be devoted to reporting the recent experimental results on various properties of the low-temperature liquid He^3 system together with appraisals of the appropriate theoretical predictions.

Several excellent reviews are available, and these may be consulted for detailed and comprehensive coverage of the following special topics: the Landau theory and the evaluation of the phenomenological parameters—Abrikosov and Khalatnikov[1]; microscopic theories of liquid He³, including a very helpful bibliography—Sessler [2]; the theory of normal Fermi liquids with particular emphasis on correlation and response functions—Pines and Nozières [3]; and recent experiments on liquid He³ at very low temperatures—Wheatley [4].

6.1. THE LANDAU THEORY OF THE FERMI LIQUID

Landau's theory [5] of the Fermi liquid assumes that the excitations of the interacting particles can be derived starting from the spectrum of the ideal FD gas. Hence, our discussion proceeds from the ideal gas, the ground state of which is characterized by complete occupation of all momentum levels less than p_F and all higher levels empty. In general, the surface in momentum space defined by the highest occupied levels of the ground state of a FD system is called the *Fermi surface*; for the ideal gas, the levels are isotropically distributed, so that this surface is a sphere with radius $p_F = (2m\epsilon_F)^{1/2}$, where ϵ_F is given by equation (2.14) for particles with spin $\frac{1}{2}$. If we use the particle density N/Ω and mass m appropriate for liquid He³, $p_F = 0.82 \times 10^{-19}$ g-cm/sec and the degeneration temperature $pT_F = \epsilon_F/k_B = 4.9°$K. From what we have already mentioned about the liquid (Section 1.4.2), this is clearly much too large—by more than a factor of 10—giving us some indication of how poor a representation the ideal gas is for the real liquid and how important the interactions are.

In order to construct excited states for the ideal system at $T \neq 0°$K, we must remove one or more particles from inside the Fermi sphere and place them outside. By doing this, we create a number of "holes" within the sphere equal to the number of particles that have been excited. Thus an elementary excitation of the ideal FD gas consists of the pair: particle excitation with $p_+ > p_F$ plus hole excitation with $p_- < p_F$. The mean number of particles in the pth state is $\langle n(p) \rangle$, given by

$$\langle n(p) \rangle = \frac{1}{\exp[(\epsilon_p - \mu)/k_B T] + 1} \tag{6.1}$$

where μ is the chemical potential. At $T = 0$, $\langle n(p) \rangle$ as a function of ϵ is represented by the heavy solid curve in Fig. 2.1. For weakly excited states, it is more economical energetically to promote a particle from just inside the Fermi sphere to just outside it, so that for small T, the distribution about ϵ_F will be smeared out, as indicated schematically by the lighter solid curve in the figure. The energy of the excitations is measured relative to ϵ_F, so that the relations

$$\left. \begin{array}{l} \epsilon_+ = (p_+^2/2m) - \epsilon_F \\ \epsilon_- = \epsilon_F - (p_-^2/2m) \end{array} \right\}; \quad \epsilon = \epsilon_+ - \epsilon_- = (p_+^2 + p_-^2)/2m \tag{6.2}$$

$$-2\epsilon_F$$

give the energy of a particle–hole pair. From these, we readily deduce that $(\epsilon/p)_{min} = 0$, and therefore, according to the Landau criterion, an ideal FD gas should not exhibit superfluidity.

Landau considered that as interactions between particles are introduced, transforming the ideal gas into a Fermi liquid, the form of the energy spectrum should not be altered. There are, of course, important differences between the two systems, and these may best be indicated from the way in which Landau defined the quasiparticles of the interacting ensemble. Each quasiparticle is considered as an independent elementary excitation associated with a real particle which moves in a self-consistent field created by the interactions with all its neighbors. The quasiparticle is a state of the entire system, and this state is uniquely specified by the spin and the momentum quantum numbers. Unlike the case for degenerate bosons, the quasiparticles of a Fermi liquid bear a one-to-one correspondence and are equal in number to the real particles.

There are several ways in which the ideal system is altered through the mutual interactions between quasiparticles, and, accordingly, we need new definitions to describe the quasiparticle mass, the distribution function, and the energy–momentum relation. Because of the interactions, an excitation moving through the liquid will have an effective mass m^* different from the bare particle mass m. In general, m^* may be greater or less than m and is determined by the manner in which the quasiparticle energy changes with momentum at the Fermi surface; that is,

$$m^* = \left(\frac{\mathbf{p}}{\partial\epsilon/\partial\mathbf{p}}\right)_{\mathbf{p}=\mathbf{p}_F} = p_F/v_F \tag{6.3}$$

where v_F is the quasiparticle group velocity at the Fermi surface in the same direction as $\mathbf{p}_F$. In the Landau theory, m^* must be determined from experiments.

Because of the self-consistent field assumption, the total energy E is no longer the sum of the individual quasiparticle energies; instead, it is a functional of the quasiparticle distribution function. We may first express the number of quasiparticles per unit volume as

$$N/\Omega = \int n(p)\, d\mathbf{P} \tag{6.4}$$

where $d\mathbf{P}$ stands for the volume element in phase space $2\Omega h^{-3}\, dp_x\, dp_y\, dp_z$, the factor 2 taking into account the possible spin orientations. Now, the best we can do to define the energy ϵ of a single quasiparticle is to determine the incremental change in energy of the system, δE, due to the addition of one quasiparticle to it. Thus,

$$\delta E = \int \epsilon_{\mathbf{p}}\, \delta n(p)\, d\mathbf{P} \qquad (6.5)$$

In these equations, $n(p)$ has exactly the same *form* as in equation (6.1), but with the crucial difference that $\epsilon_{\mathbf{p}}$ is itself a functional of the distribution function. It is through this property that $\epsilon_{\mathbf{p}}$ depends upon the temperature and the density of the system.

In the absence of a magnetic field, the energy of the quasiparticles does not depend upon the spin. However, when this spin dependence becomes important, equation (6.5) must be modified to include the quantum-mechanical spin density matrix. The right side of the equation is to be multiplied by $\frac{1}{2}Tr_\sigma$, the trace of the matrix describing the spin states.

The energy–momentum relation for the quasiparticles of a Fermi liquid may be written for the general case as

$$\epsilon(\mathbf{p}, \boldsymbol{\sigma}) = \epsilon_0(\mathbf{p}, \boldsymbol{\sigma}) + \tfrac{1}{2}Tr_\sigma \int f(\mathbf{p}, \boldsymbol{\sigma}; \mathbf{p}', \boldsymbol{\sigma}')\, \delta n(\mathbf{p}', \boldsymbol{\sigma}')\, d\mathbf{P}' \qquad (6.6)$$

Here, $\epsilon_0(\mathbf{p}, \boldsymbol{\sigma})$ is the quasiparticle spectrum corresponding to the equilibrium energy at $0°K$ and zero pressure; the second term on the right provides the density and temperature dependence of the spectrum, with $\delta n(\mathbf{p}', \boldsymbol{\sigma}')$ the change in the distribution function from the $T = 0°K$ case. The function f, which is the fundamental ingredient for a Fermi liquid, represents the interaction occurring during the collision between two quasiparticles with momentum $\mathbf{p}$ and $\mathbf{p}'$. Landau has indicated that f is related to the forward scattering amplitude† of two quasiparticles. For simplicity, we shall use the notation f, n, ϵ, understanding that each of these has as arguments the appropriate spin and momentum operators.

When both $\mathbf{p}$ and $\mathbf{p}'$ are near p_F, the effective mass m^* may be expressed in terms of the interaction, f. Thus

$$\frac{1}{m} = \frac{1}{m^*} + \frac{2p_F}{h^3} \int F(\theta) \cos\theta\, d\Gamma \qquad (6.7)$$

where $d\Gamma$ is an element of solid angle on the Fermi surface and $F(\theta)$ explicitly represents f as an expansion in Legendre polynomials with the form

$$\frac{8\pi p_F m^*}{h^3} F(\theta) = F_0 + F_1 \cos\theta + F_2\left(\frac{3\cos^2\theta - 1}{2}\right) + \cdots \qquad (6.8)$$

† For the collision process $\mathbf{p}_1 + \mathbf{p}_1' \to \mathbf{p}_2 + \mathbf{p}_2'$, "forward" scattering obtains when the angle between $\mathbf{p}_1$ and $\mathbf{p}_1'$ equals the angle between $\mathbf{p}_2$ and $\mathbf{p}_2'$ and all momenta are coplanar.

In this notation, equation (6.7) becomes simply (since $\frac{1}{3}F_1$ equals the average value of $F_1 \cos \theta$)

$$\frac{1}{m} = \frac{1}{m^*}\left(1 + \frac{1}{3}F_1\right) \tag{6.9}$$

Alternatively, with $[(1/\Omega)(\partial \mathbf{P}/\partial \varepsilon)_\mu]$ as the density of quasiparticle states per unit volume at the Fermi surface, we may arrive at

$$m^* = \frac{\pi^2 \hbar^3}{p_F}\left[\frac{1}{\Omega}\left(\frac{\partial \mathbf{P}}{\partial \epsilon}\right)_\mu\right] \tag{6.10}$$

The various definitions for m^* are useful to keep in mind.

The assumption that the energy levels of the Fermi liquid can be derived in a one-to-one correspondence from those of the ideal FD gas is equivalent to saying that the energy levels can be expressed in a convergent perturbation series. Only when this is true can the above quasiparticle description represent the system. An additional important prerequisite for the general validity of this representation is that the quasiparticle lifetime should not be too short. Since a quasiparticle may disappear either by decay into several other quasiparticles or, more likely, by scattering collisions with other excitations, the quasiparticle lifetime is essentially determined by τ, the mean time between collisions. Since both the number of quasiparticles which can collide with a given quasiparticle and the number of final states resulting from the collision are each proportional to $k_B T$, the frequency of collisions is proportional to $(k_B T)^2$. Thus τ is proportional to T^{-2}.

The condition that τ be finite may be expressed by the requirement that the quasiparticle energy, which is predominantly within the range $k_B T$ of the Fermi energy, must greatly exceed the quantum indeterminacy of this energy, i.e., $k_B T \gg h/\tau$. For He^3, an upper limit of the temperature for which this inequality holds has been given as 0.05°K, though it has also been thought to be as high as 0.3°K. In any case, the general Landau theory should be valid only below some very low temperature and should become a better approximation as the temperature is reduced (with a possible exception at very low T, where the liquid may transform to the correlated phase).

6.1.1. Equilibrium Properties of a Fermi Liquid

The specific heat at constant volume is obtained from equation (6.5) as

$$C_V = \left(\frac{\partial E}{\partial T}\right)_V = \int \epsilon \left(\frac{\partial n}{\partial T}\right)_V d\mathbf{P} \tag{6.11}$$

At low temperatures, the derivative of the distribution function for the

Fermi liquid is quite like that for the ideal gas, so that the limiting form for C_V of the liquid is just that of the gas with N/Ω appropriate for the liquid, but modified by the factor m^*/m. Thus, in the approximation of equation (2.18), the molar heat capacity as $T \to 0°\text{K}$ becomes

$$C_V = \frac{m^*}{m} C_V^{(\text{ideal FD})} \approx \frac{m^* \pi^2 N_A k_B^2 T}{2m \epsilon_F} \qquad (6.12)$$

We note that: (1) through equation (6.10), C_V depends essentially upon the density of states at the Fermi surface; (2) since C_V is proportional to T, the entropy is the same as C_V; and (3) if the experimental heat capacity were to be found to be linear at very low temperatures, then m^* could be determined from the slope of C_V *vs.* T.

The effects of spin are introduced explicitly when the nuclear magnetic susceptibility is considered. In the ideal FD gas, both C_V and χ are determined solely by the density of states near the Fermi surface, or, in effect, by the distribution function. In the case of the Fermi liquid, the introduction of the interactions between quasiparticles somewhat complicates matters. But if we assume that the dependence of f on spin originates entirely from exchange, then we may write $f(\mathbf{p}, \mathbf{p}'; \boldsymbol{\sigma}, \boldsymbol{\sigma}') = F(\mathbf{p}, \mathbf{p}') + G(\mathbf{p},\mathbf{p}')\boldsymbol{\sigma} \cdot \boldsymbol{\sigma}'$ so that C_V depends only upon $F(\mathbf{p}, \mathbf{p}')$, whereas χ may ultimately be expressed in terms of $G(\mathbf{p}, \mathbf{p}')$, an independent phenomenological function describing quasiparticle collision processes. In this notation, it is possible to express χ relative to χ_{FD}^0, the zero-temperature susceptibility of an ideal FD gas [equation (2.20)]:

$$\frac{\chi}{\chi_{FD}^0} = \frac{m^*}{m}\left[1 + \frac{2m^* p_F}{h^3} \int G(\theta)\,d\Gamma\right]^{-1} \qquad (6.13)$$

In principle, the measurement of χ may provide an alternative method of determining m^*, provided the function $G(\theta)$ can be established. Similarly to $F(\theta)$, $G(\theta)$ may be expanded in the form

$$(8\pi p_F m^*/h^3)G(\theta) = G_0 + G_1 \cos\theta + \cdots \qquad (6.14)$$

and thus equation (6.13) may be recast as

$$\frac{\chi}{\chi_{FD}^0} = \frac{1 + \frac{1}{3}F_1}{1 + G_0} \qquad (6.15)$$

(Note: in some work, G_0 is written as $Z_0/4$)

As stated earlier, the Landau Fermi-liquid theory is expected to become invalid above some temperature, $0.05 < T < 0.3°\text{K}$, when applied to He^3. However, Balian and de Dominicis ([6]) have pointed out that the theory should apply to the equilibrium properties, for which the limitations associated with the quasiparticle lifetimes are not significant, at all temperatures so long as the perturbation expansion converges. In view of this, Richards ([7]) has extended to higher order the formalism for the specific heat and the susceptibility. His results for the former are

$$C_V = \frac{\pi^2 N_A k_B}{2}\left(\frac{T}{T_F^*}\right)\left[1 + \frac{3\pi^2}{10}(1 + \Phi)\left(\frac{T}{T_F^*}\right)^2\right] \tag{6.16}$$

where T_F^* is given by

$$T_F^* = p_F^2/2k_B m^* \tag{6.17}$$

and Φ is a phenomenological parameter involving the second derivative of f with respect to the momenta, evaluated at the Fermi surface. (Note that the T^3 term is not a phonon contribution.) Similarly, χ is obtained as

$$\chi = \frac{3N_A \mu_M^2}{2k_B T_F^{**}}\left[1 - \frac{\pi^2}{12}\left(\frac{T}{T_F^{**}}\right)^2\left(1 + \frac{6}{5}\Phi\right)\right] \tag{6.18}$$

(where T_F^{**} is related to T_F^* through the spin-dependent part of the quasiparticle interaction) in the approximation that the spin exchange interaction can be expressed as the temperature-independent Weiss molecular field [otherwise, equation (6.18) involves another function J which includes the momentum variation of the spin-dependent part of f]. μ_M is the quasiparticle magnetic moment. Richards has also described how Φ and J may be determined from the experimental observations on the pressure dependence of the velocity of sound and the susceptibility, respectively. Both Φ and J are also related to the Legendre polynomial expansions.

6.1.2. Nonequilibrium Properties of a Fermi Liquid

The transport properties of a Fermi liquid in the absence of a magnetic field follow from the conservation laws for energy, momentum, and particle number, and from a quasiclassical Boltzmann equation satisfied by the distribution function n:

$$\frac{\partial n}{\partial t} + \frac{\partial n}{\partial \mathbf{r}}\frac{\partial \epsilon}{\partial \mathbf{p}} - \frac{\partial n}{\partial \mathbf{p}}\frac{\partial \epsilon}{\partial \mathbf{r}} = I(n) \tag{6.19}$$

where $I(n)$ is the collision integral and $\mathbf{r}$ is the spatial vector. We give here the results deduced from the general Landau theory by Abrikosov and Khalatnikov ([1]) for the coefficients of viscosity and thermal conductivity and by Hone ([8]) for the spin diffusion coefficient. The collision processes treated are of the type: two quasiparticles with momenta $\mathbf{p}_1$ and $\mathbf{p}_1'$ interacting to give two quasiparticles with momenta

$\mathbf{p}_2$ and $\mathbf{p}'_2$. The transition probability is written as $W(\theta, \phi)$, where θ is the angle between $\mathbf{p}_2$ and $\mathbf{p}'_2$ and ϕ is the angle between the planes defined by $(\mathbf{p}_1, \mathbf{p}'_1)$ and $(\mathbf{p}_2, \mathbf{p}'_2)$; $W(\theta, \phi)$ may be estimated from $F(\theta)$.

The coefficients of viscosity, heat conduction, and self-diffusion are given approximately by†

$$\eta = \frac{64\hbar^3 p_F^5}{45 m^{*4} k_B^2 T^2} \left\{ \left[\frac{W(\theta, \phi)}{\cos(\theta/2)} (1 - \cos\theta)^2 \sin^2\phi \right]_{av} \right\}^{-1} \tag{6.20}$$

(where the average is taken over angles) or

$$\eta = \mathscr{A}/T^2 \tag{6.21}$$

$$\lambda = \frac{8\pi^2 \hbar^3 p_F^3}{3 m^{*4} T} \left\{ \left[\frac{W(\theta, \phi)(1 - \cos\theta)}{\cos(\theta/2)} \right]_{av} \right\}^{-1} \tag{6.22}$$

or

$$\lambda = \mathscr{B}/T \tag{6.23}$$

and

$$D = \frac{32\pi^2 \hbar^6 p_F^2}{3 m^{*5} k_B^2 T^2} \left\{ \left[\frac{W(\theta, \phi)(1 - \cos\theta)(1 - \cos\phi)}{\cos(\theta/2)} \right]_{av} \right\}^{-1} [1 + G_0] \tag{6.24}$$

or

$$D = \mathscr{D}/T^2 \tag{6.25}$$

Hone has pointed out that only collisions between quasiparticles of antiparallel spins will contribute to D, while both η and λ do not depend upon spin orientation.

A necessary requirement for the propagation of ordinary sound is that local thermodynamic equilibrium should be restored in a time which is short compared with the period of the density oscillation. If τ is the mean time between collisions, i.e., the relaxation time for the medium, and ω the angular frequency of the disturbance, then $\omega\tau \ll 1$ describes the fulfillment of this requirement. Under these conditions we may compute the velocity u_1 in a Fermi liquid by relating the compressibility to the displacement suffered by the Fermi surface as the particle density in the sphere is changed. Thus, with $\rho = N/\Omega$,

$$u_1^2 = \frac{1}{m} \left(\frac{\partial P}{\partial \rho} \right)_s = \frac{N}{m} \frac{\partial \mu}{\partial N} \tag{6.26}$$

Since, at the Fermi surface, $\mu = \epsilon(p_F)$, $\partial\mu/\partial N$ can be given in terms of
† $W(\theta, \phi)$ has units g-cm^8-sec^{-3}.

$\partial\mu/\partial p_F$ such that the final expression for u_1^2 becomes

$$
\begin{aligned}
u_1^2 &= \frac{p_F}{3m} \frac{\partial\mu}{\partial p_F} \\
&= \frac{p_F}{3m}\left[\frac{p_F}{m} + \frac{2p_F^2}{h^3}\int F(\theta)(1 - \cos\theta)\,d\Gamma\right] \\
&= \frac{p_F^2}{3m^2}\frac{1 + F_0}{1 + \frac{1}{3}F_1}
\end{aligned}
\tag{6.27}
$$

Landau ([9]) has predicted that when $\omega\tau \gg 1$, defining the *collision-less regime* (that is, the mean free path of the quasiparticles exceeds the wavelength of the sound, so that local thermal equilibrium cannot be reestablished), a new type of wave propagation should be possible, which he called "zero sound." Whereas ordinary sound involves expansions and contractions of the Fermi sphere without distortion of the shape of the surface but displaced in momentum space, Landau proposed that in zero sound, the Fermi surface becomes "elongated in the forward direction of the propagation of the wave, and flattened in the opposite direction."

An expression for u_0, the velocity of zero sound, was obtained by insertion of the distribution function n into a Boltzmann-like collision integral and by considering the propagation of a wave with phase factor $\exp(-i\omega t + i\mathbf{k}\cdot\mathbf{r})$, to which both $\delta\epsilon$ and δn were assumed proportional. In the approximation that terms in F_0 and F_1 alone may represent $F(\theta)$, the following dispersion relation resulted:

$$
\frac{\gamma}{2}\log\left(\frac{\gamma + 1}{\gamma - 1}\right) - 1 = \frac{1 + \frac{1}{3}F_1}{F_0(1 + \frac{1}{3}F_1) + \gamma^2 F_1}
\tag{6.28}
$$

where

$$
\gamma = \omega/kv_F
\tag{6.29}
$$

In the latter equation, v_F, the Fermi velocity, is defined by relation (6.3), $u_0 = \omega/k$ is the group velocity of zero sound in the propagation direction $\mathbf{k}$, and $\omega = 2\pi v$, where v is the frequency in cycles/sec. Thus, if F_0 and F_1 can be determined, u_0 follows easily, especially in the limits of strong and weak interaction.

If the interactions are weak, i.e., $F_0 \to 0$, then $\gamma \to 1$, indicating that $u_0 = v_F$. Under the same conditions, $u_1 = v_F/\sqrt{3}$, the factor $1/\sqrt{3}$ arising from the thermalization of ordinary sound in three directions. Thus, $u_0 > u_1$.

If, instead, the interactions are strong, then as $F_0 \to \infty$, γ approaches the value $(F_0/3)^{1/2}$. The presence of interactions causes the magnitudes of u_0 and u_1 to come closer together.

We turn now to the attenuation characteristics of the two types of sound. In both limiting cases, $\omega\tau \ll 1$ (hydrodynamic regime) and $\omega\tau \gg 1$ (collisionless regime), the absorption of sound is quite weak. However, the region between these two extremes is one of both strong absorption and strong dispersion, and when $\omega\tau \sim 1$, it should become difficult to distinguish between the two types of waves. The absorption coefficients for zero sound and ordinary sound can therefore be described only in the two limits of $\omega\tau$, and this may be done starting with the dispersion relation. Following the notation of Abrikosov and Khalatnikov (^{1}), it is convenient to express the results using the symbols $\sigma = i\tau k v_F$ and $\xi = (i\omega\tau - 1)\sigma$.

For ordinary sound at low frequencies, $\sigma \to 0$, so that $\xi\sigma \to +1$ and $\xi \to \infty$. This allows a simplification of the dispersion relation, from which α_1, the absorption coefficient of first sound, may be extracted as the imaginary part of the wave vector:

$$\alpha_1 = \text{Im } \mathbf{k} = \left(\frac{2\omega^2\tau v_F^2}{15u_1^3}\right)\left(1 + \frac{F_1}{3}\right) \qquad (6.30)$$

For ordinary monatomic substances, it is customary to write as a good approximation for the sound attenuation

$$\alpha_1 = (2\omega^2/3\rho u_1^3)\eta \qquad (6.31)$$

which, when combined with equation (6.30), yields

$$\eta = \tfrac{1}{5}\rho\tau_\eta v_F^2(1 + \tfrac{1}{3}F_1) \qquad (6.32)$$

Hence, experimental data for the viscosity may be used to provide an estimate of τ_η, the relaxation time for viscosity. [Each of the transport coefficients, η, λ, and D, may be characterized by a separate relaxation time; however, within a factor the order of unity, these should all be essentially the same as the quasiparticle collision time τ. Thus we may also write

$$D = \tfrac{1}{3}v_F^2\tau_D(1 + G_0) \qquad (6.33)$$

and

$$\lambda = \tfrac{1}{3}v_F^2\tau_\lambda c_V \qquad (6.34)]$$

For the higher frequencies, i.e., in the collisionless regime, $\sigma \to \infty$ and $\xi\sigma \to \infty$, with $\xi = \gamma + i\xi'$. Here, ξ' represents the imaginary part of the zero sound velocity such that $|\xi'| \ll \gamma$. From the dispersion relation, it is found that the absorption coefficient for zero sound is

$$\alpha_0 = \text{Im } \mathbf{k} = \frac{1}{\gamma\tau v_F} - \frac{\omega\xi'}{\gamma^2 v_F} \qquad (6.35)$$

It can be shown that ξ' is proportional to $1/\omega\tau$, and therefore α_0 is frequency-independent, as contrasted to the ω^2 dependence of α_1. Since $1/\tau$ gives a measure of the number of collisions between quasiparticles and this in turn is proportional to T^2, α_0 and α_1 have quite different temperature dependences. From equation (6.35), we see that α_0 increases as T^2, while according to equation (6.30), α_1 is proportional to T^{-2}. These features are illustrated schematically in Fig. 6.1, where α is plotted against T for several frequencies. We see how the two types of sound merge in a region not analytically determined.

Landau has pointed out that equation (6.35) is based on a classical argument and that the correct quantum mechanical expression is given by

$$\alpha_0 = \alpha_0^{(\text{classical})}[1 + (\hbar\omega/2\pi k_B T)^2] \tag{6.36}$$

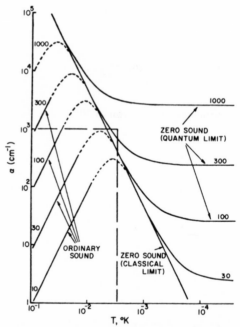

Fig. 6.1. Attenuation of sound predicted for liquid He^3 as a function of temperature. Numbers on curves indicate sound frequencies in Mc/sec. [From C. E. Gough and W. F. Vinen, in *Low Temperature Physics LT-9* (J. G. Daunt, D. O. Edwards, F. J. Milford, and M. Yaqub, eds.), p. 118, Plenum Press, New York (1965)].

Insofar as zero sound waves at very low temperatures are states characteristic of the motion of the Fermi liquid, the spectrum of the liquid will possess a phononlike branch, $\epsilon = u_0 p$, just as for a Bose fluid. Consequently, we should expect to find for the specific heat a term proportional to T^3. Since for $T \ll 1°\text{K}$, the linear term of equation (6.12) should dominate almost any T^3 term, experimental verification of the phonon branch appears extremely difficult: however, it cannot be excluded.

To arrive at equation (6.28) for zero sound, the spin part of the distribution function has been neglected. If, however, it is included, then still another type of wave, a spin wave, is predicted. Such a wave consists of the propagation of fluctuations in the spin density rather than of fluctuations in the particle density. The calculations for the properties of spin waves are the same as those for zero sound except that the functions F are to be replaced by the functions G. Landau [9] considered it unlikely, but not out of the question, that liquid He³ at very low temperatures exhibits the spin mode. On the other hand, Mermin [10] has proved that according to the Landau theory at least one or the other of these modes must exist in the collisionless regime of a normal Fermi liquid, such as He³.

6.1.3. The Landau Phenomenological Parameters: Microscopic Theories vs. Experiment

In the preceding sections, we have shown how the various properties of the Fermi liquid depend upon the phenomenological parameters F_0, F_1, G_0, and m^* related to $f(\mathbf{p}, \sigma; \mathbf{p}', \sigma')$ and its derivatives. It would seem that each parameter may be derived from more than one experimentally determined property of He³. This apparent redundancy should be helpful in achieving an accurate representation of the real liquid if indeed it is a Fermi liquid. For example, experimental heat-capacity data at very low temperatures should provide a number for m^*/m, which, through equation (6.9), furnishes an estimate of F_1. When this is combined with the experimental values for χ/χ_{FD}^0, G_0 may be extracted from equation (6.15). This value of G_0 should then be consistent with the experimentally determined diffusion coefficient through equation (6.33) or equation (6.24) and the calculated estimates [8] of the collision terms. Conversely, if He³ is not a Fermi liquid, consistency among the variously determined parameters should be lacking. The actual situation is not so simple, since the equations we have been discussing involve only the first one or two terms of a series, and if these do not conform to experiment, the theorist could always say, "We must add some more terms." Therefore the redundancy suggested above does not actually exist. However, there already is a good deal of consistency from experimental evidence among the parameters, with one notable exception; m^* as obtained from specific-heat data is vastly different from the value suggested by the susceptibility data. We shall return to this point in the next section.

If the phenomenological parameters have physical significance for liquid He^3, they should be derivable from a microscopic theory. Abrikosov and Khalatnikov ([1]) have indicated how the Yang and Lee formalism may be extended to the dilute Fermi hard-sphere gas to predict in principle the functions $F(\theta)$ and $G(\theta)$. While the results are interesting, they describe a range of densities too restricted to include the actual He^3 system.

As a natural way of treating the quasiparticle interactions by first principles, one might propose the Hartree–Fock self-consistent field method; however, this procedure cannot be properly applied because of the singularity of the two-body He potential at short distances. Brueckner and Gammel ([11]) have largely circumvented this difficulty by using a modified Hartree–Fock scheme originally devised by Brueckner for successfully treating the strong interactions encountered in nuclear matter. As in the Brueckner–Sawada treatment of He^4 (see Section 5.1.4b), the method employs the "T" matrix, which in the present case is related to Landau's f. In order to obtain physically meaningful values of the single-particle energy $\epsilon(\mathbf{p})$ for $p > p_F$, an artificial cutoff had to be introduced into the calculation.† When this was done, quite realistic values resulted for the binding energy E_0, $C/C_{ideal} = m/m^*$, and χ/χ_{FD}^0 all at $T = 0°K$. On the other hand, corrections to the theory are not easily made, nor is the theory convenient for generalizing to higher temperatures.

We may appreciate the difficulty of the "first principles" $T = 0°K$ liquid He^3 theory by the fact that Brueckner and Gammel's was the only such investigation until 1966, when Woo ([12]) reported a perturbation-theory attack on the problem. This work was based upon the novel approach, by Feenberg et al. ([13]), of relating He^3 to a boson system through a two-body correlative approximation. The potential energy function for Woo's calculations was provided by Massey ([14]) who obtained self-consistent parameters for an LJ (12-6) potential and the corresponding (quantum-mechanical) pair distribution function for He^4 (see Section 5.1.4c). Woo's estimate of E_0 appears to be a slight improvement over that of Brueckner and Gammel, but it is not easy to assess how meaningful this improvement is. Also calculated were values of the density, compressibility, and χ/χ_{FD}^0, all in order-of-magnitude agreement with experiment. No prescription was given for the spectrum, and hence, no prediction of specific heat or effective mass could be given.

† L. J. Campbell, private communication; also, Thesis, University of California at La Jolla (1965).

Also in 1966, Beck and Sessler ([15]) refined the "T" matrix method by obtaining a "thermodynamically consistent T-matrix" for calculating the properties of liquid He³. Their results for E_0 and the density are compared in Table 6.I with experiment and with the results of the calculations mentioned above; it is seen that Beck and Sessler have provided the closest fit so far to the observations.

Table 6.I. Comparison of Calculated and Observed Values of the Ground State Energy per Particle (E/N) and Interparticle Separation (r) for Liquid He³

	Experiment	Brueckner and Gammel([11])	Woo ([12])	Beck and Sessler ([15])
E/N (°K)	−2.53	−0.96	−1.35	−1.39
r (10^{-8} cm)	2.43	2.60	2.51	2.47

While the calculation of the Landau parameters from first principles still leaves much to be desired, there is nevertheless good evidence from field-theoretical studies† to indicate that the Landau formalism for the Fermi liquid may be rigorously derived through a convergent perturbation series relating the interacting system to the ideal gas. In particular, these investigations provide a clear description of a quasi-particle. Sessler ([17]) has aptly summarized the theoretical viewpoint:

> "One can describe the present situation by saying that it is known what a quasiparticle is, but as yet it is not known how to calculate its properties from the properties of free He³ atoms. In a sense, doing the hard calculation to relate a quasiparticle to a particle is not so important as knowing that there is such a relation and that the quasiparticle is a well-defined concept."

An exploration of the region of validity of the perturbation series, first made by Thouless ([18]), has disclosed that at sufficiently low temperatures, divergences should appear due to binary particle interactions. Thus, the failure of perturbation theory implied a transition to a new phase in liquid He³. Below the transition, the situation should be analogous to that described by the Bardeen–Cooper–Schrieffer (BCS) theory of superconductivity, where the important correlations are between pairs of electrons with equal but opposite-sign momenta. A search for the type of correlations possible in liquid He³ included consideration of the free-space phase shifts for He³ pairs at energies near the Fermi surface ($p_F/\hbar \approx 0.3$ Å^{-1}) as a measure of the effective interaction. The S-state ($l = 0$) phase shift at p_F is strongly negative, representing repulsion. However, the largest positive phase shift is for

† See, for example, Galitskii and Migdal or Luttinger and Ward ([16]).

$l = 2$ (see Fig. 3.3b, where $q_F = p_F r_0/\hbar \approx 2.0$) which therefore suggests a nonspherically symmetric attractive interaction. On this basis, a number of predictions have been made for the properties of the new phase. These will not be detailed here, but see, for example, the review by Sessler ([19]). The point we wish to stress is that the existence of the suspected superfluid state does not invalidate the Fermi liquid theory; rather, it is a consequence of the interactions implied by the theory.

For the experimentalists, the primary obstacle to a thorough testing of the Fermi liquid theory is the achievement of sufficiently low temperatures for making the appropriate measurements. Fortunately, this major technological step is on the verge of being hurdled by new refrigeration methods, e.g., the mixture refrigerator mentioned in Section 1.4.1. Meanwhile, we must be content to assess the progress already made, and in the following, we will try to point out what we do and do not know about the low-temperature properties of liquid He³. Generally, our discussion will be concerned with behavior along the saturated vapor pressure curve (SVP); but in some instances, it will be convenient to include data obtained at higher pressures (the latter will be more completely covered in Chapter 9). Also, the experimental details will for the most part be omitted; these may be found in the original papers. Finally, in Section 6.3, we assemble from the experiments performed thus far a consistent set of parameters which create the Fermi liquid profile for He³.

6.2. EXPERIMENTAL RESULTS FOR LIQUID He³ AT LOW TEMPERATURES

6.2.1. Nuclear Magnetic Susceptibility of He³

Above the degeneracy temperature T_F, the nuclear magnetic susceptibility of an ideal FD gas asymptotically approaches the classical Curie law, i.e., $\chi_{FD} = \chi_C$, and $\chi_C T = \mathscr{C}$, the Curie constant [cf. equation (1.47)]. Below T_F, χ_{FD} deviates markedly from the classical behavior by becoming independent of T as $T \to 0°K$ (Pauli paramagnetism). Before we discuss liquid He³, it will be interesting to inquire how well the real gas conforms to the ideal predictions.

Experiments by Romer ([20]) have suggested that at $\sim 3°K$, the susceptibility of He³ vapor should approach the ideal FD gas behavior only at densities lower than 3×10^{-3} mole/cm³, i.e., departure from the Curie law should begin at this density. However, a careful examination of χ at this temperature by Opfer et al. ([21]) has revealed that even for densities as low as 3×10^{-4} mole/cm³, χ remains within 1 % of the Curie susceptibility. While the ideal FD gas has $m^*/m = 1$, the data are consistent with $m^*/m \approx 11$. Thus, under these conditions, He³ is still a nonideal FD gas. Opfer *et al.* have analyzed the interactions responsible for this nonideality in terms of the second virial coefficient of He³ gas, and found that their approximate theoretical treatment is in substantial agreement with the experimental data.

Since, even in the dilute vapor, interactions between particles are significant, it is not surprising that the liquid susceptibility should be markedly different from an ideal FD gas. Near the end of Chapter 1, the early liquid data were briefly mentioned (Fig. 1.14) and it was noted that these could be fitted by the noninteracting FD gas theory if T_F were taken as 0.45°K instead of the value 5°K based upon the actual density. This is equivalent to the statement that $\chi/\chi_{FD}^0 = 11.1$, or if we wish, that $m^*/m = 11.1$, but such a value of the effective mass is, as we shall soon see, incompatible with specific-heat measurements.

We may as a consequence make two categorical statements: (1) The ideal FD gas cannot be used as a representation for He³ liquid; and (2) in the Landau Fermi-liquid theory, the thermal and magnetic properties are not simply related through a unique numerical value for the Fermi temperature, but instead we may distinguish between two such temperatures: T_F^* as determined from the specific-heat data, i.e., from equations (6.12) and (6.17), and T_F^{**} as the magnetic degeneration temperature characterizing spin orientation, cf. equation (6.18). In the interacting system, the concept of the unique degeneration temperature associated with the ideal gas is no longer valid, and, in general, the degeneration condition may vary from one property to another. For a given property, the critical temperature will decrease as the interactions become stronger, and hence will decrease with increasing density, contrary to the ideal-gas case [equation (2.14)].

If, on the other hand, we incorporate the predictions of the Landau theory, equation (6.15), together with other empirical data determining m^* and F_1, we may find that $G_0 \approx -0.7$. In other words, there is a strong tendency for spin alignment such that in liquid He³ the paramagnetism is large compared with the limiting ideal FD system at liquid density, with the spin-dependent interactions accounting for the unexpectedly large susceptibility.

Since the work of Fairbank *et al.* mentioned in Section 1.4.2, further measurements of χ for the liquid have been reported, principal among which are those of Anderson *et al.* ([22]), Thomson *et al.* ([23]), Beal and Hatton ([24]), Abel *et al.* ([25]), and Schwettman and Rorschach ([26]). For an assessment of these data, it is important to realize that it has not been possible to determine absolute values of χ. Instead, an attempt has been made to normalize the susceptibility to values of χ obtained in a region where the Curie law is obeyed. In the earlier work ([22,23]), $\chi T/\mathscr{C}$ was considered to be unity near 1.2°K; later, it was shown ([24,26]) that the deviations from classical behavior at this temperature amount to

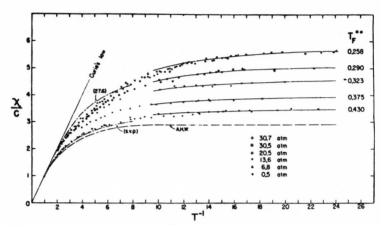

Fig. 6.2. Susceptibility of liquid He[3] as a function of inverse temperature at several pressures. AHW from Anderson et al. ([78]); (SVP) and (27.6) from Fairbank et al., ref. ([26]), Chapter 1. [From Thomson et al. ([23]).]

~5% and that $T > 2°K$ is a safer region for normalization. Over the range $1.2° < T < 3.1°K$, χ for a given temperature displays the classical pressure dependence (up to 35 atm).

The results of the various magnetic investigations tend to differ somewhat not only because of the modifications in normalization procedures employed, but probably also because of the different measuring techniques employed. A spin-echo, or pulsed rf, method ([27]) has been used by the Illinois group ([22,25]), while variations of continuous-wave or static nuclear magnetic resonance measurements have been used by others ([23,24,26]). In the latter method, a steady magnetic field H_0 is applied to the sample while a weak rf field perpendicular to H_0 excites the spins at their Larmor frequency $\omega_0(H_0)$. In the steady field, the two Zeeman levels of He[3] nuclei are separated by the energy $2\mu_M H_0$, where μ_M is the magnetic moment, and at thermal equilibrium, the lower state will have an excess population. At resonance, i.e., ω_0, an amount of power will be absorbed from the rf field proportional to the population difference between the two spin states, thereby giving the nuclear susceptibility.†

Nevertheless, since all of the results are in good qualitative agreement, it will be unnecessary for our purposes to subject them to a detailed comparison. The data of Thomson et al. ([23]) are typical for $T > 0.03°K$, and these are shown in Fig. 6.2 for several pressures up to

---

† We shall have some additional comments on the spin-echo method in Section 6.2.3c, but for details of both procedures we refer to the original papers. For a full account of magnetic resonance theory and techniques, a text such as *Principles of Nuclear Magnetism* by A. Abragam, Oxford (1961), is recommended.

31 atm. It is seen that at higher temperatures, all of the isobars are asymptotic to Curie's law, and that at lower temperatures, the susceptibility in each case approaches a constant temperature-independent value. The limiting susceptibility, $\chi^0(P)$, for an isobar determines the quantity $T_F^{**}(P) = 3\mathscr{C}/2\chi$ (P), the effective magnetic Fermi degeneracy temperature, appropriate for the corresponding fluid density. As the density increases, T_F^{**} decreases.

Abel et al. [25] have extended the measurements of χ down to 0.0035°K at low pressure. Their results are shown in Fig. 6.3 displayed as a function of T^*, defined as

$$\chi_C/\chi^0 = T^*/T \qquad (6.37)$$

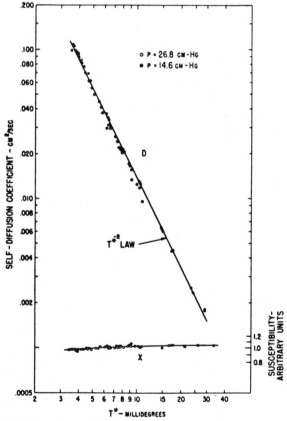

Fig. 6.3. Susceptibility and self-diffusion coefficient of liquid He³ as a function of T^* [from Abel et al. [25]].

from which we see that $T^* = \chi_c T/\chi^0 = \mathscr{C}/\chi^0 = \frac{2}{3}T_F^{**}$. The diffusion coefficient D is also shown in the figure, and on the assumption that the Kelvin temperature is defined by its proportionality to $D^{-1/2}$ (to be discussed in Section 6.2.3c), the method of plotting shown here allows the temperature dependence of χ to be determined without the complications of calibrating an additional thermometer. At the lowest temperatures, T^* was estimated to differ from T by only $0.0001°$K.† These data together with those in Fig. 6.2 offer convincing evidence for the constancy of the susceptibility at very low temperatures, in accordance with the predictions of Landau's theory.

Beal and Hatton [24] have analyzed some of their susceptibility measurements $(0.07° < T < 0.20°$K$; 0.7 < P < 27$ atm$)$ to test the finite-temperature Landau theory proposed by Richards [7]. Equation (6.18) has the form

$$\chi = \chi^0(1 - bT^2) \qquad (6.38)$$

where b is a pressure-dependent parameter. They found that equation (6.38) is consistent with the experiments up to $0.20°$K and 0.7 atm, the slopes of χ vs. T^2 being linear over this region. At higher densities, the linear range collapses and extends up to only $0.11°$K at 27 atm. (It is characteristic of both the Fermi gas and Fermi liquid that as ρ increases, higher order terms in the expansions for properties such as χ and C_V are required for a given temperature interval.) From their data and those of Anderson et al. [22] and Thomson et al. [23], Beal and Hatton calculated the following values of b:

Reference	[24]		[22]		[23]	
P (atm)	0.7	27	SVP	30	SVP	30
b	3.7	9.0	3	17	7.5	12

In all cases, b increases linearly with P. If in equation (6.18) Φ is taken as zero (Weiss molecular field approximation), then $b = \pi^2/12(T_F^{**})^2$. Using the values of T_F^{**} reported by Beal and Hatton, b is then calculated as 2.7 at SVP and 8.2 at 30 atm.

Prior to these results, Goldstein [28] had exploited the properties of the Weiss field to describe the magnetic properties of liquid He³. Because of interactions in the system, an externally applied magnetic field $\mathbf{H}$ is replaced by an effective field $\mathbf{H}_{eff}$, and in the limit $\mu_M \mathbf{H}_{eff} \ll k_B T$, the Curie law is thereby modified to read (Curie–Weiss law)

$$\chi = \mathscr{C}/(T + \Theta) \qquad (6.39)$$

† See, however, B. M. Abraham and Y. Eckstein, Phys. Rev. Letters **20**, 649 (1968).

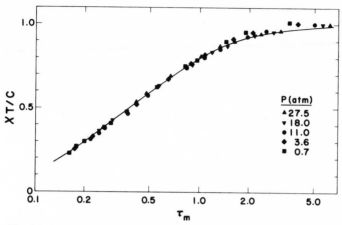

Fig. 6.4. Susceptibility of liquid He³ at several pressures as a function of $\tau_m = T/T_F^{**}$. Solid line comes from Goldstein's theory ([28]). [After Beal and Hatton ([24]).]

Here, Θ is a characteristic temperature representing the total exchange energy of one atom with remaining atoms in the system. Goldstein's contribution was to relate the nonideal paramagnetism expressed by equation (6.39) to the experimentally determined ratio $(T/T_F^{**}) = \tau_m$. The result is that the liquid susceptibility should be a universal function of τ_m over the whole range of P and T for which the liquid exists. Figure 6.4 demonstrates the remarkable agreement of Goldstein's predictions with all of the observations of Beal and Hatton ([24]). Here, the "best" smooth values ([4,24]) for T_F^{**} as a function of P (Fig. 6.5) have been used for making the comparison.

6.2.2. Thermal Properties of Liquid He³ at low Temperatures

The first measurements of the heat capacity of liquid He³ were reported by De Vries and Daunt ([29]) in 1953. The lowest temperature reached was 1.3°K, and from the data, an unlikely value of 10°K was inferred for the Fermi degeneracy temperature. Successive investigations to lower temperatures have produced a varying aspect for C in several radically distinct stages.† Accompanying each of these has been a corresponding shift in interpretation of the data. While experience has taught us (or at least should have) that a pioneering effort

---

† In this section, we do not differentiate by subscripts the various heat capacities, C_{sat}, C_V, C_P, since at the low temperatures we consider, quantities such as $(C_P - C_V)/C_P$ are negligibly small; in those exceptional cases where this omission might be misleading, proper identification will be made.

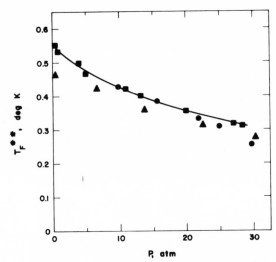

Fig. 6.5. Pressure variation of T_F^{**}. ■ Beal and Hatton [24];
● Anderson *et al.* [22]; ▲ Thomson *et al.* [23]. [After Beal
and Hatton [24].]

into a new temperature range requires independent confirmation
before substantial conclusions can be drawn, the confusion has often
been compounded by a distressing lack of agreement between data
coming from different laboratories—and sometimes from the same
laboratory. Thus, although thermal data is now available down to
about 0.003°K, indicating we have come a long way since the first work
was done, the end of the road is not yet in sight. Table 6.II lists the
important milestones in our progress to date.

Figure 6.6 shows the smoothed experimental heat capacity of
liquid He³ above about 0.1°K in comparison with that of liquid He⁴
in the same range. De Vries and Daunt [29] extended their original
measurements down to 0.57°K, finding that the curve flattens out,
which thoroughly invalidated their first conjecture about T_F. Moreover, the extended data definitely could not be fitted by assuming
either of the Fermi temperatures then popular, i.e., 5°K or 0.45°K
(curves appropriate for these values of T_F are also shown in the figure).
This produced considerable consternation as well as the first indication
that the magnetic and thermal properties could not be described by
the same ideal FD gas model—and thus by no ideal gas model.

Soon thereafter, both Roberts and Sydoriak [30] and Abraham
et al. [31] reported heat capacity data that showed less scatter than the
Ohio State work, but nevertheless confirmed the essential trend.
Calculation of the entropy [30] revealed that at about 0.5°K, $S \approx R \ln 2$,

Table 6.II. Summary of Liquid He³ Heat Capacity Measurements

Reference	Temperature range (°K)	Pressure range (atm)	m/m^* (low P)	C/RT (°K)$^{-1}$ (low P)	Remarks
[29]	1.3–2.3	SVP	—	—	$T^* = 10°K$
[29]	0.57–1.3	SVP	—	—	No T^* fit } 4% He⁴
[30]	0.54–1.7	SVP	—	—	$S_{0.5} \approx R \ln 2$
[30]	0.37–2.36	SVP	—	—	—
[31]	0.23–2.0	SVP	—	—	—
[33]	0.085–0.75	~0.02	—	—	—
[34]	0.085–0.75	0–29	2.00 ± 0.05	—	—
[36]	0.056–0.40	SVP–27.9	2.19 ± 0.13	—	—
[37]	0.008–0.040	~0.02	2.35 ± 0.20	—	—
[38]	0.02–0.1	0.12–34.8	2.82 ± 10%	2.78 ± 10%	m^*/m as $f(P)$
[39]	0.008–0.045	0.02–26.6	—	—	m^*/m as $f(P)$
[40]	0.015–0.3	0.12–28.8	—	2.89 ± 0.12	$C/RT = \alpha + \beta T$ { $T < 0.5°K$, $P > 6$ atm
[4,47]	0.003–0.052	0.28–27.0	—	3.06	—
[46]	0.0035–0.015	SVP	—	—	Anomaly at $T = 0.0055°K$

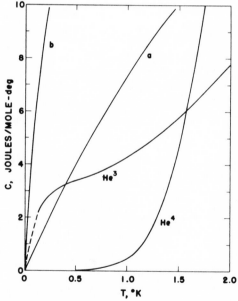

Fig. 6.6. Specific heat of liquids He³ and He⁴ at low temperature. Also shown are curves for the ideal FD gas with (a) $T_F = 5°K$ and (b) $T_F = 0.45°K$.

indicating that nuclear spin alignment must begin above this temperature.

At about this time, the effects of the nuclear spin system upon other properties of the liquid began to be appreciated, especially by Goldstein ([32]), who derived a phenomenological theory of liquid He^3 based upon the measured values of the spin susceptibility, $\chi(T)$. For a system of spins $\frac{1}{2}$, the molar entropy $S_\sigma(T)$ associated with those spins not oriented by the internal field is given through Boltzmann's theorem relating entropy to thermodynamic probability by

$$S_\sigma(T) = (N_\sigma/N_A)R \ln 2 \tag{6.40}$$

where N_σ is the number of spin-disordered particles, N_A Avogadro's number, and R the gas constant. Through the definition of the susceptibility, Goldstein rewrote this expression as

$$S_\sigma(T) = [\chi(T)/\chi_C^0(T)]R \ln 2 \tag{6.41}$$

with $\chi_C^0(T)$ being the limiting Curie susceptibility. Goldstein partitioned the total entropy of the liquid He^3 system into two components, the spin entropy and that due to all other degrees of freedom (non-spin), $S_{n\sigma}(T)$; i.e.,

$$S(T) = S_\sigma(T) + S_{n\sigma}(T) \tag{6.42}$$

The heat capacity may be treated similarly, with

$$C_\sigma(T) = T(dS_\sigma/dT)$$
$$= RT(\ln 2)\{d/dT[\chi(T)/\chi_C^0(T)]\} \tag{6.43}$$

Thus, Goldstein relates the thermal and magnetic properties of the liquid through the effective "ideal gas magnetic degeneration temperature" and asserts that the spin interactions of the real liquid are accounted for by the empirical ratio $\chi(T)/\chi_C^0(T)$.

At high temperatures, S_σ approaches the constant value for complete spin disorder, i.e., $R \ln 2$, while as $T \to 0°K$, the behavior of S_σ is predicted to be

$$\lim_{\text{low } T} S_\sigma = \frac{3R}{2}(\ln 2)\left(\frac{T}{T_F^{**}}\right)\left[1 - \frac{\pi^2}{12}\left(\frac{T}{T_F^{**}}\right)^2\right] \tag{6.44}$$

When T_F^{**} was taken as $0.45°K$, the characteristic temperature for spin orientation as determined from ideal Fermi gas theory and the early susceptibility measurements, Goldstein observed from the specific heat measurements ([30]) that even at $1.5°K$, S_σ should be an important contribution to the total entropy. Moreover, below $1°K$, S should be predominantly S_σ.

The deduction of the corresponding results for the spin heat-capacity is straightforward. At high temperatures, C_σ approaches zero, and in the low-temperature limit, C_σ has the same form as equation (6.44)—and, incidentally, as equation (6.16). C_σ has been calculated to comprise some 40 % of the total heat capacity at 0.4°K and predicted to be essentially the entire amount near absolute zero. Then the limiting slope, $(d/dT)(C_\sigma/R)$, at $T = 0°K$ (or C_σ/RT near $T = 0°K$), should be $(\frac{3}{2}T_F^{**})\ln 2$, or about 2.31 $(°K)^{-1}$. Figure 6 illustrates the division of the total heat capacity into C_σ and $C_{n\sigma}$ compared with the experimentally determined $C(T)$. The non-spin contribution appears to be almost linear up to 1.5°K.

Although some objection has been raised that partitioning the thermodynamic variables into spin and non-spin contributions is an over-simplification, the fact remains that Goldstein's theory has successfully predicted numbers for the state properties of liquid He³ at $T \neq 0°K$. The theory gives a good account of the limiting low temperature heat capacity as well as the expansion coefficient (see Chapter

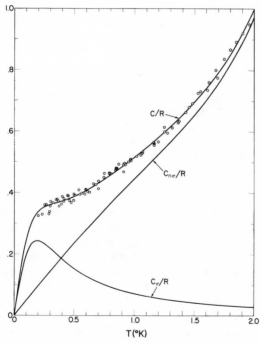

Fig. 6.7. Total observed specific heat of liquid He³ at SVP and contributions from spin and non-spin degrees of freedom [from Goldstein ([52])].

9) and, in addition, has predicted several anomalous $P-V-T$ and thermal properties of the liquid which have been subsequently verified. In this respect, it has spawned a number of worthwhile experiments.

The next giant step in extending the heat capacity measurements to lower temperatures was taken beginning in 1958 by the Ohio State group ([33-35])—see Table 6.II. By then, Landau had proposed his Fermi liquid theory providing the limiting form for C in terms of m^*/m. Also, Brueckner and Gammel ([11]) had just reported their microscopic theory, in which they calculated $m^*/m = 1.84$. Hence, a quest to determine this ratio experimentally was definitely in order; and indeed, at the lowest temperatures, Brewer et al. ([34]) found C apparently linear in T with a slope yielding $m^*/m = 2.00 \pm 0.05$. However, the question remained whether a sufficiently low temperature had been reached to ensure a truly linear region. Subsequent experiments answered this in the negative. As can be seen from Table 6.II, successive assaults on this problem by Strongin et al. ([36]) and Anderson et al. ([37,38]) pushed the value of m^*/m successively higher. The figure 2.82 reported by Anderson et al. ([38]) was considered to be a comfortable fit with Goldstein's theory ([32]), which gave $m^*/m = 2.78$ when the small non-spin contribution to the heat capacity was included.

According to the Fermi liquid theory, m^*/m should increase rather rapidly with rising pressure. On the other hand, the onset of the linear region of C is expected to occur at lower temperatures as pressure is increased, and therefore the experimental evaluation of m^*/m becomes correspondingly more difficult. The ratio derived from the data of Anderson et al. ([38]) and of Brewer and Keyston ([39]) are in surprisingly good agreement and indicate that at $P = 26.6$, m^*/m is about 1.8 times its value at SVP. It is likely that this agreement is somewhat fortuitous, since it is not at all clear that the C vs. T curves forming the bases for these conclusions have been extended into the linear region.

Beginning about 1961, it became fashionable to emphasize the limiting value of C/RT rather than m^*/m, since the latter implied a heat capacity linear in T and it was becoming apparent that claims for observing such a region carried considerable risk. In fact, the bulk of the data seemed to indicate that at pressures greater than SVP, C/RT was itself linear in T. An independent reinvestigation of the heat capacity under pressure by the Illinois group ([40]) yielded 2.89 ± 0.12 $(°K)^{-1}$ as the limiting value for C/RT at $P = 0.12$ atm, consistent with their previous work. And for $T < 0.05°K$ and $P > 6$ atm, they found the best fit to their data given in the form: $C/RT = \alpha + \beta T$, a function quite alien to the Fermi liquid theory. The coefficient α was determined to be $3.74(°K)^{-1}$ at 6.45 atm, rising to $4.44(°K)^{-1}$ at 28.8 atm, which is a more gentle increase with pressure than displayed by the experimental m^*/m ratio.

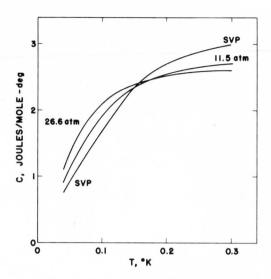

Fig. 6.8. Specific heat of liquid He³ at several pressures
[after Brewer and Keyston (³⁹)].

Despite several differences in detail, the various studies of the pressure dependence of C have been in agreement about the overall trend. The family of smoothed curves of C_P vs. T at several pressures, shown in Fig. 6.8, appear to cross at a single temperature near 0.17°K.

Recent results (⁴⁷) of the Illinois group on the heat capacity of liquid He³ have been summarized in Wheatley's article in *Quantum Fluids* (⁴). These, along with data from several previous investigations, are plotted in Fig. 6.9 at two extreme pressures (0.28 and 27.0 atm) and in the temperature range between 3 and 140 mdeg K. Wheatley has acknowledged that earlier experiments by his group were possibly inaccurate due to unknown amounts of background heating, a difficulty which has been eliminated in the latest work. Through the use of a cleverly designed calorimeter, which could be filled with two different amounts of liquid (N_1 and N_2 moles, $N_2 > N_1$) while keeping other properties of the apparatus fixed, the heat capacity of $(N_2 - N_1)$ moles of He³ could be directly obtained as the difference of total heat capacity for the two fillings. These new results at low pressure suggest a limiting value of C/RT still larger than found before $[\sim 3.06(°K)^{-1}]$, though the extrapolation of the results to 0°K is somewhat uncertain due to possible curvature. At the higher pressure, however, the case

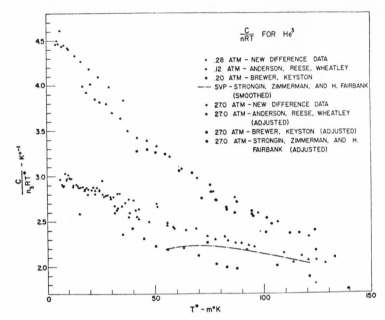

Fig. 6.9. Specific heat of liquid He^3 plotted as C/N_3RT vs. T^* according to several investigations [from Wheatley ([4])].

for a linear C/RT relation is somewhat stronger. In any event, Wheatley was reluctant at this stage to offer an interpretation of the data, preferring to leave theorizing to the theorists. So far there has been no dearth of those accepting the challenge.

Before considering a few of the more interesting interpretations and speculations about the behavior of the specific heat at the lowest temperatures, we mention some of the developments in the search for the transition into the correlated phase, a cause which has provided one of the strongest motives for extending downward the temperature range of heat capacity measurements. Because the transition is expected to occur through fermion pairing of angular momentum states, there should be marked changes in the properties of the liquid as the new phase is entered. By considering the attractive D-state interactions near the Fermi surface, Soda and Vasudevan ([41]) predicted that the specific heat should exhibit an abrupt jump reminiscent of that associated with the superconducting transition. The susceptibility should also change drastically—to lower values, since the pairing leaves fewer free spins. Leggett ([42]) has discussed this point in some detail. Finally, the transport properties should be affected, the most unusual prediction being for a sort of unidirectional superfluidity due to the asymmetry of pairing. Measurements of C probably offer the easiest means of detecting the new phase should it exist.

The possibility that liquid He³ might become superfluid has produced a rather amusing contest between the theoreticians and the experimentalists over the determination of the transition temperature, T_c. The theoreticians got off to a head start in 1960 with predictions ([43,44]) that T_c should be about 0.08°K, just beyond the reach of specific-heat data then available; and they have not as yet relinquished that lead. Subsequent refinements in the theory have pushed the predicted T_c nearly continually downward, with the present consensus placing T_c somewhere between 2×10^{-4} and 8×10^{-3}°K([45]).

The calculation of T_c is a very difficult one. It is based on the general BCS theory of finding T_c for the superconducting transition, and is given by ([44]):

$$T_c = 2.28 \frac{\hbar^2 p_F^2}{k_B m^*} \exp\left(\frac{\pi}{2} \frac{\hbar^2}{m^*} \frac{p_F}{\langle \phi|V|\mathbf{p}_F \rangle}\right) \qquad (6.45)$$

Because the transition temperature depends rather sensitively upon the density of states at the Fermi surface and the interaction potential between particles expressed through the matrix element $\langle \phi|V|\mathbf{p}_F \rangle$, two quantities which are not well known, it is not surprising that T_c should be quite elusive.

Meanwhile, an exciting byplay has taken place within the ranks of the experimentalists. In 1964, Peshkov ([46]) first announced a specific-heat anomaly at $T = 0.0055$°K, which he considered to signal the transition into a superfluid phase. At nearly the same time, Wheatley's group at Illinois had measured C over the region of the proposed anomaly without finding it. In the controversy that followed, several experimental procedures were at issue, primarily concerning: (1) the purity of the samples; (2) the measurement of temperatures; and (3) the establishment of thermal equilibrium in the samples. In order to answer criticism on these points, the investigations were continued and expanded at both Moscow ([46]) and Illinois ([25,47]). This additional work only served to entrench each of the protagonists in his original position. As far as can be discerned, Peshkov remains convinced that the Illinois group did not achieve equilibrium between the He³ sample and the refrigerating salt and therefore did not observe the anomaly because the sample never reached a temperature below 0.005°K [see p. 217 of Wheatley ([4])]. On the other hand, Peshkov's work is difficult to interpret since the supposed anomaly in He³ occurred just when the specific heat of his refrigerating salt also became anomalously large, requiring a subtraction of two large quantities to achieve the desired results.

Wheatley's rebuttal is particularly strong. For the reliability of the measured temperatures, he cites the consistency observed between the specific heat and the nuclear susceptibility as compared with the $1/T^2$ law for the diffusion coefficient (Fig. 6.3). As for the attainment of thermal equilibrium, the principal obstacle to equilibration between sample and salt is believed to be the Kapitza boundary resistance, R_K, which generally increases rapidly with decreasing temperature, going something like T^{-3} (see Section 6.2.3b). When a heat pulse is delivered to the calorimeter, the delay in reaching thermal equilibrium throughout the sample may be characterized by the thermal time constant, τ, which is directly related to R_K and to properties of the material contained in the calorimeter. If τ becomes too large, some heat may be lost, causing spurious specific-heat measurements. For some as yet unexplained reason, the time constant for the Illinois calorimeter ([48]) rose to a maximum of ~ 80 sec at 0.010°K and then *decreased* to ~ 25 sec as the temperature was reduced to 0.002°K. It was therefore concluded that in the critical range, experimental conditions were extremely favorable for obtaining reliable heat capacity data. On the other hand, Wheatley's analysis of Peshkov's heating curves suggested that τ became greatest just where the anomaly is claimed to have been observed, and that the anomaly itself represents heat losses rather than a transition to a superfluid region.

Although Peshkov's claims cannot be entirely dismissed, we feel that the bulk of the evidence argues against them. Consequently, we assume here that convincing proof of the transition has yet to be produced. In any event, it is certain that additional independent work is required before the controversy can be laid to rest.

We return now to consider several theoretical speculations about the character of the liquid He^3 heat capacity at very low temperatures. The results of Abel *et al.* ([25]) suggested to P. W. Anderson ([49]) that for $T < 0.2$°K, C/T should have the form

$$C/T = A \log(B/T) \qquad (6.46)$$

which prompted him to ask: "Does Fermi liquid theory apply to He^3?" He concluded that "yes" might be a proper answer if some type of collective excitation of the liquid could be found possessing singular properties. Balian and Fredkin ([50]) proposed that the coupling between He^3 atoms and zero sound might exhibit such a singularity, but would lead to

$$C/T = A[\log(B/T)]^{1/2} \qquad (6.47)$$

which, in the region 0.005° to 0.1°K, is nearly equivalent to equation (6.46). The later data of Abel *et al.* ([47]) at 0.28 atm "fit but do not define" a straight line on a logarithmic plot, and at 27 atm, do not even fit such a line. Physically, a singularity in C and S at $T = 0$°K is not appealing, since it is then not possible to expand these quantities in a series as $T \to 0°K$. Furthermore, Pitaevskii[51] has indicated that the arguments leading to a term in log T are incorrect.

In other efforts to explain the low-temperature behavior of C, Beal and Hatton have attempted to reconcile the extended Fermi liquid formalism of Richards [7] with the experimental C and χ data. Writing equation (6.16) in the form

$$C/T = A(1 - dT^2) \tag{6.48}$$

and taking into account the distinctions between d in terms of T_F^* and b of equation (6.38) in terms of T_F^{**}, they found that b when determined by C was a factor of three larger than when determined by χ. These results also raise questions concerning the correctness of the Fermi liquid formalism for He³.

On the other hand, Goldstein [52] has, through his universal susceptibility law [28] and the empirical total heat capacity for $T > 0.2°K$, derived a numerical expression for C at lower temperatures. Provided no anomalies appear below 0.05°K, his analysis predicts a limiting form for C/T parabolic in the temperature both at SVP and at higher pressures.

A conjecture has been made by Kirzhnitz and Nepomnyashchii [53] that at some as yet unachieved low temperature, a rather "broad" second-order phase transition should occur, not to the superfluid state, but to one which is *spatially* inhomogeneous. Here, long-range attractive forces between pairs of excited particles and "holes" within the Fermi sphere are expected to produce the transition, which should be observed by a broad precursor anomaly in the specific heat.

We finally mention an approach to the low-temperature properties of liquid He³ which to date appears to offer the greatest promise. Berk and Schrieffer [54] have considered how spin correlations might be responsible for the anomalously high paramagnetic susceptibility and low transition temperature observed for certain superconducting metals. Their suggestion that similar considerations ought to apply to other nearly ferromagnetic systems, such as liquid He³, has been developed further by Doniach and Engelsberg [55]. The basic idea here is that the strong paramagnetic interactions can produce in the Fermi system persistent spin fluctuations (called "paramagnons") which in turn may scatter fermions (in field theory language, paramagnons are contributions to the single-particle fermion self-energy due to spin fluctuations). At low temperatures, the influence on the specific heat due to the scattering of particles by paramagnons can be expressed [55] as a correction to the m^*/m ratio, that is,

$$\frac{C_V}{C_V^0} = \frac{m^*}{m} + A(T/\theta)^2\{\log(T/\theta) - B\} \tag{6.49}$$

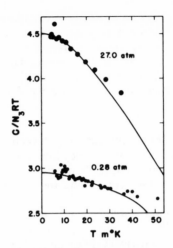

Fig. 6.10. Fit of paramagnon theory (solid curves) to specific heat data of Abel et al. ([47]) [after Doniach and Engelsberg ([55])].

where C_V^0 is $C_V^{(\text{ideal FD})}$ of equation (6.12), B is a cutoff parameter, and θ is the characteristic temperature for spin fluctuations determined from the ratio $\chi_{\text{Pauli}}/\chi_{\text{obs}}$. Figure 6.10 illustrates how the He³ specific-heat data ([47]) at SVP and at 27 atm are fitted by equation (6.49) when $\theta = 1.3°$K and $m^*/m = 3.08$ are taken for the SVP curve and $\theta = 0.78°$K and $m^*/m = 5.78$ for 27 atm. Note that for each curve there are *four* adjustable parameters for making the fit!

Should the paramagnon theory be correct, it would mean that Fermi liquid theory is applicable to He³, but that it can and should be extended.

6.2.3. Transport Properties of Liquid He³ at Low Temperatures

6.2.3a. Viscosity. The early data ([56]) on the viscosity of liquid He³ at SVP indicated a rise from ~ 19 μP at 3.0°K to ~ 28 μP at 1.2°K; and even though Zinov'eva found η to increase more rapidly as T decreased from 1.1° to 0.5°K, there was still no evidence of Fermi liquid behavior.

The first observation of the T^{-2} dependence for η was reported by Abel et al. ([57]) based on measurements of the absorption of high frequency sound ($v = \omega/2\pi = 5$ and 15 Mc/sec) between about 0.04° and 0.1°K. Analysis of the data was made using the classical expression for α_1 with the assumption that all sources of dissipation other than viscosity may be neglected. This approximation leads to equation (6.31), which is probably quite good for He³, although only below 0.1°K was the attenuation proportional to ω^2. Between 0.04° and 0.06°K, the Fermi liquid behavior emerged with the measurements giving $\eta = 2.8\ T^{-2}\ \mu$P. (Also see Section 6.2.4.)

Betts et al. ([58,59]) have determined η by measuring the damping of torsional oscillations of a quartz crystal immersed in the liquid and excited piezoelectrically at its resonant frequency. The earlier experiments ([58]) were carried out between 0.14° and 2.1°K, and at the lowest temperature, seemed to be heading toward the points of Abel et al. ([57]), though it was apparent that the gap could not be bridged smoothly. Later ([59]), the range was extended down to 0.04°K, with results as shown in Fig. 6.11. As can be seen, at the lowest temperatures, the viscosity has risen by a factor of nearly 100 over the value at the vapor–liquid critical point. Below 0.07°K, the data define the relation: $\eta = (3.8 \pm 0.6)T^{-2}\ \mu$P. A full explanation of the discrepancy between these values and those given by Abel et al. has not yet been possible. In the region above 1°K, the points of Betts et al. ([58]) are also higher—by some 10 to 15 %—than those of Taylor and Dash ([56]) obtained with the oscillating-disk technique. Although these differences are not considered outside experimental accuracy, some question remains as to

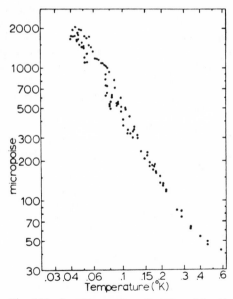

Fig. 6.11. Low-temperature viscosity of liquid He³ at SVP [from Betts et al. ([59])].

whether the various methods of measuring η might inherently yield slightly different results. This situation remains to be clarified.

From the values of η and the approximate m^* obtained from specific-heat data, equation (6.32) may be used to obtain the relaxation time for viscosity; τ_η turns out to be about $(1.9 \times 10^{-12})T^{-2} \sec/(°K)^2$. Hone ([60]) originally calculated the viscosity coefficient using equation (6.21) to be $1.5\ T^{-2}\ \mu P$ at SVP; more recently ([4]) this has been given as $2.31\ T^{-2}\ \mu P$. At higher pressures, η is expected to decrease. The agreement of the calculations with the experimental values at SVP is quite remarkable considering the possible uncertainties in the quasi-particle collision probabilities $W(\theta, \phi)$ used for the calculations.

Rice ([72]) has considered the effect of spin fluctuations on the viscosity. He finds

$$1/\eta T^2 = \alpha_\eta - \beta_\eta (T/\theta)^3 + \cdots \qquad (6.50)$$

where α_η and β_η are specific constants for the viscosity and θ has the same significance as in equation (6.49); also compare with equations (6.52) and (6.57). Quantitative comparison with experiment is difficult because of the inconsistencies mentioned above.

6.2.3b. Thermal Conductivity. An important consideration in the design of experiments for measuring the thermal conductivity of liquid He^3 at low temperatures is the thermal boundary resistance, R_K, already mentioned in our discussions of the specific heat. Formally, R_K is defined as $A\Delta T/\dot{Q}$, where ΔT is the temperature jump at the boundary caused by the energy flow $\dot{Q}$ passing across the liquid–solid interface of area A. The phenomenon, first noticed in experiments with He^4 (by Kapitza, see Section 4.3), has been attributed by Khalatnikov ([61]) to the mismatch between the acoustic phonons of the liquid and the solid at the boundary. He predicted on this basis a T^{-3} temperature dependence for R_K; and although this conclusion was for a general liquid, some feeling persisted that the resistance was somehow associated with the peculiarities of superfluid helium. However, Lee and Fairbank ([62]) found experimentally that R_K for He^3 in contact with copper above $0.25°K$ obeyed a T^{-2} law with

$$R_K(He^3–Cu) = 130/T^2 \deg cm^2\ W^{-1}$$

When this result was compared with

$$R_K(He^4–Cu) = 45/T^2 \deg cm^2\ W^{-1}$$

as found by Fairbank and Wilks ([63]) in a similar apparatus, it became clear that the effect does not require the presence of superfluid.

The acoustic treatment was pursued further by Bekarevich and Khalatnikov ([64]) as a possible means of observing zero sound in He^3 on the expectation that phonons of the solid would excite this mode during energy transfer across the boundary. Again a T^{-3} dependence was predicted for R_K at low temperatures as a consequence of Fermi liquid behavior. The same result has been obtained somewhat differently by Gavoret [65] who found that the T^{-3} law is also valid at high temperatures. Unfortunately, the low-temperature experimental determinations of R_K have not been very consistent with these calculations, nor, for that matter, reproducible from various experiments. Anderson et al. [37] had initially verified the order of magnitude and the temperature dependence of the predictions for a He³-epoxy interface in the temperature region 0.018° to 0.04°K. But subsequent, more extensive studies [66] using combinations of liquid He³ or He⁴ at various pressures in contact with copper or epoxy surfaces revealed that the theoretical values of R_K quite inadequately represent the observations with respect to magnitude, temperature dependence, and pressure dependence.

There are apparently many things we do not understand about the boundary resistance. Therefore, whenever R_K becomes a significant correction to the primary quantity of investigation, an independent evaluation of R_K for the boundary conditions in question is required. Better still, this correction should be avoided if possible.

Challis and Wilks [67] reported some of the first measurements of the thermal conductivity of liquid He³. They used the flat-plate method, in which R_K at two Cu–He³ interfaces was in series with the thermal resistance of the liquid. Fortunately, R_K is not too large in the temperature range covered (1.3° to 3°K), so that the results were qualitatively correct. This was confirmed by the work of Lee and Fairbank [62], who measured the thermal resistance of a column of liquid He³ contained in a vertical tube. Because the temperature difference due to a given heat current was obtained from thermometers placed along the tube walls, across which the heat flux was essentially zero, the problem of the Kapitza resistance was avoided entirely (though R_K was also measured independently). Thus the coefficient of thermal conductivity, λ, could be obtained from the simple relation

$$\lambda = \dot{Q}L/A \, \Delta T \tag{6.51}$$

where L is the distance between thermometers and A the cross-sectional area of the tube. These experiments spanned the temperature range from 0.24°K to 2.7°K over which λ increased slowly from 7×10^2 to 16×10^2 erg/cm-sec-°K. Thus, $d\lambda/dT$ here is positive. Not only is this dependence opposite to that expected for a Fermi liquid, but it is also contrary to the behavior of most ordinary liquids. In addition, below 1°K, the measurements did not conform to the kinetic gas theory behavior ($\lambda = 2.5\eta C_V$) observed above this temperature.

In 1961, the Illinois group ([68]) investigated λ in the temperature interval 0.026° to 0.2°K using essentially the same method as Lee and Fairbank. Within experimental error, the data from these two investigations are consistent in the region of overlap. From 0.04 to 0.026°K, the new thermal-conductivity results fit the relation $\lambda = (48/T)$ erg/cm-sec, while recent calculations ([4]) using equation (6.22) give $(79.7/T)$ erg/cm-sec for this quantity.

Further studies of the thermal conductivity including the pressure dependence of λ have been reported by Anderson et al. ([69]). The data extend only to 0.06°K, but they appear to be considerably more self-consistent than those of earlier investigators. A partial summary of the λ values below 0.8°K is given in Fig. 6.12. We also note that as the pressure is increased, λ at a given temperature decreases and the temperature of the minimum in λ (at constant P) is lowered as well. Thus, with rising pressure, the temperature at which λ becomes characteristic of a Fermi liquid is shifted downward, quite in accordance with theoretical expectations. On the other hand, at higher temperatures, the pressure dependence of λ is reversed, as shown in Fig. 6.12 from the recent measurements of Kerrisk and Keller ([70]). This is the pressure behavior expected of ordinary liquids. As yet, there is no direct information on how the isobars cross.

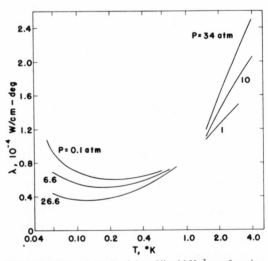

Fig. 6.12. Thermal conductivity of liquid He^3 as a function of T at various pressures [drawn from data of Anderson et al. ([69]) and Kerrisk and Keller ([70])].

Abel *et al.* ([71]) have repeated the measurements of λ at SVP from 0.030 to below 0.004°K using a new apparatus. In magnitude, the results do not agree with either of the two previous investigations ([68,69]) from the same laboratory, and between 0.004 and 0.020°K, the temperature dependence is $(1/T)^{0.92}$, not quite characteristic of a Fermi liquid. Apparently, better experimental definition of λ is still required.

Although the belief is prevalent that in the limit $T \to 0$, barring any anomalies, the transport properties should display the Fermi liquid temperature dependences, a question arises as to why departures from this behavior appear at the very low temperatures already reached. Rice ([72]) has made a rather successful attempt at resolving this problem by introducing the fermion–paramagnon interaction into the single-particle distribution function solution to the Boltzmann equation. The results take the form of a series, the leading terms of which for λ, for example, are

$$1/\lambda T = \alpha_\lambda - \beta_\lambda(T/\theta) + O[(T/\theta)^3] \tag{6.52}$$

where θ has the same significance as discussed earlier for specific heat, and α_λ and β_λ are constants characteristic for the thermal conductivity. As $T \to 0$, we see that $1/\lambda T$ is a constant, as required by Fermi liquid theory. At higher temperatures, the type of fit possible from equation (6.52) is shown in Fig. 6.13 compared with the low-pressure data of Anderson *et al.*([69]). Abel *et al.*([71]) have also claimed that this formalism is appropriate for their new data.

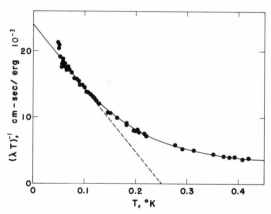

Fig. 6.13. Fit of paramagnon theory (solid line) to thermal conductivity data of Anderson *et al.* ([69]) near SVP. Dashed line is extension of curve used to fit α_λ and θ in equation (6.52) at the lowest temperatures. [After Rice ([72]).]

6.2.3c. The Diffusion Coefficient. The spin diffusion coefficient of liquid He^3 has been measured exclusively by the "spin-echo" method, in which the particles are distinguished by the phase of their nuclear spin precession in the presence of an external magnetic field. The technique, discovered by Hahn ([27]) and elaborated by Carr and Purcell ([73]), will be sketched briefly here.

Suppose we place the He^3 sample in a steady magnetic field H_0 in the z direction and at the same time arrange to have a weak but uniform field gradient G perpendicular to H_0, i.e., $dH_0/dx = G$. If, in addition, a pulsed rf field of magnitude H_1 is applied in the x direction at the Larmor frequency $\omega_0 = -\gamma H_0$ (γ is the gyromagnetic ratio, which for He^3 equals $2.038 \times 10^{-4}\,G^{-1}\text{-sec}^{-1}$), the spins will nutate with an angular frequency γH_1 during the pulse. In general, the nutations will be arbitrary, and in a time Λ, the magnetization of the spins will precess through an angle $\Lambda \gamma H_1$. It is possible to select pulse durations of the rf field such that $\Lambda \gamma H_1$ equals either 90° or 180°, two values of special interest. For if we successively apply to the thermally equilibrated spin system a 90° pulse, and then, after a short time t, a 180° pulse, we will receive after an additional time t a burst of rf or a "spin-echo" detectable with a pickup coil. What has happened as a result of our pulse sequence is that the spins have precessed back to the same orientations and positions in G which they had when the 90° pulse was delivered. It is as if we have a pack of runners all set to move at a starting line and we fire the signal to "go" (90° pulse). We assume that the runners vary in ability, but that each runs with constant speed, so that at such time when we fire a second signal they are rather spread out along the track. Upon hearing this second signal (180° pulse), each runner instantly reverses his direction and heads back to the starting line with the same speed as before. Thus, all the runners cross the line simultaneously, just as they left the starting blocks([27]).

However, there are several mechanisms by which the amplitude h_1 of the original signal may be attenuated (i.e., we may lose some runners along the way). These processes may be accounted for by the following relation for the ratio of h_2, the echo amplitude, to h_1:

$$h_2/h_1 = \exp(-2t/T_2 - \gamma^2 GD(2t)^3/12) \qquad (6.53)$$

Here, T_2 is the spin–spin relaxation time, which, in the absence of diffusion, would account for the entire fall off of intensity. However, when the diffusion coefficient is large, the second term in the exponent becomes significant and describes how, through diffusion, some spins do not return to their original location at the echo time. Actually, for liquid He^3, diffusion is the dominant damping process, so that by proper programming of pulses it is possible to measure both T_2 and D. A third mechanism for the attenuation is through the spin–lattice, or longitudinal, relaxation time T_1, which is a measure of the coupling between the spin system and the other degrees of freedom of the liquid. By a different sequence of pulses, the relation may be found

$$h_2/h_1 = 1 - \exp(-2t/T_1) \qquad (6.54)$$

Through the theory of Bloembergen *et al.* ([74]), it becomes possible to relate T_1 and D for He³ through the simple relation

$$T_1^{-1} = 0.3 \, \pi\gamma^4\hbar^2 N_0/aD \qquad (6.55)$$

where N_0 is the number of magnetic moments per unit volume and a is the atomic radius.

Although the history of attempts to reconcile the theoretical and experimental values of T_1 has been notoriously disappointing ([75]), measurements of the pulse-height ratios suitable for use with equation (6.53) provide a sensitive and accurate means of obtaining values of the diffusion coefficient. To ensure the reliability of the interpretation, several auxiliary points must be first settled. The spin-echo method measures the total diffusion of spins, which can arise either by the diffusion of atoms bearing the spins or by spin interaction of neighboring nuclei. Garwin and Reich ([76]) have convincingly argued that the spin diffusion due to the latter process is entirely negligible. They have estimated $D_{\text{interaction}}$ to be $3 \times 10^{-12} \, \text{cm}^2/\text{sec}$ (compared with the typically observed value of $D > 10^{-4} \, \text{cm}^2/\text{sec}$), so we may have confidence that the spin-echo measurements refer solely to the diffusion of atoms.

Also, the diffusion measurements in liquid He³ have usually been made under the assumptions that T_2 damping may be neglected in equation (6.53)—$T_2 \approx 1$ sec—and that experimental uncertainties due to convection, residual field gradients, sample-holder configuration, and He⁴ impurities may be neglected. Hart and Wheatley ([77]) as well as Anderson *et al.* ([78]) have discussed these points in relation to their experiments, indicating how the problems may, to a large extent, be minimized.

Turning now to the results of diffusion measurements, Garwin and Reich ([76]) pioneered the spin-echo method to produce values of D between 0.5° and 4.2°K and at pressures up to 67 atm. As a function of decreasing temperature, D for the liquid monotonically decreased, showing no indication of Fermi liquid behavior; with increasing density, D decreased. Overall, the data could be well represented by the relation

$$D = 5.9 \ln(0.16/\rho) \exp(T/2.8) \qquad (6.56)$$

to which the authors ascribe no theoretical significance.

The remaining important investigations of D at low temperature have come from Wheatley and his co-workers at Illinois. In the first of these, Hart and Wheatley ([77]) carried the measurements down to 0.067°K and found D to pass through a minimum value of $\sim 6 \times 10^{-5}$ cm²/sec at 0.55°K. At the lowest temperatures, D appeared to be proportional to $T^{-3/2}$. Anderson et al. ([78]) substantially confirmed this temperature dependence for T as low as 0.032°K. A short time later, Hone ([8]) derived the T^{-2} law for the Fermi liquid, uncovering a discrepancy between theory and experiment. This was soon resolved through further measurements by Anderson et al. ([79]), who did indeed find D proportional to T^{-2} between 0.04° and 0.02°K, the lowest temperature measured. It was suggested that previous results had been impaired by excessively long equilibrium times and inaccurate thermometry, both of which defects were remedied in the newer experiments.

Still more refined results, for ten pressures between SVP and 28.2 atm ([22]) and for temperatures extending down to 0.002°K ([25]), were subsequently obtained. As expected, D decreased with increasing pressure and exhibited the onset of Fermi liquid character at successively

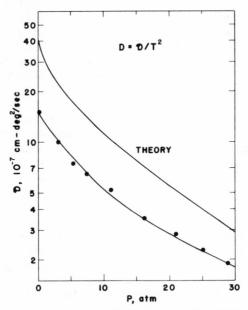

Fig. 6.14. Pressure variation of the coefficient $\mathscr{D}$ in the relation $D = \mathscr{D}/T^2$ for the self-diffusion coefficient: experiments ([22]) compared with theory ([8,60]). [After Anderson et al. ([22]).]

lower temperatures, T_D, which ranged from 0.050°K at 0.17 atm to 0.029°K at 28.2 atm. The observed pressure variation of the constant $\mathscr{D}$ in the relation $D = \mathscr{D}/T^2$ is compared in Fig. 6.14 with the theoretical predictions of Hone [8,60]. Here, the experimental values of $\mathscr{D}$ have been obtained from measurements below T_D and judged to be accurate within $\pm 7\%$, while the calculations were made using recent empirical data for evaluating the transition probability. $W(\theta, \phi)$; cf. equation (6.24). The calculated values of $\mathscr{D}$ lie about a factor of two above those observed.

We return now to Fig. 6.3, where both the diffusion coefficient and the susceptibility are plotted against the magnetic temperature, T^* ($\approx T$). It has already been mentioned (Section 6.2.1) that χ may be measured by the spin-echo technique, and we see that by switching off the field gradient **G**, this may be accomplished in the same apparatus as used for D. Then, when a 90° pulse is followed by one of 180°, the height of the echo will be undiminished from that of the original signal, provided T_2 damping is negligible. This being the case for He³, the relative susceptibility is given by the amplitude of the spin-echo. Thus, χ and D have been measured nearly simultaneously in the same apparatus under the same conditions of pressure, temperature, and thermal equilibration times. Exact procedures for carrying out these measurements have been detailed by Abel et al. [25]. The results shown in Fig. 6.3 amply demonstrate the T^{-2} dependence of D at low temperature and as well the absence of any anomaly down to 0.002°K.†

At higher temperatures, the paramagnon theory of Rice [72] is again applicable, giving

$$1/DT^2 = \alpha_D - \beta_D(T/\theta) + O[(T/\theta)^3] \qquad (6.57)$$

where α_D and β_D are specific constants derivable for the spin-diffusion process. As T approaches 0°K, $1/DT^2$ approaches a constant value. The fit of this diffusion relation to the data of Abel et al. [25] is almost as impressive as the case for thermal conductivity indicated in Fig. 6.13.

6.2.4. Sound Propagation in Liquid He³

6.2.4a. Ordinary Sound. Measurements of the velocity of ordinary sound in liquid He³ were first reported nearly simultaneously by two independent groups: Laquer et al. [80] obtained u_1 between 0.34° and 3.14°K using pulses of 5 Mc/sec sound, while Atkins and Flicker [81] operated at 14 Mc/sec over the more restricted temperature range above 1.2°K. In the temperature region of overlap, the sound velocities observed in these two investigations were in excellent agreement, although the estimated experimental errors in the former work, being about $\pm 0.2\%$, were a factor of five smaller than in the latter. In

† See footnote, p. 178.

addition, the data of Laquer *et al.* extended to sufficiently low temperatures that they could be extrapolated to 0°K with considerable confidence. Under the assumption that $du_1/dT \to 0$ at $P = 0$, they found $u_1^{(0\ \text{K})} = 183.4$ (± 0.5) m/sec, a value subsequently confirmed by Abel *et al.* ([57]) [$u_1^{(0\ \text{K})} = 182.4$ (± 0.6) m/sec] from measurements at even lower temperatures. A comparison of the temperature dependence of u_1 for He³ and He⁴ both at SVP is given in Fig. 6.15. On a reduced temperature scale with $\theta = T/T_c$ (where T_c is the liquid–vapor critical temperature), the relation $u_1(\text{He}^3)/u_1(\text{He}^4) = m_3/m_4$ at constant θ holds within a few percent in spite of the irregularities associated with the λ-region of He⁴.

The pressure dependence of u_1 has been studied by both Atkins and Flicker ([81]) and by Abel *et al.* ([57]). The latter found below 0.1°K, where u_1 is independent of T, that as the pressure increased from 0.1 to 28 atm, u_1 also increased, from 184 to 417 m/sec.

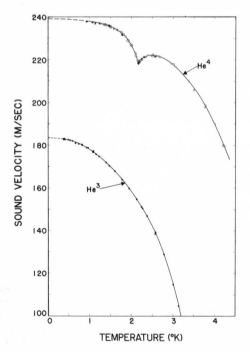

Fig. 6.15. Velocity of ordinary sound in liquids He³ and He⁴ at SVP [from Laquer *et al.* ([80])].

Through such relations as

$$\beta_S \equiv (\rho u_1^2)^{-1} \tag{6.58}$$

$$\alpha_P \equiv \alpha_{sat} + \gamma_c \beta_S (dP_{sat}/dT) \tag{6.59}$$

with

$$\gamma_c = C_P/C_V = \beta_T/\beta_S \tag{6.60}$$

the sound velocity provides an important link in the derivation of a consistent set of thermodynamic properties of the liquid. (Here, β_S is the adiabatic compressibility, β_T the isothermal compressibility, α_P the isobaric expansion coefficient, α_{sat} the expansion coefficient along the saturation curve, and (dP_{sat}/dT) the slope of the vapor pressure curve.) Both Laquer et al. ([80]) and Atkins and Flicker ([81]) have tabulated some of the thermodynamic quantities obtainable in this way using their sound velocity measurements together with other independent data for ρ_{sat}, α_{sat}, C_{sat}, and (dP_{sat}/dT)

We also recall that through equation (6.27) measurements of the specific heat and the sound velocity may be combined to yield numerical estimates for the Landau parameters F_0 and F_1 (see Table 6.IV). Both of these are, of course, functions of pressure.

6.2.4b. Zero Sound. Probably the greatest triumph of the Landau theory has been the prediction and the subsequent experimental identification of zero sound. The general nature of the difficulties inherent in the experimental approach may be appreciated from a glance at Fig. 6.1, which shows that either very high frequencies or very low temperatures—or both—are required for the detection of this phenomenon.

The 1961 studies by Abel et al. ([57]) indicated none of the attenuation characteristics of zero sound even at 15 Mc/sec and 0.045°K. Nor were these authors able to observe any evidence of sound propagation of either 25 Mc/sec or 15 Mc/sec signals at 0.008°K, even though the experimental conditions appeared favorable for the observation of zero sound—i.e., since the threshold for this mode is $\omega\tau \approx 1$ and τ is approximately $(1.9 \times 10^{-12})T^{-2}$ sec, the critical temperature T_0 for observing zero sound should be something like

$$T_0 \approx (1.2 \times 10^{-11} \, v)^{1/2} \tag{6.61}$$

a condition fulfilled by the experiments. It is possible that diffraction effects at high frequencies coupled with large absorption were responsible for the difficulties here.

Keen et al. ([82]) avoided these problems by measuring instead the acoustic impedance, Z, of the liquid. The basis for choosing this method is essentially as follows: For ordinary sound, Z is defined as

ρu_1. This quantity has figured prominently in the studies ([64,65]) of energy transfer $\dot{Q}$ across a solid boundary into liquid helium, which, according to Gavoret ([65]) obeys the relation

$$\dot{Q} = Zu_z^2 \qquad (6.62)$$

where u_z is the sound velocity at the boundary. The theory also predicts that for zero sound, $Z = \rho u_0$ (very nearly). Finally, the work of Bekarevich and Khalatnikov ([64]) suggests that Z/ρ should increase by a few percent as the temperature is lowered through the region where $\omega\tau \approx 1$. Thus, by studying the energy characteristics of an ultrasonic wave transmitted across a solid–liquid interface, Keen et al. proposed to measure the quantity Z/ρ and to search for its variation with temperature as an indication for the transition from ordinary sound to zero sound.

The experimental chamber consisted of a microwave cavity in which was suspended an X-cut quartz crystal for converting electromagnetic pulses ($v = 1000$ Mc/sec) to sonic pulses. Reflections of the sound waves between the ends of the transducer were modified when one end was immersed in liquid He^3 as compared with the case when the crystal was completely isolated. From the decay of the sonic pulses in the two cases, Z of the sample was inferred. Above $1°K$, Z/ρ reproduced the u_1 values reported by Laquer et al. ([80]), but at $\sim 0.092°K$, the measurements of Z/ρ clearly showed an increase in sound velocity, $u_0 - u_1 = \Delta u = 19 \pm 6$ m/sec, which has been taken to mark the transition to zero sound.

This result for Δu is considerably larger than predicted by Bekarevich and Khalatnikov ([64]), who considered only the limit $\omega\tau \to \infty$ in the approximation that $F(\theta)$ be given in terms of F_0 and F_1. Brooker ([83]) has extended the analysis to include all $\omega\tau$ as well as terms in F_2. Although it is not yet possible to determine F_2 with any precision, Brooker noted that a value $F_2 \approx 14$ provided a reasonable fit to the observed Δu.

Keene and Wilks ([84]) have also measured Z/ρ at pressures up to 12.5 atm, finding that as P increased, both Δu and T_0 decreased. At the highest pressure, Δu almost completely disappeared.

More recently, Kirby and Wilks ([85]) used 122 Mc/sec radiation to observe Z/ρ in the same apparatus as described above. The transition temperature was lowered to $0.034°K$, in accord with theory, and Δu was determined to be 14 ± 3 m/sec.

The above studies, while providing very strong evidence for the existence of zero sound, are nevertheless somewhat indirect. However, observation by Wheatley's group ([86]) of the distinctive attenuation characteristics of zero sound, accompanied by an appropriate velocity change, has provided incontrovertible proof of the phenomenon. The

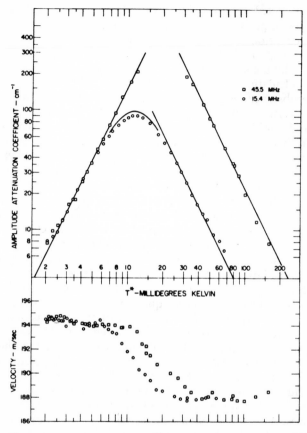

Fig. 6.16. Attenuation and propagation velocity of sound in liquid
He³ showing the characteristics associated with the transition from
first sound to zero sound for two frequencies, v = 15.4 and 45.5
Mc/sec [from Abel et al. [86]].

attenuation coefficient and propagation velocity for sound with
v = 15.4 and 45.5 Mc/sec were measured over a path length of liquid
He³ equal to 1.38×10^{-2} cm and at temperatures down to 0.002°K at
$P = 0.32$ atm. The attenuation results are graphed in Fig. 6.16. On
the low T side of the maxima, the attenuation can be described by
$\alpha_0 = (1.56 \times 10^6)T^2$ cm^{-1}, and on the high side, by $\alpha_1 = (2.68 \times 10^{-18})$
$\times \omega^2 T^{-2}$, beautifully confirming the temperature- and frequency-
dependence expected from Landau's theory (also cf. Fig. 6.1). Sufficiently low temperatures were apparently not reached for the quantum

effects predicted by equation (6.36) to be manifested, i.e., here, $\hbar\omega < k_B T$. In passing, we note that the value of α_1 just cited provides through equation (6.31) a new estimate for the viscosity coefficient, namely, $\eta = 2.3 T^{-2} \mu P$. This is some 20% lower than obtained previously by the same method ([57]), but is still in excellent agreement with the calculations.

The observed velocity shift in these experiments (also shown in Fig. 6.16) is $\Delta u = 6$ m/sec, which is remarkably close to that obtained when the Fermi-liquid parameters—F_0, F_1, and v_F as given in Table 6.IV—are inserted into equation (6.28). No recourse to terms in F_2 and higher is necessary, as in the case of the acoustic impedance data. As yet, the observed discrepancies in Δu have not been explained, though it is possible that either the theory connecting Z with the energy transfer into the liquid may be unsatisfactory in detail, or the relation $Z/\rho = u$ may not be strictly valid in the zero-sound region.

Shah ([87]) has reported the velocity shift characteristic of the transition to zero sound at the comparatively high temperature of about 0.51°K as observed from the intensities of X-rays scattered at an angle of 1.73° from liquid He³ at temperatures between 0.37° and 1.6°K. Through the theory of Abrikosov and Khalatnikov ([88]), which treats the scattering of γ rays from the liquid, the data were analyzed to yield the liquid structure factor $L(\omega, T)$. The situation here is quite analogous to that for the scattering of neutrons from liquid He⁴ (as discussed in the previous chapter) in that a photon incident upon the liquid sample may either create or destroy an elementary excitation of the liquid. The resulting liquid structure factor is related to the local density fluctuations which, under ordinary circumstances ($\omega\tau \ll 1$), represent the adiabatic processes of first sound; however, at very high frequencies, the nonhydrodynamic processes ($\omega\tau \gg 1$) modify $L(\omega, T)$ by the factor C_P/C_V. At low temperatures this ratio is nearly unity; consequently great experimental sensitivity is required to detect this effect on the sound field.

The scattering angle used by Shah corresponded to momentum transfers of about $p_F/6$ (or a wave vector equal to 0.123 Å^{-1}) and a phonon frequency $\omega = 2.26 \times 10^{11}$ rad/sec. At temperatures above 0.8°K, the scattering data are consistent with previously observed ordinary sound velocities, while at the transition, the inferred value of Δu is in good agreement with that found by Abel et al. ([86]).

A comparison of some of the parameters pertinent to the zero sound experiments is presented in Table 6.III. In the last two columns, we have calculated τ_η at the transition temperature T_0, as well as $\omega\tau_\eta$ at T_0, using $\tau_\eta = (1.9 \times 10^{-12}) T^{-2}$ sec^{-1}. It is curious that $\omega\tau_\eta$ for the first two entries in the table should agree so well with the others, since T_0 for each of these experiments lies far above the Fermi liquid region,

Table 6.III. Comparison of Some Results from Zero-Sound Experiments

Type of measurement	$\omega = 2\pi\nu$ (rad/sec)	Transition temp. T_0 (°K)	Δu (m/sec)	$\tau_\eta = 1.9$ $\times 10^{-12}T_0^{-2}$ (sec^{-1})	$\omega\tau_\eta$ at T_0
X-ray scattering [87]	2.26×10^{11}	0.51	6.3 ± 0.2	7.3×10^{-12}	1.65
Acoustic impedance [82]	6.28×10^9	0.092	19 ± 6	2.2×10^{-10}	1.38
[85]	7.65×10^8	0.034	14 ± 3	1.64×10^{-9}	1.25
Attenuation [86]	2.86×10^8	0.0193		5.1×10^{-9}	1.46
Velocity [86]	2.86×10^8	0.018	6.6 ± 0.1	5.8×10^{-9}	1.66
Attenuation [86]	9.67×10^7	0.0113		1.48×10^{-8}	1.43
Velocity [86]	9.67×10^7	0.011	6.6 ± 0.1	1.57×10^{-8}	1.52

where neither τ_η nor any other known relaxation time is proportional to T^{-2}.

It seems worthwhile to point out here that Pines [89] has proposed as an explanation for Woods' results shown in Fig. 5.9 that zero sound may be excited in liquid He⁴. He has considered the conditions for the appearance of zero sound in He⁴ (above and below T_λ) and in He³ (above the Fermi liquid region) to be that in addition to $\omega\tau \gtrsim 1$, there should be a strong polarization potential. Here, τ is some appropriate quasiparticle lifetime. If these notions are correct, it would appear that Landau's original ideas about the oscillation of the Fermi surface represent a special case of a more general phenomenon.

6.2.5. Dilute Solutions of He³ in Liquid He⁴ at Very Low Temperatures

The first indications that liquids He³ and He⁴ should not be miscible in all proportions (see Fig. 1.11) came in 1952 from the vapor pressure measurements of Sommers [90], which demonstrated that even at high temperatures, mixtures of the two isotopes were nonideal and exhibited positive deviations from Raoult's law. Straightforward application of classical nonideal solution theory predicted an absorption of heat on mixing and a separation of phases below about 0.7°K. Shortly afterward, direct experimental confirmation of the mixing heat was obtained [91]; and in 1956, Walters and Fairbank [92] using nuclear magnetic resonance techniques, observed the phase separation below a critical temperature $T_{s.c} = 0.83$°K. Prior to this, Prigogine et al. [93] had concluded that due to differences in zero-point energy (i.e., differences in mass and interparticle spacing), the two isotopes should exist in completely separate phases at $0°K$. More recently, Uhlenbeck ([94]) has emphasized the importance of statistics for the phase separation, and this has been further argued in more detailed studies by Cohen et al. ([95]).

However, the possibility that dilute solutions of He³ in He⁴ may exist in a single phase at $T = 0°K$ is contained in the early theory of Landau and Pomeranchuk ([96]), which described the effects of impurities in liquid He⁴. The presence of a small amount of He³ impurity was expected to contribute an additional branch to the energy spectrum, namely,

$$\epsilon_3 = -E_3 + p^2/2m_3^* \tag{6.63}$$

Thus the He³ atoms were treated essentially as independent particles with effective mass m_3^* (associated with the motion of the polarization cloud produced by a He³ atom on a He⁴ atom), but with a binding energy $-E_3$ in the mixture. At the other end of the concentration range, Zharkov and Silin ([97]) favored a similar spectrum for He⁴ as an impurity in He³:

$$\epsilon_4 = -E_4 + p^2/2m_4^* \tag{6.64}$$

De Bruyn Ouboter et al. ([98]) have derived thermodynamic properties of liquid He³–He⁴ mixtures from specific-heat data and found the theories of Pomeranchuk and of Zharkov and Silin to be valid for low concentrations of impurities and for temperatures down to $0.4°K$. They determined $N_A E_4$ to be 53.6 J/mole and $N_A E_3$ to be ~ 23.8 J/mole. The effective mass m_3^* has been measured in a number of experiments involving dilute He³ solutions [e.g., second sound ([99]), oscillating disks ([100]), etc.] with results generally within $\pm 10\%$ of $m_3^*/m_3 = 2.6$. No direct measurements of m_4^* are available, but using regular solution theory, Edwards and Daunt ([101]) have estimated $m_4^*/m_4 = 5.5$. (A regular solution has an ideal entropy of mixing, but a nonzero heat of mixing.)

In their treatment of regular solutions, Edwards and Daunt have derived approximate expressions for the mole fraction of He³ dissolved in He⁴ for both limiting concentration ranges. These are

$$x_l = [2(2\pi m_3^* k_B T)^{3/2} V_4^0/N_A h^3] \exp[(N_A E_3 - L_3^0)/RT] \tag{6.65}$$

and

$$(1 - x_u) = [(2\pi m_4^* k_B T)^{3/2} V_3^0/N_A h^3] \exp[(N_A E_4 - L_4^0)/RT] \tag{6.66}$$

where x_l and x_u are the He³ molar concentrations in the lower (He⁴-rich) and upper (He³-rich) phases $[x = N_3/(N_3 + N_4)]$; L_3^0 and L_4^0 and V_3^0 and V_4^0 are, respectively, the molar latent heats and volumes of the pure isotopes at $T = 0°K$. In these expressions, the exponentials are crucial. Using equation (6.66) and the values of m_4^* and $N_A E_4$ mentioned above, the authors inferred that phase separation in He³-rich mixtures occurs at relatively high temperatures and at 0°K is surely complete, since L_4^0 is numerically larger than $N_A E_4$ by a comfortable margin. Thus the exponential is negative and $(1 - x_u)$, i.e., the He⁴ concentration of the upper phase, becomes vanishingly small. However, the best estimates for $N_A E_3$ appeared greater than L_3^0, so that at very low temperatures, the exponential in equation (6.65) remains positive, suggesting that in dilute He³ solutions, there should be no phase separation.

Specific-heat measurements by Edwards et al. ([102]) of seven solutions with x ranging between 0.04 and 0.15 provided experimental confirmation of the low-temperature stability of dilute He³ solutions. These are shown in Fig. 6.17. For temperatures down to ~0.07°K, the specific-heat jump characteristic of phase separation was observed for all concentrations but two at $x = 0.04$ and 0.06. In the single-phase region, the specific-heat curves can be well represented by the ideal FD gas expression when m^* is taken as $2.5 m_3$ and Kerr's ([103]) values for the solution densities are used. Heat capacity data for solutions with $x = 0.013$ and 0.05 have been extended down to about 0.004°K by Anderson et al. ([104,105]) also without showing any indication of phase separation. It appears rather certain that at SVP, mixtures of He⁴ containing up to about 6% He³ are miscible at even the lowest temperatures.

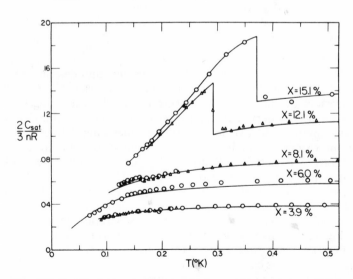

Fig. 6.17. Specific heat vs. temperature for several dilute solutions of He³ in He⁴ [from Edwards et al. ([102])].

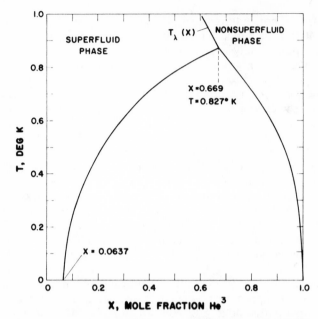

Fig. 6.18. Low-temperature T vs. composition phase diagram for He^3–He^4 mixtures [region near $T_{s,c}$ drawn from data of Graf et al. ([106]); region of low x drawn from data of Ifft et al. ([119]) which gives $x = 0.0637 \pm 0.005$ as the limiting solubility].

Now we may construct the experimentally determined x–T phase diagram for He^3–He^4 liquid mixtures as shown in Fig. 6.18. Here we have included the recent work of Graf et al. ([106]) who, using a capacitance method, observed the phase separation curve in the vicinity of the maximum to be two nearly straight lines intersecting in a cusp. This unexpected result is nevertheless consistent with earlier determinations by Roberts and Sydoriak ([107]), even though these had been extrapolated to give a rounded maximum. The experiments place the maximum at $x = 0.669 \pm 0.005$ and $T_{s,c} = (0.872 \pm 0.003)°$K. Graf et al. ([106]) also measured $T_\lambda(x)$ from thermal equilibrium rates. It appears that $T_\lambda(x)$ terminates at the phase-separation peak.

Figure 6.19 displays for dilute He^3 solutions the x-dependence of the Fermi temperature T_F and the binding energy $E_3(x)$, given by $[E_3(x) - L_3^0]/k_B$, as calculated by Edwards et al. ([102]).

One obviously important consequence of the above results is the possibility of studying a Fermi liquid (actually, a nearly ideal FD gas)

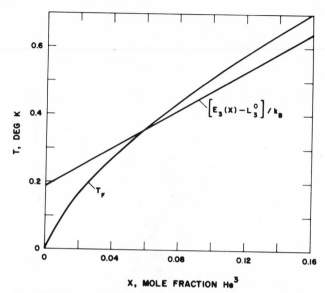

Fig. 6.19. Concentration dependence of the Fermi temperature, T_F, and the quantity $[E_3(x) - L_3^0]/k_B$ for dilute solutions of He³ in He⁴ [after Edwards *et al.* ([102])].

over a range of degeneration temperatures (or alternatively, Fermi momenta) not otherwise easily attained. Accordingly, dilute He³ solutions at low temperatures have provided a fruitful area of research. The nuclear susceptibility of dilute He³ solutions has been investigated by Husa *et al.* ([108]) at temperatures above 0.35°K and by Anderson *et al.* ([105]) down to about 0.003°K. At higher temperatures and for $x < 0.10$, the behavior of χ was found to be that of an ideal FD gas with the number density of the He³ in solution and an effective mass $m^* = 2.5m_3$. For $x > 0.10$, interactions became slightly apparent. Deviations from the ideal gas law remain small even at very low temperatures for the low concentrations ($x = 0.013$ and 0.05) investigated by Anderson *et al.* In contrast to pure He³, χ for the dilute mixtures is describable in terms of the same T_F as deduced from specific-heat measurements.

The Illinois group has measured the spin-diffusion coefficient ([105]) and the thermal conductivity ([71]), also for $x = 0.013$ and 0.05 as well as for pure He³. The results are shown, respectively, in Figs. 6.20 and 6.21. For the mixture, D obeys the T^{-2} law below about 0.030°K, whereas the T^{-1} region for λ is not reached until about 0.007°K. For

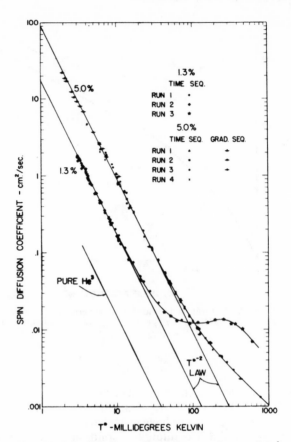

Fig. 6.20. Spin-diffusion coefficient for two mixtures of He^3
in He^4 (x = 0.013 and 0.05) compared with D of pure He^3
[from Anderson et al. (^{105})].

the mixtures, we see that λ passes through a minimum at considerably
lower temperatures than for pure liquid He^3. This has been interpreted as arising from a competition between the T^{-1} He^3 quasiparticle conductivity and a He^4 phonon conductivity.

Abraham et al. (^{109}) have observed the attenuation of sound for
frequencies of 20, 60, 100, and 140 Mc/sec and for T as low as 0.04°K
in a 5%·He^3 solution. Above 0.4°K, the results are similar to those for
pure He^4 (see Section 8.4.2b), α_1 rising to a maximum near T_λ, then
falling rapidly to a minimum near 2°K, but rising again to a second
maximum near 0.9°K, and finally decreasing. However, at lower temperatures, Abraham et al. found a third maximum not characteristic of

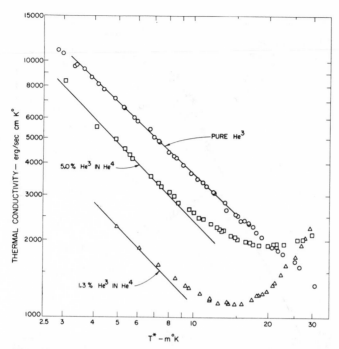

Fig. 6.21. Thermal conductivity of two mixtures of He³ in He⁴ ($x = 0.013$ and 0.05) compared with λ of pure He³ [from Abel et al.[71]].

the pure liquid. This extra attenuation in the mixture has been considered by them to arise from the direct interaction of the He³ with acoustic phonons as a consequence of the impurity excitation spectrum, equation (6.63). On the high-temperature side of the maximum, α_1 was found to vary with ω, whereas on the low side, it appears to become independent of frequency, decreasing something like $T^{2.3}$ to $T^{2.6}$. While this behavior is reminiscent of a transition to zero sound, the propagation velocity of the sound remained essentially constant at the value characteristic for pure liquid He⁴. Theoretical analyses of the sound attenuation have been given by Eckstein [110] and more recently by Baym [111], both arriving at an expression for α_1 with the form

$$\alpha_1 = A\omega^2\tau/(1 + \omega^2\tau^2) \qquad (6.67)$$

where τ is the time between He³ quasiparticle collisions and A is a constant involving the Fermi liquid parameters F_0, F_1, m^*, and v_F as well as other properties of the liquid. When $\omega\tau \gg 1$—as is the case for the experiments below $\sim 0.3°$K—equation (6.67) tells us that α_1

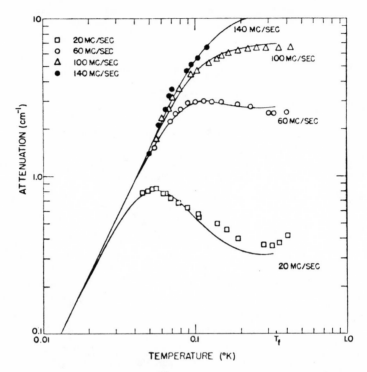

Fig. 6.22. Attenuation of first sound in a dilute solution of
He^3 in He^4 ($x = 0.05$). Solid curves are calculations (^{111})
and data points are from Abraham *et al.* (^{109}) [from Baym
and Ebner (^{111})].

should be independent of frequency and proportional to T^2. While
similar methods were used by both authors, Baym's derivation as
reported by Baym and Ebner (^{111}) contains refinements which lead to a
considerably better—and quite impressive—fit to the experimental
data, as shown in Fig. 6.22. The authors suggest that this consistency
establishes the correctness of the absolute normalization of the attenuation measurements. Eckstein has also derived the condition for the
existence of a zero-sound mode in mixtures, indicating that the effects
of the He^3–He^4 interactions place additional restrictions on the
occurrence of this mode as compared with the situation for pure He^3.

The inescapable conclusion from the empirical results is that
whereas in pure He^3, the quasiparticle interactions are strong, in dilute
He^3 solutions, the effective He^3–He^3 interactions must be exceedingly

weak. The exact nature of these interactions dictates the conditions for the possible transition to a superfluid state—or one of fermion "supermobility," as coined by Cohen and van Leeuwen. Thus, such a state would be one in which separate BE and FD superfluid systems coexist. the latter occurring through angular momentum state pairing of fermions. In their 1961 paper ([95]), these authors investigated the comparative strengths of the hard-sphere repulsive forces and of the attractive interaction between two He³ atoms arising from their exchange with He⁴ phonons. They considered that statistics and the actual mass ratio were crucial to the existence of a state of supermobility. The net attraction was found to be exceedingly weak, indicating that the transition temperature, T_c, should be so low as to preclude its experimental discovery.

Because of the near-cancellation of the opposing forces, the microscopic calculation of T_c is obviously very difficult, and as yet, only limited headway has been made in our understanding of dilute He³ solutions from this viewpoint—see, for example, Emery ([112]) and Massey and Woo ([113]).

On the other hand, Bardeen, Baym, and Pines (BBP) ([114]) have constructed an empirical interaction potential, V_k, the Fourier transform of $V(r)$, which is weakly attractive and depends upon the relative quasiparticle momentum $\mathbf{k}$. The spatial average $V(r)$, designated V_0, has been derived from the slope of the $[E_3(x) - L_3^0]/k_B$ vs. x curve shown in Fig. 6.19, while the momentum dependence has been determined from the spin diffusion measurements of Anderson et al. ([105]). The effective overall potential becomes

$$V_k = -|V_0| \cos(\beta k/\hbar) \qquad (6.68)$$

with

$$|V_0| = 0.075 \, m_4 u_1^2/n_4 \qquad (6.69)$$

and $\beta = 3.16$ Å ; u_1 is the sound velocity in pure He⁴ and n_4 is the number density of pure He⁴. Using this potential (see Fig. 6.23), BBP concluded that the transition to a supermobile fermion state is quite sensitive to x and that the most favorable concentration for the existence of such a state is $x = 0.016$, with $T_c \approx 2.2 \times 10^{-6}$ °K and $l = 0$ angular momentum pairing. In addition, increasing the pressure on the system would reduce T_c. While V_k is admittedly somewhat crude, BBP have argued that a substantial increase in T_c, even from an improved potential, is precluded by the extremely small scattering probability of quasiparticles with antiparallel spins—these are the processes which determine D and hence V_k also.

In discussing the interaction potential, BBP have pointed out two additional facets of the dilute mixtures. The first is that the attenuation

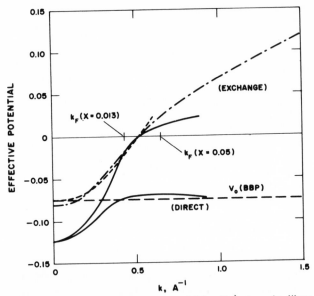

Fig. 6.23. Effective interaction potential for He^3 atoms in dilute solutions of He^3 in He^4 as a function of wave number $\mathbf{k} = \mathbf{p}/\hbar$; dashed curves BBP ([114]); dotted-dashed curve, Ebner ([115]); solid curves, Campbell ([118]). Ordinate has units of $m_4 u_1^2/n_4$ [see equations (6.68) and (6.69)]. In each pair of curves, the upper one represents the exchange interaction, the lower one the direct interaction.

of zero sound in the fermion component should be so strong as to prevent experimental detection of this mode [equation (6.28) requires $(F_0 + F_1) > 0$ for the propagation of zero sound, whereas for the solutions, $(F_0 + F_1) < 0$, as calculated from $V_\mathbf{k}$ ([86])]. The second point is that the most important physical property of the system contributing to the net He^3–He^3 interaction is the increase in molar volume accompanying the replacement of a He^4 atom by a He^3 atom in the solution— and this is the source of the numerical constant in equation (6.69).

Because in dilute solutions, He^3 behaves like a weakly interacting quasiparticle gas, the formalism developed for He^3 gas in Chapter 3 has been in several instances successfully applied to the solutions. Ebner ([115]) has extended the momentum range of the BBP potential using the classical gas expression for D [equation (3.73) with $\Omega^{(1,1)}$ defined by equation (3.67) and with $\mu = m^*/2$] together with the empirical spin-diffusion results for solutions. The nature of these refinements to $V_\mathbf{k}$ compared with the original BBP curve is shown in Fig. 6.23.

For dilute solutions, where two-body He^3 interactions are predominant, Emery ([116]) has shown how the collision probabilities

$W(\theta, \phi)$ appearing in the transport equations (6.20), (6.22), and (6.24) may be expressed in terms of the phase shifts. Emery[117] approximated the effective potential by a repulsive hard core with a square-well attraction. The interaction strength was determined from experimental D values. Using this potential, he has calculated the phase shifts and obtained estimates for the transport and other properties of dilute solutions. Further, he has found that the effect on the potential due to the presence of He⁴ is attractive at short range and repulsive at long range (> 2.6 Å). Since the total He³–He³ interaction is attractive for small momenta, it seems likely that a superfluid fermion phase exists for dilute solutions. Although T_c is again estimated to be of the order 10^{-6} °K, Emery[117] has argued that the experimental data for D already obtained at higher temperatures gives solid evidence that the transition must occur.

In another study using the gas formalism, Campbell[118] has deduced the He³–He³ potential beginning with the LJ-1 potential modified to take into account the expanded volume occupied by the He³ atom in solution. This theory has only one phenomenological parameter, the effective mass of the He⁴ atom, so that it is very nearly a first-principles theory. Phase shifts calculated from the potential were used to calculate the direct and the exchange part of the Landau Fermi-liquid function $f(\mathbf{p}, \boldsymbol{\sigma} ; \mathbf{p}', \boldsymbol{\sigma}')$ and thus also $W(\theta, \phi)$ (in the BBP theory, V_0 is the direct part, a constant, and V_k the exchange part). Campbell's effective potential also appears in Fig. 6.23.

All of the above-mentioned theoretical assaults on the effective He³ potential in dilute solutions give qualitatively similar results for representing the experiments. All agree quite well in predicting the maximum solubility at 0°K of $x \approx 0.06$, in accord with the value inferred from measurements[119]. The observed susceptibility is also well reproduced. Since BBP and Emery use the experimentally determined diffusion coefficient to obtain V_k, it is not surprising that their work leads to reasonable values for D; but Campbell's work, which does not use D for input, also gives good predictions for this quantity. On the other hand, the BBP potential is especially poor for estimating the thermal conductivity. This is understandable in part, since the functional form of the potential (similar to the Born approximation) limits the distinctions which must be made between $W(\theta, \phi)$ for D and for the other transport coefficients (D depends upon the scattering of antiparallel spins only, but all spin orientations contribute to λ and η). The works of both Emery and Campbell do not suffer this deficiency, but their estimates for λ for $x = 0.05$ are nevertheless still about a factor of two larger than the experimental values. This situation remains to be resolved. As yet, data for η are not available.

6.3. PARAMETERS OF He³ AS A FERMI LIQUID

By now, the tremendous power of Landau's ideas about He³ as a Fermi liquid is quite apparent. While some questions remain about the behavior of the specific heat at very low temperatures, about the expected transition to a superfluid phase, and about the precise limiting values of some of the transport properties, sufficient data have been accumulated to provide a fairly quantitative description of the pure liquid in terms of the phenomenological parameters of the Fermi liquid theory. By way of summary, we collect here some of the more important and better established numerical values presently assigned to these parameters and to other properties of the liquid. In the main, these numbers have been culled from the publications of the Illinois group, especially references [4], [105], and [114]. Following the arbitrary choice of these authors, data are presented for the pure liquid at two pressures, 0.28 atm and 27 atm. Also given are their results for two dilute solutions of He³ and He⁴ which exhibit Fermi liquid behavior deviating but slightly from that of the ideal gas. Calculated values of the solution transport properties are due to Emery [117]. In all cases, the values reported are for temperatures sufficiently low to allow the theory to be applicable. No estimates of error are given. Much current work, especially the experimental determination of the transport coefficients, is being directed toward better establishing these parameters; it is hoped that by the time this monograph is distributed some of the numbers listed here will be considerably improved and others will be emphatically confirmed.

Table 6.IV. Calculated Parameters for He³ as a Fermi Liquid

	Pure He³ $P = 0.28$ atm	Pure He³ $P = 27$ atm	1.3% He³ in He⁴	5.0% He³ in He⁴
m^*/m	3.08	5.78	2.38	2.46
$p_F/\hbar$ (10^7 cm^{-1})	7.88	8.77	2.04	3.17
$v_F \equiv p_F/m^*$ (10^3 cm/sec)	5.38	3.19	1.80	2.71
$-\dfrac{1}{\Omega}\left(\dfrac{\partial P}{\partial \epsilon}\right)_\mu$ (10^{-38} erg-cm³)$^{-1}$	1.11	2.31	—	—
$T_F \equiv p^2{}_F/2m^*k_B$ (°K)	1.62		0.141	0.331
F_0	10.77	75.63	—	—
F_1	6.25	14.35	$\langle F_1(5.0\%) - F_1(1.3\%)\rangle$ $= 0.11$	
$G_0 = Z_0/4$	-0.665	-0.723	0.090	0.048

Table 6.IV presents some of the parameters of the Fermi liquid calculated to be consistent with the known experimental properties of liquid He³ ; Table 6.V gives some experimental and derived quantities.

Table 6.V. Experimental Parameters for Liquid He³ in the Limit of $T = 0°K$ ^{a}

	Pure He³ $P = 0.28$ atm	Pure He³ $P = 27$ atm	1.3% He³ in He⁴	5.0% He³ in He⁴
ρ (10^{-2} g/cm³)	8.628	11.39	—	—
C/RT (°K^{-1})	3.05	4.62	0.47	0.74
$T^* = \frac{2}{3} T_F^{**}$ (°K)	0.361	0.197	$\frac{2}{3} T_F$	$\frac{2}{3} T_F$
u_1 (m/sec)	182.6	388.0	$(183.1)^b$	$(184.7)^b$
u_0 (m/sec)	193.6 (194)	— (390)	—	—
ηT^2 (10^{-6} P-°K²)	2.8 (2.31)	— (0.654)	—	—
λT(erg/cm-sec)	50 (79.7)	— (19.6)	— (19.1)	— (64)
$D T^2$ (10^{-6} cm²-°K²/sec)	1.52 (5.38)	0.20 (0.644)	17 (17.2)	90 (90)
$\tau_D T^2$(10^{-13} sec-°K²)	[4.7]	[2.1]	[146]	[340]
$\tau_\eta T^2$(10^{-12} sec-°K²)	[1.9]	—	(17)	(22)
$\tau_\lambda T^2$(10^{-13} sec-°K²)	[7.5]	—	—	—
χ_{ideal}/χ	— —	— —	1.09 (1.09)	1.08 (1.048)

^{a} Numbers in parentheses have been calculated from theory; numbers in square brackets have been derived from experiment using the appropriate Fermi liquid parameters.
^{b} Calculated from equation (8) of Baym (^{111}): $u/u_x = 1 - 0.23x$.

REFERENCES

1. A. A. Abrikosov and I. M. Khalatnikov, in: *Reports on Progress in Physics* (The Phys. Soc. London) **22**, 329 (1959).
2. A. M. Sessler, in *Liquid Helium* (G. Careri, ed.), p. 188, Academic Press, New York (1963).
3. D. Pines and P. Nozières, *The Theory of Quantum Liquids*, Vol. I, Benjamin, New York (1966).
4. J. C. Wheatley, in *Quantum Fluids* (D. F. Brewer, ed.), p. 183, North Holland, Amsterdam (1966).
5. L. D. Landau, *Zh. Eksperim. i Teor. Fiz.*, **30**, 1058 (1956) [English translation, *Soviet Phys.—JETP*, **3**, 920 (1957)].

6. R. Balian and C. de Dominicis, *Nucl. Phys.*, **16**, 502 (1960); C. de Dominicis, *Physica*, **26**, 594 (1960).
7. P. M. Richards, *Phys. Rev.*, **132**, 1867 (1963).
8. D. Hone, *Phys. Rev.*, **121**, 669 (1961) [Errata, *Phys. Rev.*, **121**, 1864 (1961).]
9. L. D. Landau, *Zh. Eksperim. i Teor. Fiz.*, **32**, 59 (1957) [English translation, *Soviet Phys.—JEPT*, **5**, 101 (1957)].
10. N. D. Mermin, *Phys. Rev.*, **159**, 161 (1967).
11. K. A. Brueckner and J. L. Gammel, *Phys. Rev.*, **109**, 1040 (1958).
12. C. W. Woo, *Phys. Rev.*, **151**, 138 (1966).
13. F. Y. Wu and E. Feenberg, *Phys. Rev.*, **128**, 943 (1962); E. Feenberg and C. W. Woo, *Phys. Rev.*, **137**, A391 (1965).
14. W. E. Massey, *Phys. Rev.*, **151**, 153 (1966).
15. D. E. Beck and A. M. Sessler, *Phys. Rev.*, **146**, 161 (1966).
16. V. M. Galitskii and A. B. Migdal, **34**, 139 (1958) [English translation, *Soviet Phys.—JETP*, **7**, 96 (1958)]; J. M. Luttinger and J. C. Ward, *Phys. Rev.*, **118**, 1417 (1960).
17. A. M. Sessler, in *Low Temperature Physics, LT8* (R. O. Davies, ed.), p. 11, Butterworths, Washington (1963).
18. D. J. Thouless, *Ann. Phys. (N.Y.)*, **10**, 553 (1960).
19. A. M. Sessler, in *Helium Three* (J. G. Daunt, ed.), p. 81, Ohio State University Press (1960).
20. R. H. Romer, in *Low Temperature Physics, LT8* (R. O. Davies, ed.), p. 17, Butterworths, Washington (1963).
21. J. E. Opfer, K. Luszczynski, and R. E. Norberg, in *Low Temperature Physics, LT9* (Daunt, Edwards, Milford, and Yaqub, eds.), p. 143, Plenum Press, New York (1965); *Phys. Rev.*, **140**, A100 (1965).
22. A. C. Anderson, W. Reese, and J. C. Wheatley, *Phys. Rev.*, **127**, 671 (1962).
23. A. L. Thomson, H. Meyer, and E. D. Adams, *Phys. Rev.*, **128**, 509 (1962).
24. B. T. Beal and J. Hatton, *Phys. Rev.*, **139**, A1751 (1965).
25. W. R. Abel, A. C. Anderson, W. C. Black, and J. C. Wheatley, *Physics*, **1**, 337 (1965).
26. H. A. Schwettman and H. E. Rorschach, Jr., *Phys. Rev.*, **144**, 133 (1966).
27. E. L. Hahn, *Phys. Rev.*, **80**, 580 (1950); Physics Today, Vol. 6, No. 11, p. 4 (1953).
28. L. Goldstein, *Phys. Rev.*, **133**, A52 (1964).
29. G. De Vries and J. G. Daunt, *Phys. Rev.*, **92**, 1572 (1953); **93**, 631 (1954).
30. T. R. Roberts and S. G. Sydoriak, *Phys. Rev.*, **93**, 1418 (1954); **98**, 1672 (1955).
31. B. M. Abraham, D. W. Osborne, and B. Weinstock, *Phys. Rev.*, **98**, 551 (1955).
32. L. Goldstein, *Phys. Rev.*, **96**, 1455 (1954); **102**, 1205 (1956); **112**, 1465 (1958); **117**, 375 (1960).
33. D. F. Brewer, A. K. Sreedhar, H. C. Kramers, and J. G. Daunt, *Phys. Rev.*, **110**, 282 (1958).
34. D. F. Brewer, J. G. Daunt, and A. K. Sreedhar, *Phys. Rev.*, **115**, 836 (1959).
35. D. F. Brewer and J. G. Daunt, *Phys. Rev.*, **115**, 843 (1959).
36. M. Strongin, G. O. Zimmerman, and H. A. Fairbank, *Phys. Rev. Letters*, **6**, 404 (1961); in *Low Temperature Physics, LT8* (R. O. Davies, ed.), p. 29, Butterworths, Washington (1963).
37. A. C. Anderson, G. L. Salinger, W. A. Steyert, and J. C. Wheatley, *Phys. Rev. Letters*, **6**, 331 (1961).
38. A. C. Anderson, G. L. Salinger, W. A. Steyert, and J. C. Wheatley, *Phys. Rev. Letters*, **7**, 295 (1961).
39. D. F. Brewer and J. R. G. Keyston, *Nature*, **191**, 1261 (1961); in *Low Temperature Physics, LT8* (R. O. Davies, ed.), p. 27, Butterworths, Washington (1963).
40. A. C. Anderson, W. Reese, and J. C. Wheatley, *Phys. Rev.*, **130**, 495 (1963).
41. T. Soda and R. Vasudevan, *Phys. Rev.*, **125**, 1484 (1962).

42. A. J. Leggett, *Phys. Rev. Letters*, **16**, 273 (1965).
43. K. A. Brueckner, T. Soda, P. W. Anderson, and P. Morel, *Phys. Rev.*, **118**, 1442 (1960).
44. V. J. Emery and A. M. Sessler, *Phys. Rev.*, **119**, 43 (1960).
45. L. P. Gor'kov and L. P. Pitaevskii, *Zh. Eksperim. i Teor. Fiz.*, **42**, 600 (1962) [English translation, *Soviet Phys.—JETP*, **15**, 417 (1962)].
46. V. P. Peshkov, *Zh. Eksperim. i Teor. Fiz.*, **46**, 1510 (1964); **48**, 997 (1965) [English translation, *Soviet Phys.—JETP*, **19**, 1023 (1964); **21**, 663 (1965)].
47. W. R. Abel, A. C. Anderson, W. C. Black, and J. C. Wheatley, *Phys. Rev.*, **147**, 111 (1966).
48. W. R. Abel, A. C. Anderson, W. C. Black, and J. C. Wheatley, *Phys. Rev. Letters*, **16**, 273 (1966).
49. P. W. Anderson, *Physics*, **2**, 1 (1965).
50. R. Balian and D. R. Fredkin, *Phys. Rev. Letters*, **15**, 480 (1965).
51. L. P. Pitaevskii, *Usp. Fiz. Nauk*, **88**, 409 (1966) [English translation, *Soviet Phys.—Usp.*, **9**, 191 (1966)].
52. L. Goldstein, *Phys. Rev.*, **148**, 108 (1966).
53. D. A. Kirzhnitz and Yu. A. Nepomnyashchii. *Zh. Eksperim. i Teor. Fiz. Pis'ma*, **4**, 86 (1966) [English translation, *JETP Letters*, **4**, 58 (1966)].
54. N. F. Berk and J. R. Schrieffer, *Phys. Rev. Letters*, **17**, 433 (1966).
55. S. Doniach and S. Engelsberg, *Phys. Rev. Letters*, **17**, 750 (1966); also see D. J. Amit, J. W. Kane, and H. Wagner, *Phys. Rev. Letters*, **19**, 425 (1967).
56. B. Weinstock, D. W. Osborne, and B. M. Abraham, *Phys. Rev.*, **75**, 988 (1949); Conference on Very Low Temperatures, Massachusetts Institute of Technology, 1949 (unpublished); R. D. Taylor and J. G. Dash, *Phys. Rev.*, **106**, 398 (1957); K. N. Zinov'eva, *Zh. Eksperim. i Teor. Fiz.*, **34**, 609 (1958) [English translation, *Soviet Phys.—JETP*, **7**, 421 (1958)].
57. W. R. Abel, A. C. Anderson, and J. C. Wheatley, *Phys. Rev. Letters*, **7**, 299 (1962).
58. D. S. Betts, D. W. Osborne, B. Welber, and J. Wilks, *Phil. Mag.*, **8**, 977 (1963).
59. D. S. Betts and J. Wilks, in *Low Temperature Physics, LT9* (J. G. Daunt, D. O. Edwards, F. J. Milford, and M. Yaqub, eds.), p. 129, Plenum Press, New York (1965).
60. D. Hone, *Phys. Rev.*, **125**, 1494 (1962).
61. I. M. Khalatnikov, *Zh. Eksperim. i Teor. Fiz.*, **22**, 687 (1952).
62. D. M. Lee and H. A. Fairbank, *Phys. Rev.*, **116**, 1359 (1959).
63. H. A. Fairbank and J. Wilks, *Proc. Roy. Soc. (London)*, **231A**, 545 (1955).
64. I. L. Bekarevich and I. M. Khalatnikov, *Zh. Eksperim. i Teor. Fiz.*, **39**, 1699 (1960) [English translation, *Soviet Phys.—JETP*, **12**, 1187 (1961)].
65. J. Gavoret, *Phys. Rev.*, **137**, A721 (1965).
66. A. C. Anderson, J. I. Connolly, and J. C. Wheatley, *Phys. Rev.*, **135**, A910 (1964).
67. L. J. Challis and J. Wilks, *Proceedings of the Symposium on Solid and Liquid He*, p. 38, Ohio State University Research Foundation, Columbus (1957).
68. A. C. Anderson, G. L. Salinger, and J. C. Wheatley, *Phys. Rev. Letters*, **6**, 443 (1961).
69. A. C. Anderson, J. I. Connolly, O. E. Vilches, and J. C. Wheatley, *Phys. Rev.*, **147**, 86 (1966).
70. J. F. Kerrisk and W. E. Keller (to be published); J. F. Kerrisk, Thesis, U. of N.M., 1968.
71. W. R. Abel, R. T. Johnson, J. C. Wheatley, and W. Zimmermann, Jr., *Phys. Rev. Letters*, **18**, 737 (1967).
72. M. J. Rice, *Phys. Rev.*, **159**, 153 (1967); **162**, 189 (1967). Erratum, **163**, 206 (1967); see also J. C. Wheatley, *Phys. Rev.*, **165**, 304 (1968); D. S. Betts and M. J. Rice, *Phys. Rev.*, **166**, 159 (1968).
73. H. Y. Carr and E. M. Purcell, *Phys. Rev.*, **94**, 630 (1954).
74. N. Bloembergen, E. M. Purcell, and R. V. Pound, *Phys. Rev.*, **73**, 679 (1948).

75. E. R. Grilly and E. F. Hammel, in *Progress in Low Temperature Physics* (C. J. Gorter, ed.), Vol. III, p. 113, North Holland, Amsterdam (1961).
76. R. L. Garwin and H. A. Reich, *Phys. Rev.*, **115**, 1478 (1959).
77. H. R. Hart, Jr., and J. C. Wheatley, *Phys. Rev. Letters*, **4**, 3 (1960).
78. A. C. Anderson, H. R. Hart, Jr., and J. C. Wheatley, *Phys. Rev. Letters*, **5**, 133 (1960).
79. A. C. Anderson, W. Reese, R. J. Sarwinski, and J. C. Wheatley, *Phys. Rev. Letters*, **7**, 220 (1961).
80. H. L. Laquer, S. G. Sydoriak, and T. R. Roberts, *Phys. Rev.*, **113**, 417 (1959).
81. K. R. Atkins and H. Flicker, *Phys. Rev.*, **113**, 959 (1959); *Phys. Rev.*, **116**, 1063 (1959).
82. B. E. Keen, P. W. Mathews, and J. Wilks, *Physics Letters*, **5**, 5 (1963); *Proc. Roy. Soc.*, **A284**, 125 (1965).
83. G. A. Brooker, *Physics Letters*, **13**, 224 (1964); Thesis, Oxford (1964).
84. B. E. Keen and J. Wilks, in *Low Temperature Physics, LT9* (J. G. Daunt, D. O. Edwards, F. J. Milford, and M. Yaqub, eds.), p. 125, Plenum Press, New York (1965); also see D. S. Betts, B. E. Keen, and J. Wilks, *Proc. Roy. Soc. (London)*, **A289**, 34 (1966).
85. I. J. Kirby and J. Wilks, *Physics Letters*, **24A**, 60 (1967).
86. W. R. Abel, A. C. Anderson, and J. C. Wheatley, *Phys. Rev. Letters*, **17**, 74 (1966).
87. N. P. Shah, Thesis, Stanford University (1966); *Phys. Rev. Letters* **20**, 1026 (1968).
88. A. A. Abrikosov and I. M. Khalatnikov, *Zh. Eksperim. i Teor. Fiz.*, **41**, 544 (1961) [English translation, *Soviet Phys.—JETP*, **14**, 389 (1962)].
89. D. Pines, in *Quantum Fluids* (D. F. Brewer, ed.), p. 257, North Holland, Amsterdam (1966).
90. H. S. Sommers, *Phys. Rev.*, **88**, 113 (1952).
91. H. S. Sommers, W. E. Keller, and J. G. Dash, *Phys. Rev.*, **92**, 1345 (1953).
92. G. K. Walters and W. M. Fairbank, *Phys. Rev.*, **103**, 262 (1956).
93. I. Prigogine, R. Bingen, and A. Bellemans, *Physica*, **20**, 633 (1954).
94. G. E. Uhlenbeck, *Physics Today*, **13**, 16 (1960).
95. E. G. D. Cohen and J. M. J. van Leeuwen, *Physica*, **26**, 1171 (1960); **27**, 1157 (1961).
96. L. D. Landau and I. Pomeranchuk, *Dokl. Akad. Nauk SSSR*, **59**, 669 (1948); I. Pomeranchuk, *Zh. Eksperim. i Teor. Fiz.*, **19**, 42 (1949).
97. V. N. Zharkov and V. P. Silin, *Zh. Eksperim. i Teor. Fiz.*, **37**, 143 (1959) [English translation, *Soviet Phys.—JETP*, **10**, 102 (1960)].
98. R. De Bruyn Ouboter, K. W. Taconis, C. Le Pair, and J. J. M. Beenakker, *Physica*, **26**, 853 (1960).
99. J. C. King and H. A. Fairbank, *Phys. Rev.*, **93**, 21 (1954); D. J. Sandiford and H. A. Fairbank, *Phys. Rev.*, **162**, 192 (1967).
100. J. G. Dash and R. D. Taylor, *Phys. Rev.*, **107**, 1228 (1957).
101. D. O. Edwards and J. G. Daunt, *Phys. Rev.*, **124**, 640 (1961).
102. D. O. Edwards, D. F. Brewer, P. Seligman, M. Skertic, and M. Yaqub, *Phys. Rev. Letters*, **15**, 773 (1965).
103. E. C. Kerr, in *Proceedings of the Fifth International Conference on Low Temperature Physics* (J. R. Dillinger, ed.), p. 158, University of Wisconsin Press (1958).
104. A. C. Anderson, W. R. Roach, R. J. Sarwinski, and J. C. Wheatley, *Phys. Rev. Letters*, **16**, 263 (1966).
105. A. C. Anderson, D. O. Edwards, W. R. Roach, R. J. Sarwinski, and J. C. Wheatley, *Phys. Rev. Letters*, **17**, 367 (1966).
106. E. H. Graf, D. M. Lee, and J. D. Reppy, *Phys. Rev. Letters*, **19**, 417 (1967).
107. T. R. Roberts and S. G. Sydoriak, *Phys. Fluids*, **3**, 6 (1960).
108. D. L. Husa, D. O. Edwards, and J. R. Gaines, *Physics Letters*, **21**, 28 (1966).
109. B. M. Abraham, Y. Eckstein, J. B. Ketterson, and J. H. Vignos, *Phys. Rev. Letters*, **17**, 1254 (1966).

110. S. G. Eckstein, *Phys. Rev. Letters*, **17**, 1257 (1966).

111. G. Baym, *Phys. Rev. Letters*, **18**, 71 (1967); G. Baym and C. Ebner, *Phys. Rev.*, **164**, 235 (1967).

112. V. J. Emery, *Phys. Rev.*, **148**, 138 (1966).

113. W. E. Massey and C. W. Woo, *Phys. Rev. Letters*, **19**, 301 (1967).

114. J. Bardeen, G. Baym, and D. Pines, *Phys. Rev. Letters*, **17**, 372 (1966); *Phys. Rev.*, **156**, 207 (1967).

115. C. Ebner, *Phys. Rev.*, **156**, 222 (1967).

116. V. J. Emery, *Nucl. Phys.*, **19**, 154 (1960); *Ann. Phys. (N.Y.)*, **28**, 1 (1964).

117. V. J. Emery, *Phys. Rev.*, **161**, 194 (1967).

118. L. J. Campbell, *Phys. Rev. Letters*, **19**, 156 (1967).

119. E. M. Ifft, D. O. Edwards, R. J. Sarwinski, and M. M. Skertic, *Phys. Rev. Letters*, **19**, 831 (1967).

Chapter 7

Critical Phenomena in He^3 and He^4

Nearly one hundred years ago, T. Andrews deduced that for every gas, there should be a "critical temperature" above which the gas cannot be liquefied no matter how much it might be compressed. Further studies revealed that the critical temperature was one coordinate of a point on the P–V–T surface where differences between the intensive properties of the liquid and of the gas disappear (the P–V–T properties near the critical point are schematically diagrammed in Fig. 7.1). Since the time of Andrews, a tremendous body of literature has accumulated on the subject of critical-point phenomena, but progress in characterizing the critical point has been difficult because this point, much like the absolute zero of temperature, is approachable but not attainable.

Interest in critical phenomena has recently heightened as a result of the convergence of three rather widely-spaced findings. The first of these has come from the celebrated 1944 paper of Onsager ([1]), in which the properties of the two-dimensional Ising lattice were calculated rigorously and exactly—truly a prodigious accomplishment. The model for the Ising lattice places on each site an atom in one of two states—spin up or spin down—with interactions occurring only between neighboring pairs of atoms and depending only upon whether the spins are parallel or antiparallel. Originally, this arrangement was proposed ([2]) as a crude representation for ferromagnetism; but it has subsequently been shown by Yang and Lee ([3]) to be formally equivalent to a "lattice gas" interacting via a finite-ranged potential. Onsager's work provided proof of the existence of a critical temperature T_c for the two-dimensional Ising lattice and, in addition, demonstrated that the heat capacity as T_c is approached from either lower or higher temperatures becomes infinite logarithmically, i.e., $C \sim \log|T - T_c|$. The corresponding results for the lattice gas indicate that this same singular behavior appears as T_c is approached along the critical isochore.

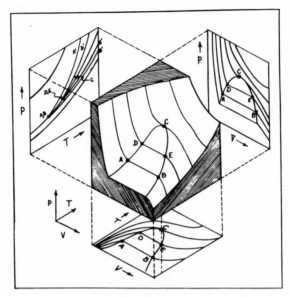

Fig. 7.1. *P–V–T* properties of a one-component system near the liquid–vapor critical region; C is the critical point. Projection on the *P–T* plane shows typical isochores; on the *P–V* plane, isotherms; and on the *T–V* plane, isobars. Curve ADCEB is the coexistence curve [drawn from Fig. 5.2-1 of Hirschfelder *et al.*, ref. ([1]) of Chapter 3].

Thus these conclusions for the heat capacity contradicted the traditional notions, which were that C_P should become infinite at T_c, but C_V should remain finite and exhibit a finite discontinuity. However, since the model for the calculations was two-dimensional and the three-dimensional case could not be solved—and has not yet been exactly solved—there was initially not much concern that the "rules" for real systems were in jeopardy. This was true until the second and third of the significant observations referred to above came to light. In 1957, Fairbank *et al.* ([4]) reported a logarithmic singularity in the heat capacity of liquid He^4 when measured along the saturated vapor pressure curve (C_{sat}) to within 10^{-6} deg of the λ-transition. Then, somewhat later, careful determinations of C_V for argon ([5]) and oxygen ([6]) in the vicinity of liquid-vapor critical points also suggested the logarithmic behavior.

It is not surprising that following these events stock in the Ising lattice model has risen dramatically along with interest in the entire subject of critical points. Not only have the classical concepts about

C_V been attacked by the emergence of this model, but several other rather revolutionary ramifications have been suggested by it. First of all, the applicability of the model to real systems raises the likelihood that all critical phenomena, including liquid–vapor critical points, λ-transitions, ferromagnetic transitions at the Curie point—in fact, all the so-called cooperative or order–disorder transitions—have fundamental common origins. This universality suggests, as for the Ising model, that the short-range forces play a significantly greater role near T_c than previously suspected ([7, 8]) and furthermore, that the detailed nature of these forces is not very important.

Despite the enthusiasm generated by the above viewpoint, we should be cautioned by the recognition that it is still based upon a relatively small amount of experimental data. In particular, the notion that C_V should retain the logarithmic character right up to T_c involves a bold extrapolation; we must therefore consider this conclusion to be tenuous. The entire subject urgently demands further investigation.

The singular points exhibited by the helium isotopes offer outstanding opportunities for studying critical phenomena; accordingly, contributions to this subject are appearing in increasing numbers in the current literature. In our attempts to summarize the trends of these investigations, it would be useful to keep in mind the cogent questions asked by M. S. Green ([9]) in his introduction to the Proceedings of the Conference on Critical Phenomena held in 1965. An edited selection follows:

What is the nature of the singularities associated with critical phenomena?

What role do quantum effects play in these?

Which if any transport properties are anomalous in the critical region?

Do all critical systems display a logarithmically singular specific heat?

Are all critical phenomena truly analogous?

If so, what is the common underlying cause for the analogous behavior?

Many avenues have been explored in approaching these questions. In the next section, we shall briefly review several which have proved most rewarding for interpreting the experimental results for helium. Following this, we discuss the observed behavior of He³ and He⁴ in the liquid–vapor coexistence region and then finally the properties near the λ-transition between He I and He II. Other critical regions may occur in the helium isotopes, namely the predicted cooperative transition in liquid He³, the consolute points for liquid He³–He⁴ mixtures as a function of pressure, and the liquid–vapor coexistence regions for He^3–He^4 mixtures as a function of concentration. Since experimental data for these situations are at best sparse, they will not be considered here.

7.1. THERMODYNAMIC CHARACTERIZATION OF THE CRITICAL POINT

7.1.1. The Ehrenfest Classification of Transitions

Although the Ehrenfest classification of higher order phase transitions is now known to describe accurately only a very few real systems, the terminology it generated still persists and its thermodynamic basis is rigorously correct. In this latter regard, Ehrenfest considered the behavior of the Gibbs free energy, $G = H - TS$, to be crucial in determining the character of a phase transition, and the transition is said to have an "order" corresponding to the lowest order derivative of G with respect to P or T that becomes discontinuous at the transition. Hence, a first-order phase transition is accompanied by a latent heat as well as finite volume and entropy changes, effects which are completely described by the Clapeyron equation. On the other hand, for second-order transitions, V and S are both continuous and there is no latent heat, but there are jumps in C_P, α_P (isobaric expansion coefficient), and β_T (isothermal compressibility). Thus, for a second-order phase change between phases 1 and 2, Ehrenfest wrote the analog of Clapeyron's equation as

$$\frac{dP}{dT} = -\frac{[\partial S(2)/\partial T]_P - [\partial S(1)/\partial T]_P}{[\partial S(2)/\partial P]_T - [\partial S(1)/\partial P]_T} = -\frac{[\partial V(2)/\partial T]_P - [\partial V(1)/\partial T]_P}{[\partial V(2)/\partial P]_T - [\partial V(1)/\partial P]_T}$$

$$= \frac{1}{VT}\frac{C_P(2) - C_P(1)}{\alpha_P(2) - \alpha_P(1)} = \frac{\alpha_P(2) - \alpha_P(1)}{\beta_T(2) - \beta_T(1)} \tag{7.1}$$

The Ehrenfest scheme may be continued to arbitrarily high orders by taking further derivatives of equation (7.1), but the distinctions between various orders become successively more subtle and less practical for identification purposes.

Whereas the condensation of an ideal BE gas proceeds as a first-order phase change, the real Bose fluid, liquid He^4, displays no latent heat at the λ-point; furthermore, both V and S are continuous at T_λ. The λ-transition can therefore be considered as at least of second order.

7.1.2. The Pippard Relations

In his thoughtful—and delightful—monograph on classical thermodynamics, Pippard ([10]) has categorized a number of variations in the behavior of C_P according to the Ehrenfest scheme for first-, second-, and third-order transitions. For two of these variations, one of second-order and the other of third, he has pointed out that the Ehrenfest relations for dP/dT [cf. equation (7.1)] generate indeterminate ratios of the form ∞/∞. The shapes of the two types of heat capacities in question are very similar to that observed for λ-transitions, suggesting that the Ehrenfest classification is ambiguous concerning the transition in liquid He⁴.

A principal source of difficulty met in the practical application of equations such as (7.1) is the necessity of evaluating precisely at the transition-point quantities like C_P, α_P, etc., which are rapidly varying in this region. To circumvent the hazards of such a procedure, Pippard has proposed an approximation for the shape of the entropy surface near the transition which allows dP/dT to be determined at finite displacements of P and T from the transition point. Since a λ-transition is generally a function of pressure as well as temperature, the entropy surface is considered as $S(P, T)$. A projection of this surface of the $S-T$ plane is shown in Fig. 7.2. The transition will occur along a line on this surface—the λ-line, also indicated in the figure. Pippard's assumption was to represent the entropy surface by

$$S(P, T) = S_\lambda(P) + f(P - \epsilon T) \qquad (7.2)$$

where $\epsilon = (dP/dT)_\lambda$, the slope of the λ-line. A similar relation was proposed for the volume surface $V(P, T)$. This amounts to considering the surfaces near the transition to be cylindrical with constant radii

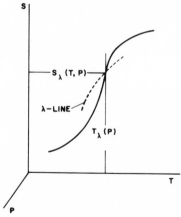

Fig. 7.2. $S-P-T$ diagram of a one-component system (e.g., He⁴) displaying a λ-transition. Solid line is a typical projection on the $S-T$ plane; dashed line is the λ-line in three dimensions.

and with generators parallel to the λ-line, an approximation which improves the more closely the transition line is approached. Thus α_P and C_P, for example, may be represented as

$$\alpha_P = \beta_T(dP/dT)_\lambda + (1/V_\lambda)(dV/dT)_\lambda \tag{7.3a}$$

$$\approx \beta_T \epsilon + \alpha_0 \tag{7.3b}$$

and

$$C_P = V_\lambda \alpha_P T_\lambda(dP/dT)_\lambda + T_\lambda(dS/dT)_\lambda \tag{7.4a}$$

$$\approx V_\lambda \alpha_P T_\lambda \epsilon + C_0 \tag{7.4b}$$

Both equations (7.3a) and (7.4a) are thermodynamically rigorous and equivalent to the Ehrenfest relations, while equations (7.3b) and (7.4b) include the Pippard approximations of setting the quantities $V_\lambda^{-1}(dV/dT)_\lambda$ and $T_\lambda(dS/dT)_\lambda$ equal to the constants α_0 and C_0, respectively. In particular, if we consider the change in C_P across a cylinder enclosing the λ-line, we find that

$$\Delta C_P = \epsilon V T_\lambda \Delta \alpha_P \tag{7.5}$$

which becomes identical to equation (7.1) when the radius of curvature of the cylinder is made to go to zero. Chase et al. ([11]) have indicated that for the λ-transition in He^4, these considerations are not valid when $|T - T_\lambda| > 10^{-4}\,°K$.

The Pippard relations have been generalized by Buckingham and Fairbank ([12]) through relaxation of the requirement that the entropy surface be cylindrical about the λ-line. On this basis, the authors have developed a complete system of thermodynamic equations for describing the observed properties of liquid He^4 near the transition. In this formalization, equation (7.4a), for example, is rewritten as

$$\frac{T_\lambda}{T}C_P = \frac{T_\lambda}{\rho_\lambda}\left(\frac{\rho_\lambda}{\rho}\right)\alpha_P\left(\frac{\partial P}{\partial T}\right)_t + T_\lambda\left(\frac{\partial S}{\partial T}\right)_t \tag{7.4c}$$

where $t = t(T, P) = T - T_\lambda(P)$ and the assumption is not made that $(\partial S/\partial T)_t$ is constant. As $t \to 0$, the Ehrenfest relations are again recovered. Some results using this method will be mentioned later on, but the reader is referred to the original article for details of the derivation.

7.1.3. Landau's Theory of Second-Order Phase Transitions

An alternative way of classifying phase transitions includes a specification of symmetry properties of the phases in question in addition to a description of the thermodynamic variables. For example, a liquid–vapor transition involves a change of state but in a sense no change of symmetry, since the relative spatial configuration of the particles is the same on both sides of the transition. At the other extreme, we are familiar with transformations between two crystal modifications of a single material, accompanied by abrupt and well-defined shifts in symmetry. These are two cases of what we have called first-order transitions. In the scheme we consider now, the analog of a second-order phase change is associated with a discontinuous variation in symmetry properties but no changes in the state of the system. In such a transition, two phases cannot be in equilibrium, and therefore no latent heat is involved. The system is entirely of either one symmetry species or another.

The symmetry element characterizing a second-order transition has been appropriately called the "order parameter," which we denote by η. One convenient way of giving η meaning is to consider a crystal lattice with two equivalent sites per unit cell, $(+)$ and $(-)$, so that the occupation number of each type of site in the crystal is given by N^+ and N^-. Then we define η by the relation

$$\eta = (N^+ - N^-)/(N^+ + N^-) \qquad (7.6)$$

from which $0 \leqslant |\eta| \leqslant 1$. The type of transition we then consider as second order is between the phase in which $0 < |\eta| \leqslant 1$ and that for which $\eta = 0$. The former phase is considered the symmetrical or ordered phase; conversely, that in which $\eta = 0$ is the less symmetrical or disordered phase.

Following the above reasoning, the modern tendency is to consider all phase transitions to fall into two classes: either first-order in the Ehrenfest sense, or not first-order. For the latter we generally use the term "second-order," even though in the Ehrenfest sense the transition may be of higher order.

A thermodynamic formulation of second-order phase changes following the molecular field approach and incorporating the notion of the order parameter has been developed by Landau [13]. The basic assumption of the method is that the Gibbs function, or the chemical potential μ, depends upon η as well as on P and T and that an expansion in powers of η can represent μ in the region near the transition. Thus

$$\mu(P, T, \eta) = \mu_0(P, T) + \alpha(P, T)\eta + A(P, T)\eta^2 + B(P, T)\eta^3$$
$$+ C(P, T)\eta^4 + \cdots \qquad (7.7)$$

Landau has acknowledged that the transition for a second-order phase change is most likely a singularity on the Gibbs surface $G(P, T)$, and, consequently, the validity of representing this singularity by a power series with an arbitrary number of terms is open to serious question.

However, he has claimed that by terminating equation (7.7) at a fairly low order, its applicability should not be badly impaired near the transition region.

The characterization of the coefficients of η^n can be accomplished through essentially mathematical arguments plus the conditions $\partial\mu/\partial\eta = 0$, $\partial^2\mu/\partial\eta^2 > 0$. For the case in which the second-order transition occurs along a continuous line on the surface $G(P, T)$ equation (7.7) reduces to

$$\mu = \mu_0(P, T) + A(P, T)\eta^2 + C(P, T)\eta^4 \tag{7.8}$$

with the transition line determined by $A(P, T) = 0$. For the $\eta = 0$ phase, $A < 0, C > 0$; for the $\eta \neq 0$ phase, $A > 0, C < 0$. If we consider the $\eta \neq 0$ phase at constant pressure, and if, near the transition temperature T_c, we approximate A by

$$A(T) = a(T - T_c) \tag{7.9}$$

then it can be shown that in the vicinity of T_c, the order parameter is given by

$$\eta^2 = -\frac{A}{2C} = \frac{a}{2C}(T_c - T) \tag{7.10}$$

The thermodynamic consequences of this treatment predict that along the transition line, C_V, C_P, β_T, α_P, and $(\partial P/\partial T)_V$ all suffer finite discontinuities.

When applied to the λ-transition in liquid He^4, the above formalism has several flaws. Besides the fact that the derivation of equation (7.8) is not rigorous, the entire theory neglects the effects of fluctuations, and for liquid helium, these are very large near T_λ [however, Ginzburg [14] has shown how the theory may be made valid when fluctuations are included]. Nevertheless, we find it difficult to overestimate the importance equation (7.8) has assumed in the phenomenological description of quantum fluids. It forms the basis for the Landau–Ginzburg theory of superconductivity [15], and as well for the Ginzburg–Pitaevskii theory of superfluidity [16]. Through this parallel development, the fundamental similarities between these two quantum phenomena have become clearly exposed, with the current literature continuing to reveal new insights and additional testimony to the power of the method. Unfortunately, space does not permit us to pursue the analogy; we shall be able to touch only briefly upon some of the notions pertinent to superfluidity. The essential assumptions of the Ginzburg–Pitaevskii approach are the applicability of Landau's molecular field theory to the λ-transition and the identification of the order parameter with Ψ, "the effective wave function of the superfluid part of the liquid," such that

$$\rho_s = m|\Psi|^2 \qquad (7.11)$$

where m is the mass of the helium atom. Further comments concerning the justification of associating ρ_s with the order parameter will be given later on in this chapter; some dynamic properties of the superfluid following from equation (7.11) will be developed in Chapter 8.

Returning now to the formalism for second-order transitions, we consider the consequences of a statement by Landau that the transition line must terminate (at both ends) at a first-order phase boundary—e.g., for He⁴, the λ-line extends between the melting curve and the vaporization curve. The termination point of the line is called by Landau "the critical point of the second-order transition ... in some sense analogous to the ordinary critical point." The analysis of this critical point demands the addition of a term $K(P, T)\eta^6$ to the series (7.8), since at (T_c, P_c), the coefficients A and C both vanish. Landau concluded that at the critical point: C_P should tend to infinity as $(T_c - T)^{-1/2}$, as should α_P and β_T; however, C_V and $(\partial P/\partial T)_V$ suffer finite discontinuities.

7.1.4. Tisza's Thermodynamics

Tisza ([17]) has developed a system of thermodynamics which involves no *ad hoc* assumptions concerning critical singularities, but includes as a logical consequence the anomalous transitions associated with critical points and λ-points. For our present purpose, one of the significant features of this system is the introduction of "quasithermodynamic" variables η_i representing intrinsic symmetry properties of homogeneous states of matter. Thus, two phases are distinct if they have different densities (e.g., liquid and vapor), or if they have the same density but differ in η_i (e.g., the right- and left-handed modifications of trigonal quartz). Tisza has criticized the Ehrenfest relations as depending upon an incomplete definition of what a "phase" is, while claiming that the introduction of the η_i corrects this deficiency.

Although it is clear that Landau's work is reflected here, there are important differences. Among the possible symmetry operations representable by the η_i in Tisza's formulation is that defined by equation (7.6) describing configurational order. Tisza has emphasized the physical significance of both branches, $+\eta$ and $-\eta$, referring to these as "doublet modifications." (We note that the power series derived by Landau contains only even powers of η, so that any distinction in sign is lost from the beginning.) In liquid He⁴, the λ-transition is, according to Tisza (and, of course, others), associated with momentum ordering;

and while η of the low-temperature phase is again related to $|\Psi|$, the doublet character of η implies that the ground state of liquid He^4 is doubly degenerate. Tisza has suggested that time reversal might be the symmetry operation accounting for this.

Tisza's system of thermodynamics avoids the hazards involved in representing the critical-point singularity by a power series expansion in η. Instead, since the transition is considered to occur where the system is pushed to the edge of the region of thermodynamic stability, the conditions for this stability were investigated taking into account the quasithermodynamic variables η where required. The argument has led to a distinction between two types of critical points, those of the condensation type in which η plays no part, and those of the order–disorder type for which η is important. The thermodynamic singularities appearing in both types of transitions may be concisely considered through what Tisza calls the *stiffness matrix*, **S**,

$$
\mathbf{S} =
\begin{bmatrix}
\left(\dfrac{\partial T}{\partial S}\right)_V & \left(\dfrac{\partial T}{\partial V}\right)_S \\[2ex]
-\left(\dfrac{\partial P}{\partial S}\right)_V & -\left(\dfrac{\partial P}{\partial V}\right)_S
\end{bmatrix}
=
\begin{bmatrix}
\dfrac{T}{C_V} & \dfrac{T}{C_V}\left(\dfrac{\partial P}{\partial T}\right)_V \\[2ex]
\dfrac{T}{C_V}\left(\dfrac{\partial P}{\partial T}\right)_V & \dfrac{1}{V\beta_S}
\end{bmatrix}
\tag{7.12}
$$

and its inverse, the *compliance matrix*, **C**,

$$
\mathbf{C} =
\begin{bmatrix}
\left(\dfrac{\partial S}{\partial T}\right)_P & \left(\dfrac{\partial S}{\partial(-P)}\right)_T \\[2ex]
\left(\dfrac{\partial V}{\partial T}\right)_P & \left(\dfrac{\partial V}{\partial(-P)}\right)_T
\end{bmatrix}
=
\begin{bmatrix}
\dfrac{C_P}{T} & V\alpha_P \\[2ex]
V\alpha_P & V\beta_T
\end{bmatrix}
\tag{7.13}
$$

Here, β_S is the adiabatic compressibility. Equations (7.12) and (7.13) have been derived from the fundamental equation for the internal energy, $U = U(S, V)$, expanded in quadratic form. The conditions for thermodynamic stability are that **S** and **C** not be singular. As the critical region is approached, the compliance coefficients, C_P, α_T, and β_T become infinite, signalling the termination of the stability region. Also, **S** may be transformed to a diagonal representation with the elements $\lambda_1 = T/C_V$ and $\lambda_2 = (V\beta_T)^{-1}$. At the critical point, λ_2 becomes zero, but C_V is expected to remain finite.

7.1.5. Critical-Point Indices

For quite a long while, it has been appreciated that certain properties of a system near its critical point can be well approximated in terms of functions with the form $(X_c - X)^n$, where X may represent such state variables as T, ρ, and P, and the index n is characteristic of the various properties. Several theoretical models also lead to this behavior. For instance, for a single-component fluid obeying the van der Waals equation of state, the difference between the density of the liquid and of the vapor in equilibrium with the liquid—i.e., $(\rho_l - \rho_g)$ along the coexistence curve—should disappear as $(T_c - T)^\beta$, with $\beta = \frac{1}{2}$; also, the compressibility along the critical isochore ($\rho = \rho_c$) should become infinite as $|T_c - T|^{-\gamma}$, with $\gamma = 1$. These and a number of other similar relations, which may be obtained from generalized equations of state, depend ultimately upon the assumption that the Helmholtz free energy as a function of ρ and T is analytic in the critical region and therefore may be expanded in a Taylor's series about the critical point. A recent review of these theories has been given by Fisher [8].

Because the exact solution of the two-dimensional (2-d) Ising model, which does not require the above assumption, also leads to an exponent description of the critical point [e.g., for the (2-d) Ising model, $\beta = \frac{1}{8}$ and $\gamma = \frac{7}{4}$] an extraordinary amount of interest has been generated to determine whether the theoretical three-dimensional (3-d) lattice gases and real systems may also be strictly characterized by critical indices. Notable success on the theoretical side has been achieved using sophisticated techniques for evaluating the series expansion approximations that occur in the classical problem; a review of these methods, along with references to the original work, has been given recently by Domb [18].

We may define an index $n^\pm$ for a property $X(T, \rho)$ of a fluid near its critical point as

$$n^\pm = \lim_{T \to (T_c)^\pm} [\log X(T, \rho)/\log |t|] \qquad (7.14)$$

where $t = (T - T_c)$ and the superscript $^\pm$ distinguishes T_c being approached from above $(+)$ or below $(-)$. Some of the more commonly met indices are associated with the fluid properties as follows:

$$C_V \propto |t|^{-\alpha} \qquad (7.15)$$

(in the limit $\alpha \to 0$, this relation reduces to a logarithmic singularity);

$$(\rho_l - \rho_g)/2\rho_c \propto t^\beta \qquad (7.16)$$

(the coexistence curve does not extend above T_c, so β refers only to β^-),

$$\beta_T \propto |t|^{-\gamma} \qquad (7.17)$$

$$|P - P_c| \propto |\rho - \rho_c|^\delta = |\Delta\rho|^\delta \qquad (7.18)$$

(δ gives the degree of the critical isotherm);

$$(d^2 P_{\text{sat}}/dT^2) \propto t^{-\theta} \qquad (7.19)$$

(θ also exists only below T_c); finally, we have

$$|g(r) - 1| \propto 1/r^{1+\eta} \tag{7.20}$$

where $g(r)$ is the pair correlation function.

We digress briefly to comment on equation (7.20). The most fundamental microscopic manifestations of critical-point phenomena are the thermodynamic fluctuations. For example, as T_c is approached, both the magnitude of the density fluctuations as well as the spatial range over which the fluctuations are correlated increase markedly. This accounts for the well-known phenomenon of "critical opalescence" observed for light scattering in the critical region. In the theory of Ornstein and Zernike ([19]), the light scattering intensity is directly related to the behavior of the fluctuations through the pair correlation function $g(r)$, and in the limit of $T \rightarrow T_c$, $|g(r) - 1| \sim 1/r$. Hence, in equation (7.20), η indicates the deviations from the classical Ornstein–Zernike theory. We may also define a quantity ξ as a correlation length which measures the range of the density fluctuations; as $T \rightarrow T_c$, ξ goes to infinity as $t^{-\nu'}$.

Table 7.I compares [after Fisher ([20])] the indices discussed above as obtained from various models with the experimental values. The predictions of the (3-d) lattice gas are seen to be quite realistic.

Table 7.I. Critical-Point Exponents According to Various Models Compared with Experimental Findings

Exponent	Lattice gas (2-d)	Lattice gas (3-d)	van der Waals gas ("classical gas")	Experiment (nonquantum gas)
α^+	0 ; log	$0 \leqslant \alpha^+ \leqslant 0.2$	Discontinuity	$0 \leqslant \alpha^+ \leqslant 0.2$
α^-	0 ; log	0 ; log (?)	Discontinuity	≈ 0 ; log
β	$\frac{1}{8}$	$\frac{5}{16} = 0.312$	$\frac{1}{2}$	0.33–0.36
γ^+	$\frac{7}{4}$	$\frac{5}{4}$	1	>1.1 (?)
γ^-	$\frac{7}{4}$	1.23–1.32	1	>1.2 (?)
δ	15.0	5.2	3	4.2
θ	0 ; log	$\gtrsim 0$	0	0 (?)
η	$\frac{1}{4}$	0.059	0	>0 (?)
ν'	1	0.644	$\frac{1}{2}$	>0.55

Despite the long history of attempts to characterize the thermodynamic properties of the critical point, very few experimental investigations have been extended sufficiently close to the singularity to permit accurate values to be assigned to the critical indices. Consequently, several conjectured relationships among the indices have proved useful in establishing upper and/or lower bounds for those doubtful cases. One of these relations is the inequality

$$\alpha^- + 2\beta + \gamma^- \geqslant 2 \qquad (7.21)$$

originally obtained by Rushbrook [21] for magnetic transitions and more recently shown by Fisher [8] to be applicable to fluids, perhaps as an equality [22]. Widom [23,24] has deduced the relation

$$\gamma^- = \beta(\delta - 1) \qquad (7.22)$$

and Griffiths [25] has proposed the two inequalities

$$(1 + \delta)\beta \geqslant 2 - \alpha^- \qquad (7.23)$$

and

$$\alpha^- + \beta \geqslant \theta \qquad (7.24)$$

Rowlinson [26] has reviewed these relations and evaluated their relative usefulness and correctness.

As an example of how the above formulas may be helpful, we note that δ is a particularly difficult exponent to obtain accurately from experimental $P-V-T$ data. There is reason to believe that the isotherms should really be somewhat flatter than indicated in Table 7.I ($\delta = 4.2$). Use of Widom's relation, for example, suggests a value near 4.8 to be more appropriate.

7.1.6. The Scaling Laws

As an extension—or, indeed, a simplification—of the index laws, several authors [24,27,28] have proposed theories which, while expressed differently, amount to very much the same ideas. These are often referred to as the "Widom–Kadanoff scaling laws," and they should be taken as hypotheses not yet proved by experiment. Widom [24] has suggested that the equation of state for a fluid in the single-phase region near T_c be written as

$$\mu(\rho, T) = \mu_0(T) + \Delta\rho(x + y)\Phi(x, y) \qquad (7.25)$$

where $\mu_0(T)$ is the value of μ when $\rho = \rho_c$, $x = t$, and $y \approx |\Delta\rho|^{1/\beta}$. The function $\Phi(x, y)$ is a constant for a classical van der Waals fluid, but for real fluids has the important property of being a homogeneous function of x and y with the degree of homogeneity positive. Thus the introduction of $\Phi(x, y)$ is made to account for irregularities in the specific heat, compressibility, etc., which do not conform to classical critical behavior. The assumed properties of the unknown function $\Phi(x, y)$ imply that ρ is symmetrical about ρ_c on the coexistence curve; and from an analysis of the possible forms for $\Phi(x, y)$ Widom concluded that the critical singularities must be symmetrical also.

In the microscopic sense, Kadanoff [27] has emphasized the importance of long-range correlations as the source of critical-point singularities. He first assumed that the correlation functions, for example, $g(r)$, are homogeneous functions of space governed by the fundamental length ξ and then considered what happens when $\xi \to \infty$ as $T \to T_c$. As a model, he has used the (2-d) Ising lattice and imagined the system divided into cells of side La_0, where a_0 is the lattice spacing. When ξ is smaller than La_0 (T far from T_c), $g(r)$ falls off rapidly with r, there are no correlations between cells, and the important interactions occur between the lattice sites. To obtain the properties of the system, we must take averages over a large number of these sites. On the other hand, when $\xi \gg La$ (T near T_c), the correlations between cells become crucial and the nature of the short-range interactions inconsequential. Thus, in effect, through an increase in ξ, the sensitive regions have been scaled up from site interactions to cell interactions. But L, being an arbitrary length, drops out of the picture as $\xi \to \infty$, since the number of cells we must look at to obtain average system properties now no longer matters.

In the (2-d) Ising problem the only relevant properties which may differ between the site case and the cell case are determined by the parameters t and h (the latter describes the effect of an external magnetic field). Kadanoff has speculated that the differences may be accounted for by scale factors such that $t_{\text{cell}} = L^y t_{\text{site}}$ and $h_{\text{cell}} = L^x h_{\text{site}}$, with x and y constants to be specified. Thus all critical singularities of the model should be expressible in terms of the indices x and y. Finally, these results were extended to real (3-d) systems.

The practical consequences of the suppositions by both Widom and Kadanoff are, first, to make equalities out of inequalities such as expressions (7.21), (7.23), and (7.24); and second, to symmetrize the critical singularities—that is, $n^+ = n^-$—where applicable. As a consequence, the number of independent critical exponents is reduced to two.

The scaling-law hypothesis appears very attractive and is currently the fashionable way to treat critical-point phenomena. This has been particularly true for the cases encountered in helium, as we shall see. Kadanoff et al. [29] have produced a monumental survey of static critical-point phenomena, comparing the theoretical and experimental developments with emphasis on the scaling laws, while Green *et al.* ([30]) have on the basis of these laws devised a promising new technique for analyzing data in the critical region. The latter authors have successfully applied their method to the equation of state for a variety of nonquantum fluids. In addition, some limited headway has been made by Ferrell *et al.* ([31]), and by Halperin and Hohenberg ([32]), and by Kadanoff and Swift ([53]) in using the scaling-law approach to attack the very difficult problem posed by transport phenomena in the critical region.

7.2. PROPERTIES OF He³ AND He⁴ NEAR THE CRITICAL POINTS

7.2.1. The Coexistence Curve of He⁴: The density near T_c

The natural order parameter for the liquid–gas system is $\Delta\rho = |\rho - \rho_c|$, where ρ may refer to either ρ_l or ρ_g. Consequently, the determination of β in equation (7.16) is of considerable importance. Experiments toward this end have been carried out using either the dielectric-constant method or the related optical-interferometer method. In the latter, the index of refraction n of the sample is measured and converted to density through the Lorenz–Lorentz law defining the molar refraction $[N]$

$$[N] = \frac{(n^2 - 1)M}{(n^2 + 2)\rho} \tag{7.26}$$

where M is the molecular weight. $[N]$ is a constant, depending upon the wavelength of the light used in the experiment and upon the assumption that α_M, the molar polarizability, is independent of ρ. Measurements of the dielectric constant ϵ also may determine ρ through the Clausius–Mosotti relation

$$\rho = \frac{3M}{4\pi\alpha_M}\frac{(\epsilon - 1)}{(\epsilon + 2)} \tag{7.27}$$

where again the constancy of α_M is assumed.

Although extremely accurate density data are in principle obtainable using these methods, good evidence suggests that α_M is indeed not independent of ρ. If we define Q as

$$Q = [(\epsilon - 1)/(\epsilon + 2)]\rho^{-1} \tag{7.28}$$

then $1/Q$ may be developed in a virial-type expansion,

$$1/Q = A + B\rho + C\rho^2 + \cdots \tag{7.29}$$

with $A = 4\pi\alpha_M/3M$. Johnston *et al.* ([33]) have shown that at room temperature, $1/Q$ for He^4 decreases with increasing density, and recent experiments by Sherman and Kerr ([34]) at liquid He temperatures indicate changes of several tenths of a percent in α_M. This effect may be important for the coexistence curve experiments very close to T_c, since it appears that changes in α_M are linear with density on this curve. Nevertheless, further work is required to clear up this point satisfactorily.

A problem considerably more serious involves the temperature scale and the exact absolute value of T_c for He^4. Yang and Yang ([35]) have argued on thermodynamic grounds that should C_V of He^4 display a logarithmic singularity at T_c (see Sections 7.2.3 and 7.4), either or both $(d^2\mu/dT^2)_V$ and (d^2P_{sat}/dT^2) should also become infinite. This then requires an additional term, $Kt^2 \ln t$, to describe the vapor-pressure–temperature relation which defines the scale T_{58}. Inclusion of this term would have the effect of lowering T_c by a small amount depending on the magnitude of the singularity in C_V—but a "small amount" in terms of critical properties may not be trivial. In any case, this uncertainty, together with those mentioned in Chapter 4, lessens our confidence in the assigned value of T_c and suggests caution when we speak in terms of $(T - T_c)$ for He^4.

For some time, the orthobaric density data of Edwards and Woodbury ([36]) provided the best description of the He^4 coexistence curve near T_c. These came from refractive index measurements and approached T_c to within $0.036°K$ on the T_{58} scale. The authors originally analyzed their data by extending the Landau–Lifshitz ([37]) expansion for $(\partial^2 F/\partial V^2)_{T,N}$, where $F = F(T, V, N)$ is the Helmholtz free energy. This was satisfactory near T_c; but for $t > 110$ mdeg, the method appeared to break down. Tisza and Chase ([38]) investigated the causes for this failure and suggested that a better representation of the data could be obtained by treating a system with fixed volume and variable number of particles, rather than the reverse as done by Landau–Lifshitz—i.e., by expanding $(\partial^2 F/\partial N^2)_{T,V}$ rather than $(\partial^2 F/\partial V^2)_{T,N}$. Still further improvement has been achieved by Mistura and Sette ([40]), who extended the Tisza–Chase formalism analogously to the Edwards–Woodbury modification of the Landau–Lifshitz theory. The end result has been to fit the data reasonably well over the range $0.050° < t < 0.250°K$.

Treatments of the coexistence curve mentioned above are based upon the recognition that the Helmholtz free energy is probably nonanalytic in the critical region and upon the assumption that the shape of the coexistence curve may be determined by a series expansion despite this nonanalyticity. Buckingham ([41]) has proposed that if, at T_c, C_V displays a logarithmic singularity, the limiting form of the coexistence curve should be given by the nonanalytic relation

$$\frac{X^2}{1 - \ln X} = at \qquad (7.30)$$

where a is a constant and X is what Buckingham has called the "natural variable,"

$$X = \frac{\rho_l - \rho_g}{\rho_l + \rho_g} \equiv \frac{V_g - V_l}{V_g + V_l} \neq \frac{\rho_l - \rho_g}{2\rho_c} \qquad (7.31)$$

Equation (7.30) lacks generality, being applicable only to the coexistence curve.

Edwards ([42]) has reanalyzed the Edwards and Woodbury measurements using equation (7.30) with success comparable to that obtained by the Mistura and Sette method. The results are shown in Fig. 7.3.

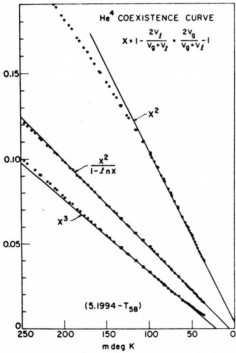

Fig. 7.3. The He⁴ coexistence curve data of Edwards and Woodbury ([36]) analyzed using Buckingham's natural variable X [Buckingham ([41])]. T_c taken as 5.1994°K on T_{58} scale [from Edwards ([42])].

The good fit to this function has been cited by Edwards as evidence that the coexistence curve is nonanalytic near T_c. An interesting feature of the variable X is that when X^n is plotted against t, $n = 1/\beta$, where β is the index in relation (7.16). From plots of X^2 (i.e., $\beta = \frac{1}{2}$) and X^3 (i.e., $\beta = \frac{1}{3}$) it can be determined that neither of these is as appropriate as the $X^2/(1 - \ln X)$ representation. The latter corresponds to an intermediate value for β of about 0.41. We also point out that the expansions of the second derivatives of $F(T, V, N)$ imply $\beta = \frac{1}{2}$.

It is evident that none of the curves in Fig. 7.3 pass through the origin, as they should if T_c were in fact the exact absolute critical temperature and if the proper expression for the coexistence curve were used. In the figure, T_c is taken as 5.1994°K according to the T_{58} scale. By assuming that $X^2/(1 - \ln X)$ is indeed the correct relation, Edwards observed that T_c should be about 0.0075°K lower than given by T_{58}, as qualitatively suggested by Yang and Yang ([35]).

Roach and Douglass ([43]) have recently made dielectric-constant measurements along the coexistence curve and analyzed their data in terms of the exponent β. In order to avoid the effects of suspected uncertainties in the T_{58} scale near the critical point, these authors used a companion relation to expression (7.16) in terms of pressure rather than of temperature, that is,

$$(\Delta\rho) \propto (P_c - P)^{\beta(P)} \tag{7.32}$$

where $\beta(P)$ is essentially the same as β. [Relations (7.32) and (7.18) should not be confused, the former being taken along the coexistence curve and the latter along the critical isotherm.] On a log–log plot of $(\Delta\rho)$ vs. $(P_c - P)$, the data can be fitted to a straight line the slope of which suggests a limiting value (as $P \to P_c$) for $\beta(P)$ of 0.345 $\pm$ 0.009. When vapor pressures were converted to temperatures on the T_{58} scale, followed by use of the relation (7.16), β was found to be 0.352 $\pm$ 0.003, in substantial agreement with $\beta(P)$. From the pressure plots and the P_{sat} vs. T_{58} relation, the critical temperature was determined by Roach and Douglass to be $T_c = 5.1890 \pm 0.0006$°K, or some 0.010°K lower than given by the T_{58} scale, corroborating the predictions of Yang and Yang ([35]) and the analysis by Edwards ([42]).

Roach and Douglass ([43]) have similarly treated additional interferometric measurements of ρ recently obtained by Edwards ([44]) over the range $0.002° < t < 0.090$°K. They found these data consistent with the parameters $T_c = 5.1877$°K and $\beta = 0.382 \pm 0.033$. Causes for the discrepancy between this value of β and that obtained from the Roach and Douglass measurements are not yet understood.

In a later paper, Roach and Douglass ([45]) have reported density measurements along five isotherms in the vicinity of the critical point. These data, plotted in Fig. 7.4, were also obtained from the dielectric-

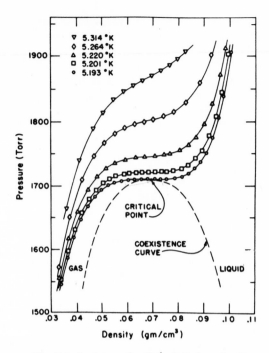

Fig. 7.4. Isotherms for He⁴ plotted as density *vs.* pressure near the critical point [from Roach and Douglass ([45])].

constant method and analyzed using a modification of equation (7.18), namely,

$$\Delta P' = \frac{A|\Delta \rho'|^{\delta} \, \mathrm{sgn}(\Delta \rho') + B(T) \, \Delta \rho'}{(1 - \frac{1}{2} \Delta \rho')} \qquad (7.33)$$

Here, $\Delta P' = (P - P_0)/P_c$; $\Delta \rho' = (\rho - \rho_0)/\rho_c$; ρ_0 and P_0 refer to the central point of an isotherm; $\mathrm{sgn}(\Delta \rho')$ is $+1$ or -1 depending on whether ρ is greater or less than ρ_0; $B(T)$ gives the slope of the linear region about the center point of the isotherms; and $(1 - \frac{1}{2} \Delta \rho')^{-1}$ takes into account an asymmetry in $\Delta P'$ for a given $\Delta \rho'$ on either side of the center point. Fits to the measurements gave

$$\delta^+ = 4.00 \pm 0.02, \qquad A^+ = 2.00 \pm 0.04, \qquad \rho > \rho_c$$

$$\delta^- = 3.91 \pm 0.01, \qquad A^- = 1.66 \pm 0.02, \qquad \rho < \cdot \rho_c$$

The scaling laws predict $\delta^+ = \delta^-$ and $A^+ = A^-$, conditions clearly not met here.

Roach and Douglass also applied the method of Green *et al.* ([30]) to their data, again finding $\delta \approx 4$, whereas the analysis of several non-quantum gases by the latter authors produced a clear case for $\delta \approx 5$. Finally, a test was made of equation (7.23) by combining the value found here for δ with that for β determined previously ([43]) and taking $\alpha^- = 0.017 \pm 0.008$ from a least-squares fit to the heat-capacity data of Moldover (see Section 7.2.3). Thus the maximum value of $[(1 + \delta)\beta + \alpha^-]$ is 1.84, in direct contradiction to Griffiths' expression. This is a very perplexing situation which requires resolution.

7.2.2. The Coexistence Curve of He³

From extrapolations to the saturated vapor pressure made along 23 isochores in the range $0.015 < \rho < 0.066 \text{ g/cm}^3$, Sherman ([46]) first explored the nature of the He³ coexistence curve. By taking $T_c = 3.324°\text{K}$ and $P_c = 873.0 \text{ mm Hg}$ from the T_{62} He³ scale of temperatures, he found the critical isochore to be at $\rho_c = 0.0418 \text{ g/cm}^3$. A log–log plot of $(\rho_l - \rho_g)$ vs. t revealed the following behavior of β: for $t \gtrsim 0.2°\text{K}$, $\beta = 0.34$; but for $t < 0.070°\text{K}$, β appeared to assume the constant value of 0.48 ± 0.02.

Sherman also obtained estimates of the indices γ and δ by taking derivatives of his primary P–V–T data. He found that γ (along the critical isochore for $T < T_c$) is 1.1, somewhat lower than the classical value of 1.25, and that $\delta \approx 3.4$, considerably below the value obtained for heavier molecules. Subsequently, Chase and Zimmerman ([47]) measured the dielectric constant of He³ along an isotherm at 3.324°K (T_{62}) and through equation (7.18) obtained $\delta = 3.49 \pm 0.1$, corroborating Sherman's results for this index.

Several authors ([48,49]) have sought an explanation for the anomalous values of β and δ for He³ in terms of quantum effects based on de Boer's ([50]) quantum-mechanical corresponding-state theory. At the time, β for He⁴ was taken as 0.41 from Edwards' work ([42]), so that this deviation from the classically expected $\beta = \frac{1}{3}$ fitted into the scheme. However, the newer value of β for He⁴ obtained by Roach and Douglass ([43]) cast considerable doubt upon the relevance of quantum effects where critical indices were concerned; and further contrary evidence has come from the recent determination of β for He³ by Zimmerman and Chase ([51]), who closely followed the experimental and data analysis techniques of Roach and Douglass. In terms of the relation $|\Delta\rho/\rho_c| = A(t/T_c)^\beta$, both branches of the coexistence curve for He³ can be uniquely represented by $A = 1.323 \pm 0.004$, $\beta = 0.3625 \pm 0.0010$. When only points for $t < 0.033°\text{K}$ were analyzed, β decreased slightly to 0.0354 ± 0.003. It thus appears that β for quantum fluids does not deviate significantly from the classical value; but we are still left with the enigma of δ.

Again the question of the absolute value of T_c becomes relevant. Zimmerman and Chase, in arriving at the above conclusions for β, first obtained from their data the value 3.3098 $\pm$ 0.0004°K for T_c of He³, or some 14 mdeg lower than T_c on the T_{62} scale. Such an error in T_c could very well contribute to the anomalously large value of β originally found by Sherman.

7.2.3. Specific Heats of He³ and He⁴ near the Critical point

Moldover and Little ([52]) have investigated the singularities in C_V for He³ at $\rho = 0.98_5 \, \rho_c$ and for He⁴ at $\rho = 0.99_8 \, \rho_c$. The experimental measurements were analyzed in two ways. One of these attempted to fit the data by a function of the form

$$C_V/R = -A \ln(t/T_c) + B \tag{7.34}$$

The results appear in the top graphs of Fig. 7.5, where C_V is plotted against $t = |T - T_c|$. The data were also reduced by plotting log C_V vs. t, as shown in the bottom sections of the figure, where the solid lines represent equation (7.15) with $\alpha = 0.2$. Such a low value of α is nearly equivalent to a logarithmic singularity [cf. the analysis for He⁴, $T < T_c$, by Roach and Douglass ([45]) mentioned in Section 7.2.1]. For

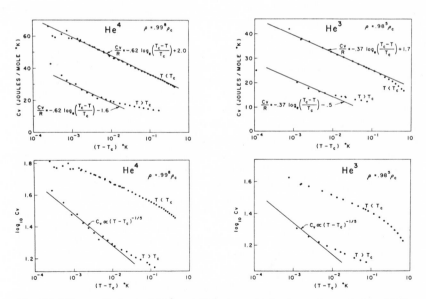

Fig. 7.5. The specific heat of He³ and He⁴ at constant volume along nearly critical isochores [Moldover and Little ([52])].

$T < T_c$ for both He^3 and He^4, equation (7.34) seems appropriate over several decades of t to within about 0.001°K of T_c. Similarly, for He^4 above T_c, the $t^{-0.2}$ law is reasonably substantiated; but for He^3 above T_c, the data appear too sparse for any conclusions to be drawn.

In their discussions of the critical point, Yang and Yang ([35]) have proposed on the basis of the de Boer ([50]) quantum mechanical theory of corresponding states that the singularity in C_V at T_c should be of the same strength in all the noble gases, except helium, for which quantum dispersion effects should serve to reduce the magnitude of the peak. A measure of the strength of the singularity is given by A in equation (7.34). In conformity with the Yang and Yang predictions, Moldover and Little found A for He^3 and He^4 to be, respectively, 0.37 and 0.62, compared with a value of 1.8 deduced for argon ([5]).

7.2.4. Propagation of Sound in He^4 near the Critical Point

As pointed out by Chase et al. ([39]), the stiffness matrix, equation (7.12), may be diagonalized to give either of two sets of diagonal elements:

$$\lambda_1 = T/C_V, \qquad \lambda_2 = 1/V\beta_T \qquad (7.35)$$

or

$$\lambda'_1 = 1/V\beta_S, \qquad \lambda'_2 = T/C_P \qquad (7.36)$$

The usual theories of the critical point have stated that β_T and C_P should become infinite as $T \to T_c$, i.e., $\lambda_2 = \lambda'_2 = 0$, but that λ_1 and λ'_1 should remain finite. If, however, a singularity exists also in C_V as some evidence we have considered suggests, then we should expect to find $\lambda_1 = \lambda'_1 = 0$ as well, and the sound velocity, $u_1 \equiv (\rho\beta_S)^{-1/2}$, should consequently disappear at the critical point.

An examination of this situation has been made by Chase et al. ([39]) using 1 Mc/sec sound, with results that tend to confirm these expectations. The velocity measurements as functions of t and of ΔP are shown separately in Fig. 7.6, while evidence suggesting the logarithmic singularity in the adiabatic compressibility (as derived from the u_1 data) is presented in Fig. 7.7. In both figures, the pressure plots are taken along the isobar $P = 1718 \pm 1$ mm Hg, and the temperature plots along the isotherm $T = 5.200 \pm 0.002$°K. The authors have reported that the exceedingly strong attenuation of the sound signal, as usually experienced near a critical point, prevented them from obtaining measurements closer than $t \approx 2 \times 10^{-3}$°K or $\Delta P \approx 2.5$ mm Hg. While the rapid falloff in u_1 as these limits are approached is suggestive of a further drop, whether u_1 actually disappears at T_c remains a matter of conjecture.

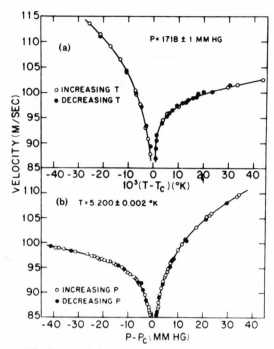

Fig. 7.6. Variation of sound velocity in He⁴ near the critical region as a function of temperature (upper graph) and pressure (lower graph) [from Chase *et al.* ([39])].

Observations ([39]) of u_1 as a function of P on isotherms above T_c display well-defined minima which, however, are rounded and become less sharp as T increases. The locus of the (P, T) values for these minima in u_1 forms on a P–T plot a smooth continuous extension of the vapor-pressure curve beyond T_c. This apparent continuity in (dP_{sat}/dT), together with the C_V data of Moldover and Little ([52]), was used to test the validity of a relation for u_1 compatible with Yang and Yang's ([35]) comments on the critical point, namely: $u_1^2 = \rho_C^{-2}(dP_{\text{sat}}/dT)^2(T/C_V)$. Within experimental error the data support this relation. However, no conclusion could be drawn about the proposed ([35]) infinity for (d^2P_{sat}/dT^2) as $T \to T_c$.

7.2.5. The Thermal Conductivity of He³ near the Critical Point

The only transport property to be investigated experimentally in the critical region of either of the heliums has been the thermal conductivity of He³. Kerrisk and Keller ([54]) have used the parallel-plate method to measure λ, using a gap of less than 0.1 cm in order to avoid effects due to convective heat transfer. Figure 7.8 shows the results of

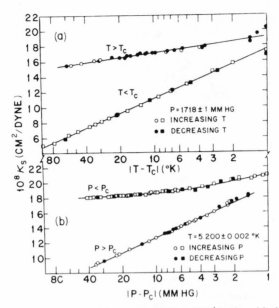

Fig. 7.7. Adiabatic compressibility of He^4 in the critical region as a function of (a) log$|T - T_c|$ and (b) log$|P - P_c|$ as deduced from the sound velocity measurements of Fig. 7.6 [from Chase et al. (^{39})].

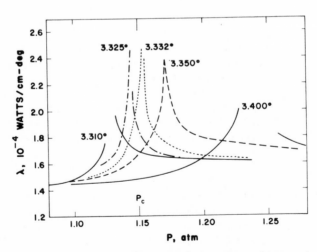

Fig. 7.8. Thermal conductivity of He^3 as a function of pressure in the critical region

λ vs. pressure for isotherms near the critical region. For $T = 3.310°K$ (on the T_{62} scale), λ increases just before intersecting the SVP line. As T_c is approached, the curves are sharply peaked; but above T_c the peaks become less pronounced and more rounded and shift to higher pressures. Nevertheless, anomalies associated with the critical point seem to persist for a considerable range in P and T away from the point itself.

The behavior shown in the figure is in many respects similar to that observed by Michels et al. ([55]) in their detailed studies of λ for CO_2. Quite probably, the qualitative differences that do appear may be associated with the positive $(\partial\lambda/\partial T)_P$ exhibited by He³ (and He⁴) as opposed to the negative slope generally found for other liquids. A worthwhile discussion of λ (and also of η) in the critical region has been given by Sengers ([56]).

We anticipate the discussion of Section 7.3.6 by noting that scaling-law arguments predict λ for He⁴I to approach $T_\lambda(P)$ as $[T - T_\lambda(P)]^{-1/3}$. Although the theoretical value of the exponent depends importantly on the superfluid behavior of He⁴ it is likely that the method of Ferrel et al. ([31]) is applicable to a wider range of critical point phenomena. And in fact, by more general arguments for a classical fluid Kadanoff and Swift ([53]) have obtained $\lambda \propto (T - T_c)^{-2/3}$ as $T \to T_c$ along the critical isochore. Unfortunately, the scatter in the He³ data precludes the possibility of unambiguously describing λ in terms of $|t|^l$ near T_c, although the increase in the thermal conductivity maximum as $T = T_c$ qualitatively follows the predictions.

7.3. THE LAMBDA TRANSITION IN LIQUID He⁴

The λ-transition in He⁴, being by far the dominant feature of this liquid, has naturally received an enormous amount of attention from both theorists and experimentalists. Until recently, the phenomenon has usually been treated as an isolated anomaly, whereas now the tendency is to consider it an example of a general class of critical singularities. This latter viewpoint was first clearly expressed in the review article by Buckingham and Fairbank ([12]), although arguments for this position had appeared, albeit sporadically, in the earlier literature. Nevertheless, the key piece of evidence about the nature of the transition was provided by the specific-heat measurements of Fairbank et al. ([4]). These and related matters have been fully described in the above-mentioned review article. Our purpose here is to provide in some respects a sequel to that article by first presenting what we believe to be the most reliable experimental data on the λ-point properties and then commenting on the significance and possible interpretations of these data.

7.3.1. The Specific Heat along the Saturation Curve near T_λ

The original results of the *tour de force* by Fairbank et al. ([4]) on C_{sat} have been extended to within a few tenths of a microdegree of T_λ in Kellers' unpublished thesis work ([4]). Figure 7.9 shows the nature of the singularity on a plot of C_{sat} vs. $\log|t'|$, where t' stands for $(T - T_\lambda)$. The two branches for temperatures above and below T_λ have equal slope and constant separation for $|t'| < 5 \times 10^{-2}\,°K$; they are represented by the solid lines in the figure according to the relation (in J/g-deg)

$$C_{sat} = 4.55 - 3.00\log|t'| - 5.20\Delta \qquad \begin{cases} \Delta = 0, & T < T_\lambda \\ \\ \Delta = 1, & T > T_\lambda \end{cases} \qquad (7.37)$$

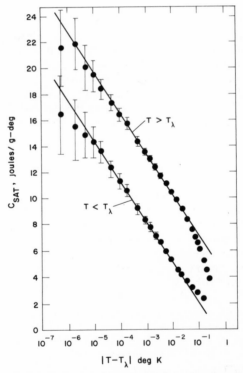

Fig. 7.9. Specific heat at SVP of He[4] as a function of $|T - T_\lambda|$. Solid lines represent equation (7.37) of text. [After Kellers ([4])].

Measurements in the extreme range near T_λ are obviously very difficult to obtain, and a certain amount of judgement on the part of the authors was understandably necessary in selecting and analyzing the raw data. While some of these uncertainties are reflected in the increasingly large error bars shown as T_λ is approached, it should also be pointed out that a considerable fraction of the runs were discarded for one reason or another. Nevertheless, the plot in Fig. 7.9 suggests, especially for the $T > T_\lambda$ branch, that for $|t'| \lesssim 10^{-5}\,°\mathrm{K}$, the deviations from equation (7.37) may be real. We shall have additional comments on this point in Section 7.4.

If for the moment we assume that C_{sat} does indeed exhibit the logarithmic singularity described by equation (7.37), then it follows that while S_{sat} is continuous through the λ-region, dS_{sat}/dT becomes infinite as T_λ is approached. Also, through integration of the thermodynamic relation involving the molar heat of vaporization H_v,

$$\frac{dH_v}{dT} = \frac{H_v}{T} + C_{sat}\,(\text{gas}) - C_{sat}\,(\text{liquid}) \approx \frac{5}{2}R - C_{sat}\,(\text{liquid}) \quad (7.38)$$

it can be shown that the H_v vs. T curve displays a point of inflection and an infinite slope at T_λ as well as a minimum some 10 millidegrees above T_λ.

7.3.2. The Density and the Expansion Coefficient of the Saturated Liquid near T_λ

The expansion coefficient of the saturated liquid, α_{sat}, was the first property to be described by a logarithmic function of t', based on the pycnometric measurements for $T < T_\lambda$ by Atkins and Edwards [57]. Later, Edwards [58], using an interferometric method, and Chase et al. [11], using a dielectric-constant method, covered the regions both above and below T_λ and extended the density observations to within $10^{-4}\,°\mathrm{K}$ of T_λ. Still more recently, Kerr and Taylor [59] have re-measured ρ_{sat}, again with a direct pycnometer technique. Results of this last work are shown in Fig. 7.10, where it is seen that ρ_{sat} passes through a maximum about 6 mdeg above T_λ. This region has been further examined by Peshkov and Borovikov [60], who place the maximum at $T_\lambda + 0.0065 \pm 0.0005°\mathrm{K}$. Finally, Elwell and Meyer [61] have measured the dielectric constant of the liquid in the vicinity of the λ-line at pressures from 0.5 to 28 atm. By extrapolation of their data, they inferred the nature of α_P at $P_{\lambda,sat}$ (the λ-point pressure at saturation).

A plot of the α_{sat} values derived from the above-mentioned ρ_{sat} measurements is presented in Fig. 7.11, where it can be seen that the two sets of pycnometer data are in substantial agreement (for $T < T_\lambda$)

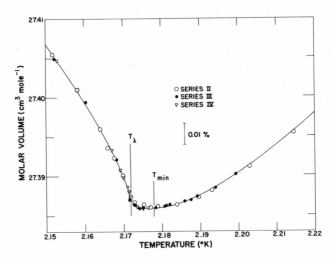

Fig. 7.10. Molar volume of liquid He^4 at SVP near T_λ [from Kerr and Taylor ([59])].

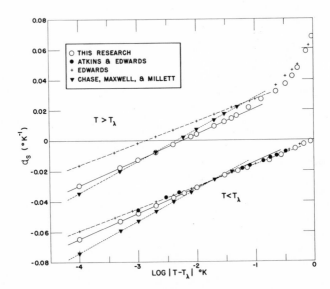

Fig. 7.11. Comparison of several experimental determinations of α_{sat} as a function of $\log|T - T_\lambda|$ [from Kerr and Taylor ([59])].

but differ somewhat from the results derived from either refractive-index or dielectric-constant measurements. While the choice between these data is somewhat ambiguous, the behavior of α_{sat} near the transition is qualitatively the same in all cases. That is, as $|t'|$ gets small, the results may be represented by a relation of the form

$$\alpha_{\text{sat}} = A \log|t'| + B \quad (^\circ\text{K})^{-1} \tag{7.39}$$

Within experimental error, $A_{\text{I}} = A_{\text{II}}$ (where the subscripts differentiate between He I and He II), but $B_{\text{I}} \neq B_{\text{II}}$, indicating a jump in α_{sat} at T_λ. In Fig. 7.12a, we plot the density dependence of A as obtained by Elwell and Meyer from their α_P results, and in Fig. 7.12b, B as deduced similarly, when α_P is substituted for α_{sat} in equation (7.39). In the latter figure, points for the α_{sat} determinations are compared with those from α_P, and this may not be too meaningful. We recall that α_{sat} and α_P are

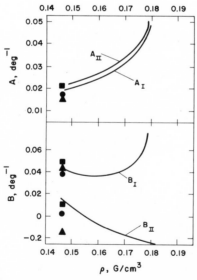

Fig. 7.12. Density variation of the coefficients in the relation $\alpha_P = A \log|t'| + B$: (a) A_{I} and A_{II} vs. ρ (where subscripts indicate He I and He II); (b) B_{I} and B_{II} vs. ρ. Also shown are constants from α_{sat} data: ■ [Chase et al. (¹¹)]; ▲ [Edwards (⁵⁸)]; ● [Kerr and Taylor (⁵⁹)]. Solid lines drawn after data of Elwell and Meyer (⁶¹).

related by

$$\alpha_{\text{sat}} = \beta_T (dP/dT)_{\text{sat}} + \alpha_P \qquad (7.40)$$

and β_T is also singular at T_λ.

7.3.3. The Propagation of Ordinary Sound near the λ-Point at Saturated Vapor Pressure

Early measurements of the velocity of ordinary sound u_1 near the λ-point were reported by van Itterbeek and Forrez [62] and by Chase [63]. More recently, Rudnick and co-workers [64,65] have considerably refined the data using low frequencies of from about 10 to 100 kc/sec to suppress dispersion effects. This has allowed the observations to be extended to within 3.5×10^{-6} °K of T_λ. The first reports by Rudnick and Shapiro [64] indicated that u_1 should become discontinuous at the λ-point. However, the later results of Barmatz [65], taken closer to T_λ and with a velocity resolution of one part in 10^5, have not confirmed this discontinuity, but have implied a unique value for the sound velocity at the λ-point, $u_1(\lambda)$, of 217.05 m/sec. These data near T_λ are shown in Fig. 7.13; in the regions of overlap, they are consistent with the earlier measurements.

The Pippard relations, equations (7.3b) and (7.4b), may be used to derive equation (7.41b) for u_1 near the transition (V in cm³/g and C_P in ergs/g-deg):

$$\frac{1}{u_1^2} = \frac{\beta_T}{V} - \frac{T\alpha_P^2}{C_P} \qquad (7.41a)$$

$$\approx \frac{C_0 - \alpha_0 \epsilon V_\lambda T_\lambda}{\epsilon^2 V_\lambda^2 T_\lambda} - \frac{C_0}{\epsilon^2 V_\lambda^2 T_\lambda C_P} \qquad (7.41b)$$

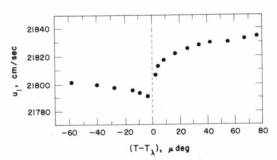

Fig. 7.13. Velocity of ordinary sound near the λ-transition at SVP [after Barmatz and Rudnick [65]].

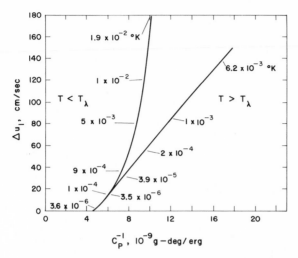

Fig. 7.14. Test of the relation $\Delta u_1 \propto 1/C_P$ for He^4 near the λ-point at SVP; temperatures indicate values of $|T - T_\lambda|$. [After Barmatz and Rudnick ([65]).]

where equation (7.41a) is thermodynamically exact. Since C_P is expected to become very large, the last relation implies no discontinuity in u_1 across the transition, as observed. From equation (7.41b), Barmatz has obtained the approximate expression: $\Delta u_1 = u_1 - u_1(\lambda) \approx A/C_P$, where A should be the same constant for He I and He II. A linear relation is obeyed by the data for $(T - T_\lambda) < 0.005°$K and for $(T_\lambda - T) < 0.001°$K, and as shown in Fig. 7.14, the two branches of a plot of Δu_1 vs. C_P^{-1} appear to coalesce at T_λ.

7.3.4. The Superfluid Density near the Transition

Clow and Reppy ([66]) have used a gyroscopic technique (see Section 8.1.1) to study the temperature dependence of the superfluid density ρ_s to within about 10^{-5} °K of T_λ. The method depends upon an earlier conclusion by the authors that the angular momentum of a persistent superfluid current displays the same temperature dependence as ρ_s. Thus, by normalizing the angular momentum measurements, they observed that ρ_s/ρ could be represented as

$$\rho_s/\rho \propto (t')^{0.67 \pm 0.03} \tag{7.42}$$

Now, in superfluid helium, the order parameter analogous to $|\rho - \rho_c| = \Delta\rho$ for liquid–vapor critical phenomena is related to the superfluid wave function. Clow and Reppy, assuming that this was given by the Ginzburg and Pitaevskii theory ([16]), used equation (7.11) for the definition of ρ_s and thereby concluded that the order parameter $|\Psi|$ should be proportional to $(t')^{0.335}$. This exponent is tantalizingly close to the value of β found for the critical points, so that the experiment appeared to confirm the proposed analogy between $\Delta\rho$ and $|\Psi|$.

On the other hand, Josephson ([67]) has pointed out the necessity for differentiating here between the superfluid density [which is defined by the hydrodynamic relation between the superfluid velocity $\mathbf{v}_s$ and the current density $\rho_s\mathbf{v}_s$—cf. equation (8.9)] and the order parameter describing the macroscopic occupation of the zero-momentum state. We call this latter quantity $\langle\psi(r)\rangle$, which, according to Josephson, is the proper analog to the order parameter usually involved in second-order phase transitions. This recalls our discussion of Section 5.1.3 concerning the distinction between ρ_0 and ρ_s. We know that at $T = 0°$K, $\rho_0 \neq \rho_s$, and since ρ_0 has not yet been observed experimentally, it is quite risky to set $|\Psi|$ proportional to $\langle\psi(r)\rangle$ at T_λ even though we know they both vanish there. As shown by Josephson, setting $|\Psi| \propto \langle\psi(r)\rangle$ implies that $\eta = 0$ in equation (7.20). Instead of equation (7.11), he then wrote

$$\rho_s \propto \langle\psi(r)\rangle^2 \xi^\eta \tag{7.43}$$

If we put $\langle\psi(r)\rangle \propto (t')^\beta$ and $\xi \propto (t')^{-v'}$, it follows from equation (7.43) that

$$\rho_s \propto (t')^{2\beta - \eta v'} \tag{7.44}$$

The Kadanoff-Widom scaling laws give the relation

$$2\beta - \eta v' = (2 - \alpha')/3 \tag{7.45}$$

where α' is the exponent in relation (7.15) when C_P replaces C_V. A logarithmic singularity in C_P at T_λ implies $\alpha' = 0$ and $(2\beta - \eta v') = \frac{2}{3}$. Josephson has suggested that since there is no evidence that η should be zero for helium at the λ-point, the results of Clow and Reppy indicate the validity of equation (7.45) rather than $\beta = \frac{1}{3}$.

Using the Andronikashvili method (oscillating stack of closely-spaced disks) Tyson and Douglass ([68]) claim to have measured ρ_s near T_λ more accurately than did Clow and Reppy. For the exponent in equation (7.42), i.e., $(2\beta - \eta v')$, they found 0.666 ± 0.006. By analyzing the $C_{sat} \approx C_P$ data of Fairbank et al. and Kellers ([4]), they deduced $\alpha' = 0.014 \pm 0.016$, or $(2 - \alpha')/3 = 0.0671 \pm 0.005$. Thus, equation (7.45) was confirmed. In addition, Tyson and Douglass showed that for helium, the exponent v' for the correlation length, i.e., $\xi = \xi_0(t')^{-v'}$, is formally identical to the exponent for ρ_s, and therefore numerically v' is essentially 2/3. This still leaves us with only one relation to determine the two unknowns, β and η. Also by assuming a low-temperature value for ξ_0 of the order of the interatomic distance, they calculated ξ to be $\sim 10^{-2}$ cm at $t' = 10^{-9}\,^\circ$K. Thus, in any experiments conducted so far, ξ is considerably smaller than the container size.

7.3.5. State Properties in the Vicinity of the λ-Line

The pressure *vs.* temperature phase diagram in the vicinity of the λ-line between the saturated vapor pressure curve and the melting curve is illustrated in Fig. 7.15. Several parameters of the λ-line selected from recent experiments are listed in Table 7.II (generally, we give only one reference for each entry; this is usually the latest report, and references to earlier work appear there).

Table 7.II. Properties of the λ-Line

Property	Value at the saturation curve	Value at the melting curve
P_λ (atm)	0.0497 (T_{58} Scale)	29.74 ± 0.05 ([70])
T_λ ($^\circ$K)	2.1720 (T_{58} Scale)	1.7633 ± 0.0001 ([70])
ρ_λ (g/cm^3)	0.14615 ([59])	0.18044 ± 0.00030 ([70])
$(dP/dT)_\lambda$ (atm/$^\circ$K)	-111.05 ± 0.10 ([70])	-55.05 ± 0.50 ([70])
$(d\rho/dT)$ (mg/cm^3-$^\circ$K)	-233.9 ± 1.1 ([70])	-42.3 ± 0.5 ([70])
u_1 (m/sec)	217.05 ([65])	340 ± 2 ([12])
C_V (J/g-$^\circ$K)	370 ± 50 ([4,12])	17 ± 2 ([12,71])
$(dS/dP)_\lambda$ (J/atm-g-$^\circ$K)	-2.25×10^{-2} ([65])	-1.3×10^{-2} ([71])
$(dS/dT)_\lambda$ [J/g-($^\circ$K)^2]	2.3 ([12,71])	0.6 ([12,71])

The λ-line. Determination of the λ-line is usually made through observation of a dramatic change in the character of some property of the liquid as T or P is varied through the λ-region. This, of course, requires an *a priori* judgement that the change in the property in question actually does occur at the true thermodynamic λ-point. A classic example of how one may be fooled in this respect concerns the changes in density near $T_{\lambda,\text{sat}}$. Until a few years ago, it was believed that $T_{\lambda,\text{sat}}$ occurred when ρ_{sat} reached a maximum, whereas now we know as a result of increased experimental precision that the maximum is several millidegrees above T_λ and that the transition is signalled instead by the rapid increase in $|d\rho_{\text{sat}}/dT|$. Another symptom often used to detect the transition is the rapid drop in thermal conduction by the liquid as T (or P) is increased through the λ-line—even though

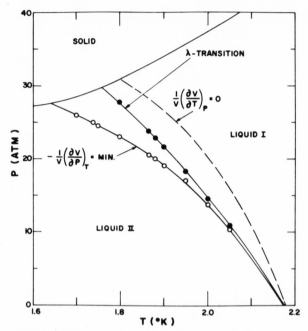

Fig. 7.15. $P-T$ phase diagram for He^4 in the vicinity of the λ-line, showing the loci for the vanishing of the expansion coefficient and the minima of the compressibility [from Grilly [72]].

until very recently, no experimental data existed to indicate how the thermal conductivity λ should behave on the high side of transition! It is still problematic whether the measurements of λ have sufficient resolution to assure the validity of this method for defining the transition (see Section 7.3.6).

It is therefore somewhat reassuring that mutually compatible $P-T$ coordinates for the λ-line can be selected from five completely distinct types of investigation: (1) from the locus of discontinuities in warm-up curves coupled with $P-V-T$ measurements [69,70]; (2) from the locus of the cusp in α_P observed in dielectric-constant measurements [61]; (3) from the locus of maxima in the isothermal compressibility above 10 atm [72]; (4) from the sound velocity measurements [65] using the Pippard relations; and (5) from the α_{sat} data [59] combined with specific-heat data [4] using equation (7.4c).

Two high-precision measurements of the slope of the λ-line, $(dP/dT)_\lambda$, have recently been reported, one by Elwell and Meyer [61], the other by Kierstead [70]. Their results are plotted in Fig. 7.16 as a function of temperature. While at conditions removed from $T_{\lambda,sat}$,

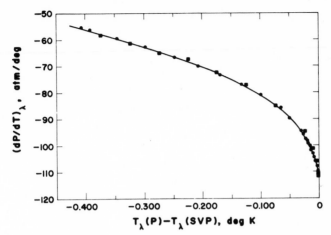

Fig. 7.16. The slope of the λ-line as a function of $T_\lambda(P)$: ■ [Elwell and Meyer[61]]; ● [Kierstead[70]]; solid line is average drawn for visualization [after Kierstead[70]].

the two sets of data are in substantial agreement, they differ considerably in the extrapolation to $T_{\lambda,sat}$: Elwell and Meyer give -114 ± 1 atm/deg for $(dP/dT)_\lambda$ at $T_{\lambda,sat}$, and Kierstead gives -111.05 ± 0.10 atm/deg. Clearly, the approach of the transition line to the lower triple point is qualitatively different from that to the upper triple point.

Kierstead[70] as well as others[61,69,71] have measured the density along the λ-line with mutually consistent results. Hence the (ρ, T, P) coordinates of the λ-line appear to be satisfactorily defined.

The $\alpha_P = 0$ Locus. Also shown in Fig. 7.15 is the locus in the P–T plane of points at which the density along an isobar becomes a maximum, i.e., where $\alpha_P = 0$. We have already mentioned that $\alpha_{sat} = 0$ at about 0.006°K above $T_{\lambda,sat}$; at higher pressures, as seen from the figure, the measurements of Grilly and Mills[73] for $24.1 < P < 30.9$ atm place the locus as much as 0.090°K above T_λ. Thus, not only is α_P negative, and therefore anomalous, in the He II region above about 1.15°K, but it is similarly anomalous in the He I region between the λ-line and $\alpha_P = 0$ locus.

The Expansion Coefficient. From dielectric-constant measurements, Elwell and Meyer[61] have closely examined the temperature variation of the molar volume along isobars in the vicinity of the λ-line. Values of α_P to within 2×10^{-5} °K of T_λ obtained from these data were fitted with the functional form of equation (7.39) (substituting α_P for α_{sat}). The results are shown in Fig. 7.12. Good agreement with this function was observed to within $5 \times 10^{-2}\,°K$ of T_λ; however, contrary to the case for α_{sat}, the curves for α_P above and below the transition are not parallel, as indicated by differences in A_I and A_II.

The Isothermal Compressibility. For normal substances, the coefficient of isothermal compressibility β_T has been observed to decrease with increasing pressure. Near the λ-line on the low-temperature side, an increase in β_T with P had been observed ([74]) as early as 1933, but only recently has this effect been examined directly in detail. Lounasmaa ([75]) measured β_T along an isotherm crossing the λ-line at $P_\lambda = 13.04$ atm and found β_T linear with $|P - P_\lambda|$ on both sides of the transition from 10^{-2} atm to within less than 10^{-3} atm of P_λ; but β_T displayed a 10% discontinuity at $P = P_\lambda$. More recently, Grilly ([72]) has obtained considerably more extensive data on β_T though with somewhat less resolution. These results are plotted in Fig. 7.17, from which we see that for $T > T_\lambda$ (2.20°K), β_T is well-behaved, whereas in the He II region, the isotherms pass through a broad minimum before rising to a cusp at the transition. The locus of these minima is shown in Fig. 7.15. Grilly found that near the transition, the observa-

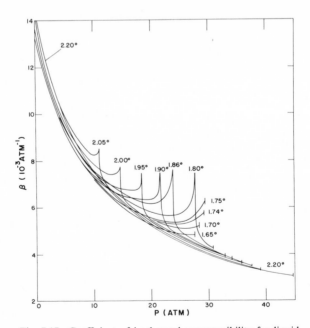

Fig. 7.17. Coefficient of isothermal compressibility for liquid He^4 as a function of pressure. Maxima of cusps indicate crossings of the λ-line [from Grilly ([72])].

tions along an isotherm were best fitted by the relation

$$(\beta_T - \beta_{2.2}) = C \log|P - P_\lambda| + D \qquad (7.46)$$

(which gives β_T at arbitrary T relative to β_T at $T = 2.20°K$) rather than by one linear in $|P - P_\lambda|$ as deduced by Lounasmaa ([75]). Here, C and D are both functions of T, with $C_I \neq C_{II}$ and $D_I \neq D_{II}$, so that as fitted by Grilly's data, equation (7.46) extrapolates to $|P - P_\lambda| = 10^{-3}$ atm, showing discontinuities in β_T consistent with Lounasmaa's observations. The resolution of the data is insufficient to determine the height of the cusps at $P = P_\lambda$.

The Pressure Coefficient. A typical isochore crossing the λ-line is shown in Fig. 7.18. From such plots, one may derive the pressure coefficient, $(\partial P/\partial T)_V = \alpha_P/\beta_T$, which is an important quantity entering into the thermodynamics of the λ-transition. Figure 7.19 illustrates $(\partial P/\partial T)_V$ at several densities as obtained by Lounasmaa and Kaunisto ([69]). Subsequent, more detailed studies of $(\partial P/\partial T)_V$, each along a single isochore, have been reported by Lounasmaa ([75]) ($P_\lambda = 13.04$ atm) and by Kierstead ([76,77]) (P_λ very close to the melting curve). The latest of these ([77]) provides data to within $2.5 \times 10^{-6}°K$ of T_λ and 5×10^{-5} atm of P_λ. All of the measurements in the vicinity of the transition have been represented by equations of the form

$$(\partial P/\partial T)_V = E \log|T - T_\lambda| + F \qquad (7.47)$$

for which $E_I \neq E_{II}$ and $F_I \neq F_{II}$. This indicates $(\partial P/\partial T)_V$ to be discontinuous and to display an asymmetric cusp about T_λ. However, it

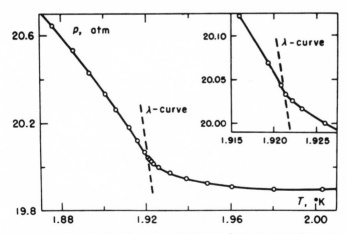

Fig. 7.18. A typical isochore ($\rho = 0.1724 \text{ g/cm}^3$) for liquid He⁴ crossing the λ-line [from Lounasmaa and Kaunisto ([69])].

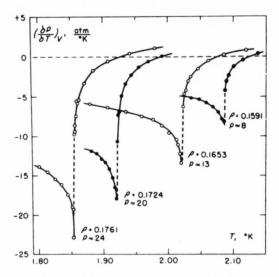

Fig. 7.19. Experimental determination of the pressure coefficient for several isochores crossing the λ-line (approximate pressures in atmospheres) [from Lounasmaa and Kaunisto ([69])].

is clear from Fig. 7.18 that $(\partial P/\partial T)_V$ can never become infinite, as extrapolation of the data using equation (7.47) suggests; and in fact, we see that $(\partial P/\partial T)_V$ can never exceed the slope of the λ-line at the point where the isochore crosses. Similarly, we suspect the implied discontinuity of being nonphysical.

Thermal Properties. The most extensive and reliable thermal properties of the liquid near the transition are derivable from the constant-volume specific-heat measurements of Lounasmaa and Kojo ([71]). A plot of log C_V vs. T for various densities is presented in Fig. 7.20, while the entropy–temperature diagram derived from these results is given in Fig. 7.21. From the former, it appears that the height of the cusp at the λ-transition decreases as the density increases, though we must realize that the spacing of points is much coarser than found in the work of Fairbank et al. ([4]). We note the curious crossing of the entropy curves in Fig. 7.21. Through the thermodynamic relation

$$(\partial S/\partial P)_T = -(\partial V/\partial T)_P = -V\alpha_P \qquad (7.48)$$

we see that the anomalous behavior of α_P and the anomalous increase of entropy with compression are intimately related. The experimental results are completely consistent with this relation.

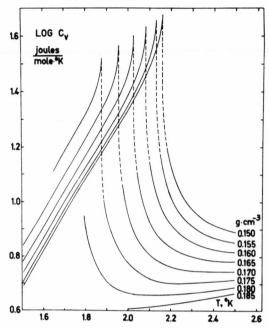

Fig. 7.20. Smoothed experimental results for log C_V of liquid He^4 plotted against temperature for several densities [from Lounasmaa and Kojo ([71])].

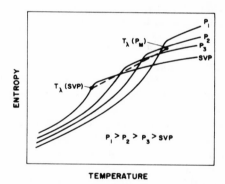

Fig. 7.21. Entropy of liquid He^4 as a function of T for several pressures, showing the anomalous region of positive $(\partial S / \partial P)_T$—schematic. Dashed curve shows the λ-line from the saturated vapor pressure to the melting pressure, P_m.

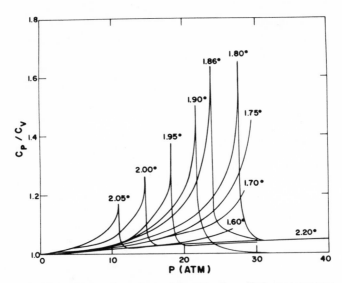

Fig. 7.22. Pressure dependence of the ratio of specific heat at constant volume to that at constant pressure for liquid He[4] at several temperatures [from Grilly ([72])].

Another thermal property of interest is $C_P/C_V = \beta_T/\beta_S = \beta_T \rho u_1^2$. Grilly ([72]) combined his compressibility data with measurements of sound velocity ([78]) and density ([74]) near the transition line to obtain the C_P/C_V results graphed in Fig. 7.22. Again the experiments are not sufficiently refined to establish the heights of the peaks.

7.3.6. Transport Properties in the Vicinity of the λ-Line

It is unfortunate that so little is known about the dynamic properties of liquid He[4] near the λ-transition. Studies ([79]) of the viscosity coefficient at SVP in He I and He II have indicated that η is continuous at the λ-point, but that $d\eta/dT$ displays a singularity. In the He II region, η appeared to have the same temperature dependence as ρ_n but the data cannot quantitatively define the approach to T_λ. Nor is there any information on η at higher pressures along the λ-line.

Behavior of the superfluid critical velocity as $T \to T_\lambda$ has recently been reported, and this will be discussed in the next chapter (Section 8.1.3b).

The only transport-phenomenon data available near the λ-line are the recent thermal conductivity measurements in He I by Kerrisk and Keller ([80]). These experiments used the same apparatus as for determining the thermal conductivity coefficient λ in the critical region

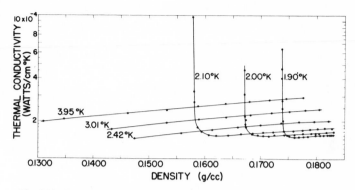

Fig. 7.23. Thermal conductivity of liquid He I as a function of density for several temperatures. For the three isotherms below 2.17°K, the curves rise steeply as the λ-line is approached [from Kerrisk and Keller ([80])].

of He³ (Section 7.2.5). They consisted of measurements along eleven isotherms between 1.77° and 2.15°K, from 34 atm down to within about 0.01 atm (or $\sim 10^{-4}$ °K) of the transition curve. As the λ-region is approached from above, all of the isotherms pass through a rather broad thermal conductivity minimum, the P–T locus of which lies parallel to and some 30–40 mdeg above the λ-line. Typical isotherm behavior on a density plot is shown in Fig. 7.23, where it is seen that λ rises very steeply near the transition.

Ferrell *et al.* ([31]) have considered the fluctuations in first and second sound modes near the λ-transition and used a scaling-law argument to deduce the following singular behavior for the thermal conductivity:

$$\lambda = \lambda_0 (2T_\lambda/t')^{1/3} \ln^{1/2}(2T_\lambda/t') e^{-4/3} \qquad (7.49)$$

where the dominant factor is $(2T_\lambda/t')^{1/3}$. These authors analyzed the raw data of Kerrisk and Keller for several instances where the "cold" plate of the thermal-conductivity cell was held at fixed P and T near the transition while successive increments in power were added to the "hot" plate (each data point in Fig. 7.23 was obtained from the $\Delta T = 0$ extrapolation of such a procedure). Typical results for this analysis are indicated in Fig. 7.24, where the solid curve represents the function of equation (7.49). The theory does indeed reproduce the shape of the experimental curve when λ_0 is normalized to the data. The calculated value of λ_0 is about one-third too small, which is satisfactory considering the approximations in the theory.

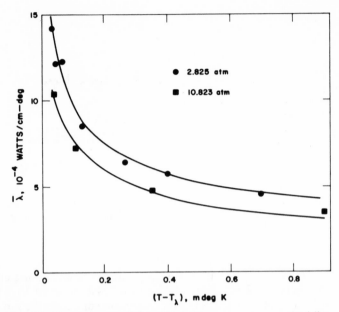

Fig. 7.24. Thermal conductivity of He I at two pressures near the λ-line. Experimental points are from Kerrisk and Keller ([80]). Solid curves are according to equation (7.49) with λ_0 adjusted to best fit the data. The ordinate is given as $\bar{\lambda} \approx \frac{3}{2}\lambda$, where the factor $\frac{3}{2}$ comes about from the averaging of λ over ΔT [see Ferrell et al. ([31]) for details]. [Drawn after Ferrell et al. ([31]).]

7.3.7. Depression of the λ-Point in Small Geometries

It has been known for some time that in small geometries, the λ-point temperature is lower than in bulk liquid. This effect does not become noticeable until the smallest linear dimension of the sample is less than the order of 1 μ; but in extremely narrow channels and in the film (both saturated and unsaturated), a decrease in T_λ of more than 1°K is possible. The theory of Ginzburg and Pitaevskii ([16]) qualitatively predicts the depression. On the other hand, there is confusion as to what properties of the liquid signal the transition, as observed maxima in the specific heat for samples of restricted geometry indicate a different T_λ than do experiments on the onset of superfluid flow determined either by heat flow or fourth sound. This is a very complex and not well-understood problem which we shall not discuss here, although we should be aware of its existence. Brewer ([89]) and Manchester ([90]) have reviewed this subject. In addition, two notes ([91]) on fourth sound point out some of the problems here, while computations ([92]) of the properties of a nearly (2-d) BE gas are also germane.

7.4. SOME COMMENTS ON THE CRITICAL SINGULARITIES IN He³ AND He⁴

From the limited number of critical systems we have examined here we are hardly justified in proposing answers to the general questions listed at the beginning of this chapter. Nevertheless, it does seem worthwhile to explore the extent to which our present restricted knowledge allows us to compare the λ-transition with the liquid–vapor critical points of He³ and He⁴ and of "classical" fluids.

If we proceed from where our knowledge is most deficient, we are forced to start with transport phenomena. The scarcity of reliable experimental data in this area surely deserves urgent consideration and remedy. However, there does appear to be a great deal of similarity among the thermal conductivity singularities for He I approaching the λ-transition, for the He³ critical point, and for the CO_2 critical point.

The role played by quantum effects in critical phenomena also remains largely undetermined. The most cogent comments on this matter have come from Yang and Yang ([35]), whose conjectures concerning the shape of the vapor pressure curve near T_c and the relative strengths of the C_V singularities in noble gases appear to have been confirmed by experiments. We recall that the basis for these predictions assumed that $C_V \to \infty$ as $\log t$, while some doubt remains whether this is the correct limiting form for C_V. In only a few systems has C_V been observed to tend to a "logarithmic infinity" at T_c, so that one can hardly claim generality for such behavior from experimental evidence. At the same time, the C_V data for He³ and He⁴ ([52]) are really not sufficiently extensive or well-defined to lend unambiguous support to the notion of a logarithmic singularity.

Strictly speaking, of course, experiments can never observe an infinite specific heat. The influence of statistical thermal fluctuations intervenes at some small temperature away from the critical point and renders physically meaningless the limiting extrapolations $t \to 0$ and $C_V \to \infty$. Similar remarks apply to the behavior of other thermodynamic coefficients. For the case of the He⁴ λ-point, Goldstein ([81]) has pointed out that for $t' < \sim 10^{-12}\,°K$, thermal fluctuations should become important, and here the system would be an unspecified mixture of He I and He II. Although many measured properties of the λ-region have been fitted by the logarithmic form, implying an infinite limiting behavior, Goldstein notes that none of these properties has really become large; furthermore, for them to become large would require extension of the observations to considerably less than $10^{-12}\,°K$ of the transition. For instance, according to equation (7.37), at $(T_\lambda - T) = -t' = 10^{-6}\,°K$, $C_{sat} = 17.35$ J/g-deg, while at $-t' = 10^{-12}\,°K$, C_{sat} is barely double that value. It is not difficult to construct a direct thermodynamic argument to demonstrate that

C_V cannot become infinite along the λ-line in He^4. In essence it proceeds as follows: Consider $S(V, T)$ and expand the total differential $dS(V, T)$ as

$$dS(V, T) = (\partial S/\partial T)_V \, dT + (\partial S/\partial V)_T \, dV$$

$$= (C_V/T) \, dT + (\partial P/\partial T)_V \, dV \qquad (7.50)$$

Then, taking the total derivatives along the λ-line and solving for C_V, we find

$$C_V = T(dS/dT)_\lambda - T(\partial P/\partial T)_V (dV/dT)_\lambda \qquad (7.51)$$

Each of the three derivatives appearing in the last equation is certainly finite, and so C_V must be finite as well—though of course it may become very large.

In the specific limit of $T_{\lambda,\mathrm{sat}}$, the above conclusion should be equally valid as elsewhere along the λ-line. Corroboration for this has been cited by Kellers ([4]), who derived a finite limiting value for C_V from his measurements of C_{sat} (Table 7.II). Goldstein ([81]) calculated a value about one-quarter of this. Also, the high-resolution sound-velocity data of Barmatz and Rudnick ([65]) indicate a finite value for u_1 at $T_{\lambda,\mathrm{sat}}$ which is thermodynamically consistent with a finite value for C_V. In this respect, the sound-velocity data for He^4 near the critical point ([39]) differ qualitatively from those at the λ-point inasmuch as the former tend to suggest the impossibility of sound propagation (i.e., $u_1 \to 0$) at the critical point. This, implying that $C_V \to \infty$ at T_c, remains a puzzling feature, but also hints at the possibility that fundamental differences exist between the λ-transition and other critical phenomena.

Because $(\partial P/\partial T)_V$ for liquid He^4 has been represented through equation (7.47) to exhibit a finite jump at the λ-line, it follows from equation (7.51) that a jump should also occur in C_V. However, our reservations about the reality of the jump in $(\partial P/\partial T)_V$ as $T \to T_\lambda$ lead us to suggest that C_V should remain continuous through the transition.

Let us now see what help we can get from the microscopic theories of C_V. Beginning with the ideal BE gas, we recall that C_V is continuous and finite through T_c but suffers a discontinuity of slope, dC_V/dT. Brout ([82]) has shown how the Hartree–Fock approximation applied to He^4 in the region above T_c leads to a qualitative change in the transition (because of the difficulty in treating the macroscopic occupation of the zero-momentum state, the theory does not include the region $T < T_c$). The result of Brout's calculation was to introduce a term in the energy which gives rise to a discontinuous specific heat at T_c as well as a steep increase in C_V as $T \to T_c$ from above. At T_c, C_V is 12 times the ideal gas value, which is too large for He^4. [An energy spectrum with an energy gap produces similar changes in C_V ([83]), but we know that such a spectrum is not proper for He^4.]

More recent refinements of the theory by De Coen and Tompa ([84]) have given a nearly quantitative representation of the experiments ([71]) including the minimum on the high side of T_λ displayed in Fig. 7.20. We are therefore led to conclude that the best evidence suggests for the λ-transition in He⁴ a finite C_V without a discontinuity at T_λ.

We turn now to C_P, which, for the classical case, exhibits the essential singularity of the critical point, becoming infinite as $T \to T_c$. We recall Landau's conclusion that $C_P \to \infty$ as $|t|^{-1/2}$, which is a considerably stronger singularity than a logarithmic one; and C_P for many classical substances does indeed become very large. For liquid He near $T_{\lambda,\mathrm{sat}}$, C_P is very nearly equivalent to C_{sat}, which ostensibly proceeds logarithmically to infinity. We have also mentioned earlier our reservations about this behavior as suggested by the trend of the data for $-t \leqslant 10^{-5}$ °K—this is presumably independent of thermal fluctuation effects. There is a possibility that C_P should be finite at the λ-point.

Again we appeal to the microscopic theory. For the ideal BE gas, C_P also becomes infinite at T_c. But for the hard-sphere BE fluid model, Sikora and Mohling ([85]) have demonstrated that as $T \to T_c$ from above, C_P tends to a finite limit but with a logarithmically infinite slope. According to the authors, this conclusion depends importantly upon the long-wavelength phonon excitations of the system. It should therefore apply to any BE fluid possessing a phononlike excitation spectrum at low momenta—and thus presumably to the real liquid He⁴. On the other hand, Patashinskii and Pokrovskii ([86]) have presented strong arguments showing that near the λ-transition, liquid He behaves as an ideal quasiparticle gas obeying the dispersion relation, $\epsilon = Ap^{3/2}$, which is not a phonon spectrum. This leads to an infinite C_P at T_λ described by a relation with the form of equation (7.37). Quite a bit depends upon which of these theories is the more realistic for liquid He and the resolution of this dilemma, since other singularities, such as in α_P and β_T, are intimately connected to the singularity in C_P.

While these uncertainties about the nature of C_P persist, it seems worthwhile to mention one of the currently popular models for other critical points which does *not* give realistic results for liquid He at T_λ. The 3-d Ising model predicts C_P to behave like: $A|t|^{-0.2} + B|t| + C$. Fairbank and Kellers ([87]) have indicated that this relation fits the experimental λ-point data over only a limited region and is especially poor for $t' < 10^{-3}$ °K.

Although there are severe doubts about the exact limiting form of the thermodynamic derivatives *at* the λ-transition, the experimental evidence taken together strongly supports logarithmic forms for such quantities as C_P, C_V, β_T, α_P, and $(\partial P/\partial T)_V$ *near* the transition. Lounasmaa ([75]), by examining the interrelations between these quantities on the basis of the Ehrenfest-like expressions of Pippard ([10]) and of Buckingham and Fairbank ([12]), has found several apparent numerical inconsistencies which cast doubt upon either the data or the theories. However, in a recent paper, Lee and Puff ([88]) have indicated how these inconsistencies may be removed. Starting with several reasonable assumptions concerning the thermodynamic fluctuations and the derivatives of the grand partition function near the λ-line, they have deduced expansions of the form:

$$X_y = X_1^{I,II} + X_2 \log|t'| + O(|t'|) \qquad (7.52)$$

where X_y is either β_T, α_P, or C_P, and $X_1^{I,II}$, and X_2 are constants with the superscripts indicating the appropriate phase, He I or He II. The $X_1^{I,II}$ and X_2 are explicitly defined by the theory in terms of the λ-point parameters, such as T_λ, P_λ, ρ_λ, ϵ, C_0, and α_0, associated with the Pippard relations. When only the first two terms in equation (7.52) are used, the agreement with the available data is reassuringly good.

In seeking a fundamental underlying similarity among various types of critical phenomenon, we find that the scaling laws seem to offer at present the most rewarding approach. As emphasized before, rather than "laws," these are hypotheses which need to be proved. We have also seen how these ideas are useful in correlating several critical properties and as well how they apparently fail—specifically, for the case of the exponent δ. Much experimental work is required in this area, which hopefully will lead to a clearer understanding of critical phenomena. In the case of He^4 the testing of these hypotheses is particularly urgent, for the nature of the λ-transition remains one of the most important unsolved problems of liquid helium.

REFERENCES

1. L. Onsager, *Phys. Rev.*, **65**, 117 (1944).
2. E. Ising, *Z. Phys.*, **31**, 253 (1925).
3. C. N. Yang and T. D. Lee, *Phys. Rev.*, **87**, 404 (1952); T. D. Lee and C. N. Yang, *ibid*, 410.
4. W. M. Fairbank, M. J. Buckingham, and C. F. Kellers, in *Low Temperature Physics and Chemistry*, *LT-5* (J. R. Dillinger, ed.), p. 50, University of Wisconsin Press (1958); C. F. Kellers, Thesis, Duke University (1960).
5. M. I. Bagatskii, A. V. Voronel, and V. G. Gusak, *Zh. Eksperim. i Teor. Fiz.*, **43**, 728 (1962) [English translation, *Soviet Phys.—JETP*, **16**, 517 (1963)].
6. A. V. Voronel, Yr. R. Chashkin, V. A. Popov, and V. G. Simkin, *Zh. Eksperim. i Teor. Fiz.*, **45**, 828 (1963) [English translation, *Soviet Phys.—JETP*, **18**, 568 (1964)].
7. G. E. Uhlenbeck, in *Critical Phenomena* (M. S. Green and J. V. Sengers, eds.), p. 3, NBS Misc. Pub. 273, Washington (1966).
8. M. E. Fisher, *J. Math. Phys.*, **5**, 944 (1964).
9. M. S. Green, in *Critical Phenomena* (M. S. Green and J. V. Sengers, eds.), p. ix, NBS Misc. Pub. 273, Washington (1966).

10. A. B. Pippard, *The Elements of Classical Thermodynamics*, Cambridge University Press (1960). See especially Chapter 9.
11. C. E. Chase, E. Maxwell, and W. E. Millett, *Physica*, **27**, 1129 (1961).
12. M. J. Buckingham and W. M. Fairbank, in *Progress in Low Temperature Physics* (C. J. Gorter, ed.), Vol. III, p. 80, North Holland, Amsterdam (1961).
13. L. D. Landau and E. M. Lifshitz, *Statistical Physics*, Chapters 8 and 14, Addison-Wesley, Reading, Mass. (1958).
14. V. L. Ginzburg, *Fiz. Tverd. Tela*, **2**, 2031 (1960) [English translation, *Soviet Phys.—Solid State*, **2**, 1824 (1960)].
15. V. L. Ginzburg and L. D. Landau, *Zh. Eksperim. i Teor. Fiz.*, **20**, 1064 (1950).
16. V. L. Ginzburg and L. P. Pitaevskii, *Zh. Eksperim. i Teor. Fiz.*, **34**, 1240 (1958) [English translation, *Soviet Phys.—JETP*, **7**, 858 (1958)].
17. L. Tisza, *Ann. Phys. (N.Y.)*, **13**, 1 (1961).
18. C. Domb, in *Critical Phenomena* (M. S. Green and J. V. Sengers, eds.), p. 29, NBS Misc. Pub. 273, Washington (1966).
19. L. S. Ornstein and F. Zernike, *Proc. Acad. Sci. Amsterdam*, **17**, 793 (1914); *Physik. Z.*, **19**, 134 (1918).
20. M. E. Fisher, in *Critical Phenomena* (M. S. Green and J. V. Sengers, eds.), p. 21, NBS Misc. Pub. 273, Washington (1966).
21. G. S. Rushbrook, *J. Chem. Phys.* **39**, 842 (1963).
22. J. W. Essam and M. E. Fisher, *J. Chem. Phys.*, **38**, 802 (1963).
23. B. Widom, *J. Chem. Phys.*, **41**, 1633 (1964).
24. B. Widom, *J. Chem. Phys.*, **43**, 3898 (1965).
25. R. B. Griffiths, *Phys. Rev. Letters* **14**, 623 (1965).
26. J. S. Rowlinson, in *Critical Phenomena* (M. S. Green and J. V. Sengers, eds.), p. 9, NBS Misc. Pub. 273, Washington (1966).
27. L. P. Kadanoff, *Physics*, **2**, 263 (1966).
28. R. B. Griffiths, *Phys. Rev.*, **158**, 176 (1967).
29. L. P. Kadanoff, W. Götze, D. Hamblen, R. Hecht, E. A. S. Lewis, V. V. Palciauskas, M. Rayl, J. Swift, D. Aspnes, and J. Kane, *Rev. Mod. Phys.*, **39**, 395 (1967).
30. M. S. Green, M. Vincentini-Missoni, and J. M. H. Levelt Sengers, *Phys. Rev. Letters*, **18**, 1113 (1967).
31. R. A. Ferrell, N. Menyhárd, H. Schmidt, F. Schwabl, and P. Szépfalusy, *Phys. Rev. Letters*, **18**, 891 (1967); *Ann. Phys. (N.Y.)*, **47**, 565 (1968).
32. B. I. Halperin and P. C. Hohenberg, *Phys. Rev. Letters*, **19**, 700, 940 (1967).
33. D. R. Johnston, G. J. Oudemans, and R. H. Cole, *J. Chem. Phys.*, **33**, 1310 (1960).
34. R. H. Sherman and E. C. Kerr, Proc. of LT-10, Vol. I, p. 325, Moscow (1967). Private communication.
35. C. N. Yang and C. P. Yang, *Phys. Rev. Letters*, **13**, 303 (1964).
36. M. H. Edwards and W. C. Woodbury, *Phys. Rev.*, **129**, 1911 (1963).
37. L. A. Landau and E. M. Lifshitz, *Statistical Physics*, Addison-Wesley, Reading, Mass. (1958), Sections 79–81.
38. L. Tisza and C. E. Chase, *Phys. Rev. Letters*, **15**, 4 (1965).
39. C. E. Chase, R. C. Williamson, and L. Tisza, *Phys. Rev. Letters*, **13**, 467 (1964); C. E. Chase and R. C. Williamson, in *Critical Phenomena* (M. S. Green and J. V. Sengers, eds.), p. 197, NBS Misc. Pub. 273, Washington (1966).
40. L. Mistura and D. Sette, *Phys. Rev. Letters*, **16**, 268 (1966).
41. M. J. Buckingham, in *Critical Phenomena* (M. S. Green and J. V. Sengers, eds.), p. 95, NBS Misc. Pub. 273, Washington (1966).
42. M. H. Edwards, *Phys. Rev. Letters*, **15**, 348 (1965).
43. P. R. Roach and D. H. Douglas, Jr., *Phys. Rev. Letters*, **17**, 1083 (1966).
44. M. H. Edwards, Proc. of LT-10, Vol. I, p. 592, Moscow (1967).
45. P. R. Roach and D. H. Douglas, Jr., *Phys. Rev. Letters*, **19**, 287 (1967); P. R. Roach, *Phys. Rev.*, **170**, 213 (1968).

46. R. H. Sherman, *Phys. Rev. Letters*, **15**, 141 (1965).
47. C. E. Chase and G. O. Zimmerman, *Phys. Rev. Letters*, **15**, 483 (1965).
48. R. H. Sherman and E. F. Hammel, *Phys. Rev. Letters*, **15**, 9 (1965).
49. M. E. Fisher, *Phys. Rev. Letters*, **16**, 11 (1966).
50. J. de Boer, *Physica*, **14**, 139 (1948); J. de Boer and B. S. Blaisse, *Physica*, **14**, 149 (1948); J. de Boer and R. J. Lunbeck, *Physica*, **14**, 510, 520 (1948).
51. G. O. Zimmerman and C. E. Chase, *Phys. Rev. Letters*, **19**, 151 (1967).
52. M. R. Moldover and W. A. Little, *Phys. Rev. Letters*, **15**, 54 (1965); M. R. Moldover, Thesis, Stanford University (1966).
53. L. P. Kadanoff and J. Swift, *Phys. Rev.*, **166**, 89 (1968).
54. J. F. Kerrisk and W. E. Keller (to be published); J. F. Kerrisk, Thesis, U. of N.M., 1968.
55. A. Michels, J. V. Sengers, and P. S. Van der Gulik, *Physica*, **28**, 1201, 1216 (1962); A. Michels and J. V. Sengers, *Physica*, **28**, 1238 (1962).
56. J. V. Sengers, in *Critical Phenomena* (M. S. Green and J. V. Sengers, eds.), p. 165, NBS Misc. Pub. 273, Washington (1966).
57. K. R. Atkins and M. H. Edwards, *Phys. Rev.* **97**, 1429 (1955).
58. M. H. Edwards, *Can. J. Phys.*, **36**, 884 (1958).
59. E. C. Kerr and R. D. Taylor, *Ann. Phys. (N.Y.)*, **26**, 292 (1964).
60. V. P. Peshkov and A. P. Borovikov, *Zh. Eksperim. i Teor. Fiz.*, **50**, 852 (1966) [English translation, *Soviet Phys.–JETP*, **23**, 559 (1966)].
61. D. Elwell and H. Meyer, *Phys. Rev.*, **164**, 245 (1967).
62. A. van Itterbeek and G. Forrez, *Physica*, **20**, 133 (1954).
63. C. E. Chase, *Phys. Fluids*, **1**, 193 (1958).
64. I. Rudnick and K. A. Shapiro, *Phys. Rev. Letters*, **15**, 386 (1965).
65. M. B. Barmatz and I. Rudnick, Proc. of LT-10, Vol. I, p. 512, Moscow (1967); M. B. Barmatz, Thesis, UCLA (1966); M. Barmatz and I. Rudnick, *Phys. Rev.*, **170**, 224 (1968).
66. J. R. Clow and J. D. Reppy, *Phys. Rev. Letters*, **16**, 887 (1966).
67. B. D. Josephson, *Physics Letters*, **21**, 608 (1966).
68. J. A. Tyson and D. H. Douglass, Jr., *Phys. Rev. Letters*, **17**, 472, 622 (1966); J. A. Tyson, *Phys. Rev.* **166**, 166 (1968).
69. O. V. Lounasmaa and L. Kaunisto, *Ann. Acad. Sci. Fennicae*, Ser. AVI, No. 59 (1960).
70. H. A. Kierstead, *Phys. Rev.*, **162**, 153 (1967).
71. O. V. Lounasmaa and E. Kojo, *Ann. Acad. Sci. Fennicae*, Ser. AVI, No. 36 (1959).
72. E. R. Grilly, *Phys. Rev.*, **149**, 97 (1966).
73. E. R. Grilly and R. L. Mills, *Ann. Phys. (N.Y.)*, **18**, 250 (1962).
74. W. H. Keesom and A. P. Keesom, *Physica*, **1**, 128 (1934); Leiden Communications Suppl. No. 7b (1933).
75. O. V. Lounasmaa, *Phys. Rev.*, **130**, 847 (1963).
76. H. A. Kierstead, *Phys. Rev.*, **138**, A1594 (1965).
77. H. A. Kierstead, *Phys. Rev.*, **153**, 258 (1967).
78. K. R. Atkins and R. A. Stasior, *Can. J. Phys.*, **31**, 1156 (1953).
79. R. D. Taylor and J. G. Dash, *Phys. Rev.*, **106**, 398 (1957).
80. J. Kerrisk and W. E. Keller, *Bull. Amer. Phys. Soc.*, Ser. II, **12**, 555 (1967).
81. L. Goldstein, *Phys. Rev.*, **135**, A1471 (1964); **140**, A1547 (1965).
82. R. Brout, *Phys. Rev.*, **131**, 899 (1963).
83. F. London, *Superfluids*, Vol. II, p. 55, John Wiley, New York (1954).
84. J. L. De Coen and H. Tompa, *Physica*, **32**, 995 (1966).
85. P. Sikora and F. Mohling, Los Alamos Sci. Lab. Report LA-DC 8333 (1967).
86. A. Z. Patashinskii and V. L. Pokrovskii, *Zh. Eksperim. i Teor. Fiz.*, **46**, 994 (1964) [English translation, *Soviet Phys.—JETP*, **19**, 677 (1964)].
87. W. M. Fairbank and C. F. Kellers, in *Critical Phenomena* (M. S. Green and J. V. Sengers, eds.), p. 71, NBS Misc. Pub. 273, Washington (1966).

88. K. C. Lee and R. D. Puff, *Phys. Rev.,* **158,** 170 (1967).
89. D. F. Brewer, in *Superfluid Helium* (J. F. Allen, ed.), p. 159, Academic Press, London (1966); Proc. of LT-10, Vol. I, p. 145, Moscow (1967).
90. F. D. Manchester, *Rev. Mod. Phys.,* **39,** 383 (1967).
91. I. Rudnick, E. Guyon, K. A. Shapiro, and S. A. Scott, *Phys. Rev. Letters,* **19,** 488 (1967); D. F. Brewer, G. W. Leppelmeier, C. C. Lim, D. O. Edwards, and J. Landau, *Phys. Rev. Letters,* **19,** 491 (1967).
92. D. F. Goble and L. E. H. Trainor, *Can. J. Phys.,* **44,** 27 (1966).

Flowing Liquid He II: Critical Velocities and Dissipation Functions

In Chapter 1, we remarked that the two-fluid equations of motion

$$\rho_s \, D\mathbf{v}_s/Dt = -(\rho_s/\rho)\,\nabla P + \rho_s s\,\nabla T \qquad (8.1)$$

and

$$\rho_n \, D\mathbf{v}_n/Dt = -(\rho_n/\rho)\,\nabla P - \rho_s s\,\nabla T - \eta_n \nabla \times \nabla \times \mathbf{v}_n \qquad (8.2)$$

where

$$D\mathbf{v}/Dt = \partial \mathbf{v}/\partial t + (\mathbf{v} \cdot \nabla)\mathbf{v} \qquad (8.3)$$

are generally valid only in the limit of vanishing velocities. However, if, for example, $\mathbf{v}_n$ becomes large, we expect, in analogy with ordinary hydrodynamics, that the laminar flow described by equation (8.2) will be modified by the onset of turbulence. Similarly, with increasing values of $\mathbf{v}_s$, it is physically reasonable that the frictionless character of the superfluid flow should be violated by the appearance of some sort of dissipation process. And, finally, at sufficiently large relative velocities, $\mathbf{v}_r = \mathbf{v}_n - \mathbf{v}_s$, the assumption that the two velocity fields are independent ought to fail, and we should see some evidence for the mutual interaction between these fields. In other words, associated with each of the velocities $\mathbf{v}_n$, $\mathbf{v}_s$, and $\mathbf{v}_r$, will be a sort of critical velocity, which we call $\mathbf{v}_{n,c}$, $\mathbf{v}_{s,c}$, and $\mathbf{v}_{r,c}$, respectively, each signaling the onset of a flow regime different from that described by the steady-state linear equations of motion and therefore indicating the necessity for including one or more additional terms into these equations.

Several alternate schemes for adding the nonlinear terms have been proposed. Here, we shall take a phenomenological approach which has been widely and successfully used. Equations (8.1) and (8.2) become, respectively,

$$\rho_s \, D\mathbf{v}_s/Dt = -(\rho_s/\rho)\,\nabla P + \rho_s s\,\nabla T - \mathbf{F}_s - \mathbf{F}_{sn} \qquad (8.4)$$

273

and

$$\rho_n \, D\mathbf{v}_n/Dt = -(\rho_n/\rho) \, \nabla P - \rho_s s \, \nabla T - \eta_n \nabla \times \nabla \times \mathbf{v}_n$$

$$+ (2\eta_n + \eta') \nabla(\nabla \cdot \mathbf{v}_n) + \mathbf{F}_{sn} - \mathbf{F}_n \qquad (8.5)$$

The superfluid equation contains two new generalized forces, $\mathbf{F}_s$ to describe frictional processes involving the superfluid alone, and $\mathbf{F}_{sn}$ to account for the interaction between normal fluid and superfluid. This mutual force is also included in the normal fluid equation, but with opposite sign, along with an extra force $\mathbf{F}_n$ due to some as yet unspecified dissipation in the normal fluid. Finally, η' stands for the coefficient of second, or bulk, viscosity which describes energy losses when changes in density occur rapidly in comparison with the relaxation time required for restoration of thermodynamic equilibrium. If the fluid is incompressible, $\nabla \cdot \mathbf{v}_n = 0$ and the bulk viscosity term in equation (8.5) vanishes.

By postulating the three generalized forces acting on the fluid, it would seem that we have pretty well covered ourselves to meet any eventuality encountered in the flow of liquid He II. However, these arbitrary forces take on meaning only when they can be associated with well-defined physical processes such that their character and occurrence may be reliably specified. In other words, we should like to know the conditions for the critical velocity which signal the onset of each type of dissipation and as well the velocity dependence of each once the critical value has been exceeded. Since an immense variety of flow processes are possible in He II and since experimental difficulties have often prevented reproducible observations from being made even for the same process, the achievement of a consistent hydrodynamic formulation for the liquid has not been easy. Nevertheless, thanks to several recent exciting experimental and theoretical developments, we are now in a position to differentiate among the various dissipation processes and quantitatively characterize them to a rather remarkable degree.

The present chapter summarizes this progress by treating in turn $\mathbf{F}_s$, $\mathbf{F}_{s,n}$, and $\mathbf{F}_n$ and the respective critical velocities. The major emphasis is placed on questions concerning the destruction of superfluidity, since these have the deepest significance. A final section is devoted to some remarks about dissipation processes at very low temperature, with particular regard to the attenuation of sound waves in the liquid.

We reemphasize that the formalism used here is far from unique, and that despite the wide range of nonlinear equations proposed for describing the thermohydrodynamical behavior of He II, no single set is altogether satisfactory. The derivation of the linear equations for

He II has generally proceeded from the usual three conservation rules for mass, momentum, and entropy, plus an additional arbitrary relation extracted from the observed behavior of the liquid in order to specify the unusual superfluid properties—most often this additional relation is simply the superfluid equation of motion [however, see Lin ([1])]. When dissipative processes are considered, extra terms must be included in the momentum and entropy balances and in the additional specifying equation. It is here that the greatest divergences appear among the various authors. Reviews of early attempts to formulate the nonlinear equations have been presented by Dingle ([2]), by Daunt and Smith ([3]), and by London ([4]). Finally, the hydrodynamics constructed by Landau and Khalatnikov and summarized recently in the latter's monograph ([5]) has several distinct advantages over the others, as will become apparent in the section dealing with sound absorption.

   The material covered in this chapter predominantly concerns linear flow process, although limited references are made to rotating helium. This emphasis should not be construed as minimizing the importance of the latter subject. Rather, it results from a combination of two circumstances: the principal interest of the author and the recent appearance of several thorough reviews of the rotating He II problem by Andronikashvili and Mamaladze ([6]).

8.1. THE DESTRUCTION OF SUPERFLUIDITY

8.1.1. Persistent Superfluid Currents

   Since our objective is to describe the manner in which superfluidity is destroyed, it is worthwhile to examine first some of the evidence for the existence of dissipationless flow. Let us consider a situation in which the normal fluid is at rest and the superfluid is moving at low speeds. Then equation (8.1) alone should describe the motion of the system, and, because there are no frictional forces implied by this relation, the fluid once put into motion should flow in this mode forever. In other words, a persistent superfluid current should be established, and the observation of such a current should be the ultimate direct test of true superfluidity. Accordingly, a considerable effort has been directed toward the creation, detection, and characterization of persistent currents.

   We may easily appreciate that for proving the existence of persistent currents, a necessary experimental arrangement is one having a continuous flow path, which suggests the use of axially symmetric geometries. A container with this character may be rotated under conditions which bring all the superfluid into solid-body rotation (for example, by rotating the system while it is cooled through the λ-point). Then the rotation is stopped and the system allowed to relax. If a persistent current exists, a corresponding amount of angular momentum should be trapped in the system, and the problem is to detect the supercurrent without destroying it.

A number of experiments ([7-12]) have implied the existence of persistent currents, but Mehl and Zimmermann ([13]) have recently reported the most notable direct evidence for this phenomenon. They rotated a thin-walled glass sphere (diameter = 3 cm) packed with powdered silica (particle size $\sim 1\,\mu$) and filled with liquid He. To detect the angular momentum nondestructively, a gyroscopic technique developed by Clow et al. ([14]) was used: after rotation of the apparatus is stopped, the sphere, which is held in a yoke suspended by a torsion fiber, is tilted through 90°; the angular momentum vector is at this stage perpendicular to the original axis of rotation and exerts a torque on the fiber, thereby producing a constant deflection. It was assumed, and experimentally verified, that the angular momentum associated with the liquid circulating through the channels formed by the silica grains is effectively clamped and tilts with the sphere. In this way, currents were prepared which lasted over 5 hr without suffering detectable loss of angular momentum. From the experimental uncertainties, the authors estimated a lower limit of the decay period τ of about 10^6 sec, based on an assumed decay law of the form $\exp(-t/\tau)$.

In a different type of experiment employing the gyroscopic technique, Reppy ([15]) has demonstrated the stability of persistent currents against changes in temperature below T_λ. In effect, he found that the quantity $\rho L_p/\rho_s$ (L_p is the persistent-current angular-momentum vector) is a unique and reversible function of the temperature, implying that a single angular momentum state is preserved independently of the number of particles participating in the motion.

8.1.2. Predictions for the Superfluid Critical Velocity, $v_{s,c}$

London ([4]) has asked the question: "Is superfluidity the absence of viscosity?" Since omission from the superfluid equation [equation (1)] of a viscous shear term $\eta_s \nabla \times \nabla \times v_s$ may be accounted for either if $\eta_s = 0$ or if $\nabla \times v_s = 0$, the answer to this question has considerable bearing on the nature of superfluidity. Both London and Landau were in agreement that it is highly unphysical for any substance to have zero viscosity, and that a fundamental condition for the existence of superfluidity is likely that $\nabla \times v_s = 0$. From this assumption, we infer: (1) the velocity profile of the flowing superfluid should be a plane perpendicular to the flow direction; and (2) superfluidity should be destroyed when $\nabla \times v_s$ no longer vanishes.

However, these deductions are oversimplifications. In regard to the first, there are problems with fixing the boundary conditions upon the superfluid at a wall, especially if $\nabla \times \mathbf{v}_s = 0$ there. Concerning the second, Nozières [16] has recently pointed out that while the above approach to explaining superfluidity is generally correct and often useful, it presents a description that is too restrictive in that the general phenomenon of superfluidity occurs in many situations where the laws of perfect fluid flow cannot apply. Such is the case when inhomogeneities are present in the system. Instead, he argues that the existence of superfluidity should depend upon a kind of long-range order which evades the effects of inhomogeneities—for He II these might be the container walls and the normal fluid—and which can be explained only on a microscopic basis, not by analogy with ideal fluid hydrodynamics.

What then are the conditions determining the destruction of superfluidity? And what is the meaning of a critical velocity? There are still no unambiguous answers to these questions, but significant progress has been made in what appears to be the proper direction. In the following, we shall develop the principal steps that have led to the present position, beginning with an outline of some of the theoretical arguments. Nevertheless, during this discussion, it will be useful to bear in mind the experimental results we wish the theory to explain. Hence we anticipate the conclusions of Section 8.1.3 by graphing in Fig. 8.1 the observed values of $\mathbf{v}_{s,c}$ as a function of channel

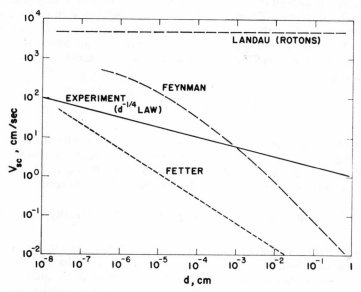

Fig. 8.1. Superfluid critical velocity as a function of channel width according to experiment (solid curve) and various theories (dotted curves).

width d. The most recent experiments suggest that $\mathbf{v}_{s,c} \approx d^{-1/4}$, nearly independent of temperature.

8.1.2a. The Onsager–Feynman Vortex–Line Model. In Fig. 8.1, we also show the results obtained by Landau ([17]) from the excitation spectrum, as mentioned earlier (Section 1.3.5). The lowest velocity satisfying the criterion

$$\mathbf{v}_{s,c} = [\partial \epsilon(p)/\partial \mathbf{p}]_{\min} \tag{8.6}$$

is determined by the roton region: it is roughly independent of both temperature and d, and much larger than the observed critical velocities. Despite the quantitative failure of the Landau criterion for $\mathbf{v}_{s,c}$, the analysis leading to equation (8.6) is believed to possess considerable merit; there has therefore been a great deal of reluctance to abandon this approach. For this relation to be compatible with experiments, it appears that a type of excitation in addition to phonons and rotons should exist in the liquid—one of low energy and large momentum.

A suggestion by Onsager in a footnote to his paper ([18]) on vorticity and a subsequent independent development by Feynman ([19]) have provided some substance for this conjecture. Both authors recognized that classical hydrodynamics allows circulation to appear in a flowing ideal fluid without violating the curl-free character of the motion provided the geometry of the system is multiply-connected. Thus, Onsager proposed that the circulation K in superfluid helium might be quantized in units of h/m (m is the mass of the helium atom) at singular points in the fluid, thereby maintaining the absence of volume vorticity.

Feynman's argument proceeded from his notions about the form of the wave function Ψ for superfluid He in uniform motion at $T = 0°\text{K}$. Here, Ψ is written as

$$\Psi = \Psi_0 \exp\left(i\mathbf{k} \cdot \sum_j \mathbf{R}_j \right) \tag{8.7}$$

with $\mathbf{R}_j$ the position of the jth atom and Ψ_0 the wave function for the fluid at rest. The total momentum of the N-particle system is $N\hbar\mathbf{k}$ with $\mathbf{k} = m\mathbf{v}/\hbar$. An intuitive argument indicates that even for slightly nonuniform motion the wave function should have the form

$$\Psi = \Psi_0 \exp\left[\frac{im}{\hbar} \sum_j \mathbf{v}_j(R_j) \cdot \mathbf{R}_j \right] = \Psi_0 \exp[i\phi(\mathbf{R})] \tag{8.8}$$

where the total phase factor $i\phi(\mathbf{R})$ is a slowly varying function of the coordinates and should represent the quantum-mechanical velocity potential for irrotational flow. When we determine from equation (8.8) the usual quantum-mechanical momentum current density, set this equal to the superfluid momentum density, $\mathbf{J} = \rho_s \mathbf{v}_s$, and take the normalization as $|\Psi|^2 = \rho_s$, the velocity may be identified as

$$\mathbf{v}_s = \frac{\mathbf{J}}{\rho_s} = -\frac{i\hbar}{2m\rho_s}(\Psi^* \nabla \Psi - \Psi \nabla \Psi^*) = \frac{\hbar}{m\rho_s}\Psi_0\Psi_0^* \nabla\phi = \frac{\hbar}{m}\nabla\phi \qquad (8.9)$$

While there is some doubt ([20]) concerning the rigor of this definition for the superfluid particle velocity it is probably not too dangerous an oversimplification. In fact, equation (8.9) has been accepted as a fundamental practical expression of superfluid behavior, satisfying our intuitive requirement for superfluidity, i.e., curl $\mathbf{v}_s = 0$.

Now consider a closed path $\mathbf{s}$ about any nonsuperfluid obstruction or "hole" in the liquid (thereby rendering the system multiply-connected with respect to superfluid motion). When exactly one turn about the path $\mathbf{s}$ is traversed, because Ψ must be single-valued the phase ϕ must change by some multiple $n = 1, 2, 3, \ldots$ times 2π. The line integral of the velocity over this path around the hole defines the circulation K, which through equation (8.9) becomes

$$K \equiv \oint \mathbf{v}_s \cdot d\mathbf{s} = \oint (\hbar/m) \nabla\phi \cdot d\mathbf{s} = n(h/m) \qquad (8.10)$$

Thus, as Onsager suggested earlier, the circulation should be quantized in units of h/m. Equation (8.10) is analogous to the Bohr–Wilson–Sommerfeld condition for stationary atomic orbits; but in the case of liquid He II we must realize that many superfluid particles—of order N—may participate in the quantized state. Next, we allow the hole to shrink to the order of atomic dimensions (hole radius $= a_0$) and find in this limit that the velocity distribution (in the axially symmetric case) implied by equation (8.10) describes a quantized vortex line with "core" radius a_0.

Feynman ([19]) has pointed out that while a nonviscous classical fluid will flow turbulently at any finite velocity, turbulence in superfluid He cannot begin at arbitrarily small velocities, but may appear only when sufficient kinetic energy can be gathered from the flow to produce one quantum of vorticity. Such a process is envisaged as the origin of the critical velocity. One cannot *a priori* determine the exact geometrical form the vorticity will assume, but if, for convenience, we take the vorticity in He II to be analogous to that of a free vortex ring of diameter d in an ordinary fluid, we may reconsider the Landau criterion and calculate the $\epsilon/\mathbf{p}$ ratio [to be precise, $\mathbf{p}$ is here the *impulse* or the time integral of the forces required to create the ring from rest ([1])]. The kinetic energy of the ring is given by (with K again the circulation)

$$\epsilon = \frac{\rho K^2 d}{4}\left(\ln\frac{4d}{a_0} - \kappa\right) \qquad (8.11)$$

and its impulse by

$$\mathbf{p} = \pi\rho\mathbf{K}d^2/4 \tag{8.12}$$

so that the Feynman condition for the critical velocity becomes

$$\frac{\epsilon}{\mathbf{p}} = \mathbf{v}_{s,c} = \frac{\mathbf{K}}{\pi d}\left(\ln\frac{4d}{a_0} - \kappa'\right) \tag{8.13}$$

Here, κ and κ' are constants of order unity, which depend upon the structure assumed for the vortex core.

Equation (8.13) is just the velocity field associated with a classical vortex ring in an unbounded medium and with a circulation h/m. If the velocity of the ring were less than $\mathbf{v}_{s,c}$, d would increase; conversely, if it were larger than $\mathbf{v}_{s,c}$, the ring would shrink. We may apply equation (8.13) to He II by taking as the simplest approximation the assumption that a boundary would have no effect upon the results. Thus, if the liquid is flowing in a circular tube of diameter d, the ring with the lowest $\epsilon/\mathbf{p}$ ratio will be the largest one compatible with the flow geometry. We then picture $\mathbf{v}_{s,c}$ to be that $\mathbf{v}_s$ at which a ring of diameter d is formed in the tube, remaining fixed relative to the wall; as $\mathbf{v}_s$ exceeds $\mathbf{v}_{s,c}$, the ring shrinks, moves out into the mainstream of the flow, and ultimately travels along with the superfluid. Critical velocities calculated in this way, taking a_0 to be ~ 2 Å, depend roughly on d^{-1} and are plotted in Fig. 8.1. While these calculations agree better with experiment than do the original Landau results, the observed d dependence is still not satisfactorily predicted.

The model leading to equation (8.13) is that of a classical vortex in an infinite medium and is certainly too simplified to describe such complex processes as must be involved in the breakdown of super-fluidity in the presence of solid boundaries. Several refinements have been attempted to take into account the interaction of various forms of vorticity with the walls of the flow tube. Fineman and Chase [21] have pointed out that for a classical vortex ring with an empty core, $\epsilon \to 0$ as d approaches the diameter of the tube. Arguing that the impulse is unaffected by the boundary, they found the nonphysical result $\mathbf{v}_{s,c} \to 0$ for a vortex created at the wall, and therefore concluded that vortex formation responsible for observed critical velocities could not occur close to a wall. Raja Gopal [22], on the other hand, has treated the same problem and found that ϵ for a vortex ring near a wall is sensitive to the structure assumed for the vortex core. When the core is taken to be of uniform finite density, ϵ decreases near the wall but remains finite. In other respects, the two investigations produced similar findings in that ϵ was calculated to reach its maximum value when $d_{\mathrm{ring}}/d_{\mathrm{tube}} \approx 0.9$ and that equation (8.13) is essentially recovered (except near the wall). However, Huggins ([23]) has reanalyzed the impulse theorem and found that in the presence of solid boundaries, the impulse necessary to create a vortex system as postulated above is not uniquely defined. He cautions that considerable care should be taken in substituting for **p** and ϵ in Landau's criterion.

8.1.2b. Experimental Evidence for the Existence of Vortex Lines. The above account of the vortex-line model is closely tied to classical hydrodynamics. Relations (8.9) and (8.10) are indeed consequences of the nature of the wave function (8.7), but beyond these tentative roots in quantum mechanics, the argument is purely classical. We may therefore wonder as to how seriously one ought to take this picture for describing the quantum phenomena at hand, especially since the $v_{s,c}$ *vs. d* relation is poorly predicted. We require reassurance that we are on the proper track. Fortunately, this is available from both theoretical and experimental origins, indicating at least the *existence* in He II of quantized vorticity describable by quasiclassical formulas.

Although a number of observations on flowing He II may be consistently interpreted in terms of the properties of quantized vorticity, the first real evidence for the model stems from an attempt by Vinen ([9]) to detect single quanta of circulation. His apparatus consisted of a cylindrical vessel along the axis of which a fine wire was stretched. The vessel was filled with liquid and set into constant rotation about the axis while the system was above the λ-transition. Rotation continued while the apparatus was slowly cooled to some temperature below T_λ. The wire was then set into vibration. Ideally, the wire vibration is doubly degenerate, since two modes are possible at right angles; but the presence of circulation about the wire should split this degeneracy into two circularly polarized vibrations separated by a frequency $\omega = \rho_s K / \mu$, where μ takes into account the masses of the wire and of the fluid displaced by it. Measurements consisted of determining ω for the system in some stable rotational state.

Vinen's results provided evidence both for the persistence and the quantization of circulation in He II. In the majority of experimental runs, the most stable condition appeared to be that for which a single quantum of circulation was attached to the wire. However, it was not unusual to find fractional amounts of h/m, and these Vinen ascribed to vortex lines attached to only a part of the length of the wire. Because the data were not entirely clear-cut, due largely to the difficulties in attaining equilibrium conditions, many who were familiar with the caprices of He II were reluctant to acknowledge the validity of Vinen's conclusions.

Repetition and extension of Vinen's experiment some five years later by Whitmore and Zimmermann ([12]) has virtually removed all of the ambiguity associated with the original results. These authors have clearly demonstrated that superfluid motion may continue for long periods, although the apparent circulation associated with this motion may increase or decrease spontaneously from time to time during any given experiment. Nevertheless, the most stable circulation values were predominantly observed to occur at low multiples of h/m. Histograms for two typical runs are shown in Fig. 8.2. Curiously, the singly quantized state appears to be less frequently attained than either 2 or 3 times h/m.

While these experiments provide rather convincing evidence for the existence of quantized vorticity in He II, they do not tell us much about the detailed structure of the associated flow. What we should like in addition is a demonstration that equations (8.11) and (8.12) are really applicable to vortices in the liquid. In a series of elegant experiments, Rayfield and Reif ([24]) have indeed shown this to be true.

In the presence of an electric field $\mathscr{E}$, the energy of a helium ion in liquid He is given by $e\mathscr{E}l$, e being the charge and l the mean free path between collisions. When $e\mathscr{E}l$ is greater than $k_B T$, the ion has enough energy for it to produce excitations in the liquid during the time

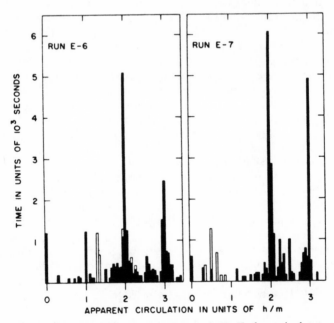

Fig. 8.2. Histograms for the occurrence in He II of quantized states of vorticity in the vibrating-wire experiment [Whitmore and Zimmermann ([12])].

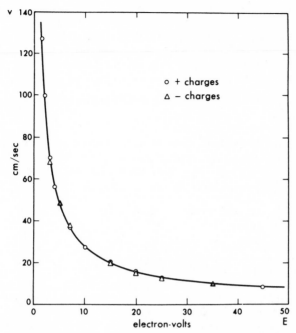

Fig. 8.3. Velocity *vs.* energy relation for charge carriers created by ions in liquid He II. Solid curve calculated assuming the charge carriers are vortex rings with core radius = 1.2 Å and with one quantum of circulation h/m. Experimental points are for positive and negative charge carriers [Rayfield and Reif ([24])].

between collisions. Rayfield and Reif have found that at temperatures between 0.28°K and 0.7°K, it is possible for ions in He II to create charge-carrying structures having the properties of vortex rings of quite large sizes—radius greater than 500 Å. In this respect, their investigations revealed:

1. The velocity **v** of the charge carrier with energy ϵ is very low ($\sim 10^{-5}$ that of a free He ion of comparable energy) and is inversely proportional to ϵ.

2. The observed relationship between ϵ and **v** is quantitatively predicted by equations (8.11) and (8.13) when κ and κ' are taken respectively as 7/4 and 1/4, as for a free classical vortex ring ([25]), and a_0 is assumed to be 1.2×10^{-8} cm. Predictions from these equations are compared with the experimental data in Fig. 8.3, demonstrating that the agreement is quite beautiful.

3. The circulation K may be evaluated directly from the ϵ and **v** data and is rather insensitive to the value assumed for a_0 so long as a_0

is taken to be of the order of atomic dimensions. K was found to be 10^{-3} cm^2-sec^{-1} which corresponds to a single unit of h/m (0.998×10^{-3} cm^2-sec^{-1}). Once this is established, the fit in Fig. 8.3 becomes very dependent upon the precise value of a_0. A more detailed analysis gave for the circulation and core radius

$$K = (1.00 \pm 0.03) \times 10^{-3} \quad cm^2\text{-sec}^{-1}$$

$$a_0 = (1.28 \pm 0.13) \times 10^{-8} \text{ cm}$$

4. From the dynamical properties of the charged carriers, the authors deduced the dispersion relation $\epsilon \propto p^{1/2}$, with $p \equiv |\mathbf{p}|$. This is characteristic of a vortex ring, not of a particle ($\epsilon \propto p^2$) nor of one of the usual He II thermal excitations.

The experimental evidence thus overwhelmingly supports the notion that free quantized vortices describable in terms of classical hydrodynamics can exist in He II. In this light, earlier experiments which provided more indirect evidence about vortex lines take on added significance. Reviews by Vinen [26] and by Hall [27] give comprehensive summaries of these investigations. Donnelly [28] has given an extensive survey of the use of ions for probing the hydrodynamic fields of liquid He.

8.1.2c. Quantum Mechanical Vortices. The development of the quantum-mechanical description of vortex states in He II has proceeded along several different paths which nevertheless lead to essentially the same equation of motion describing the superfluid. Although with various authors the form of this equation takes on slightly different appearances, depending upon the particular mathematical method used, the following is a fairly general representation:

$$i\hbar \, \partial\Psi/\partial t = -(\hbar^2/2m)\nabla^2\Psi + \Phi|\Psi|^2\Psi \qquad (8.14)$$

Here, Φ is the interaction energy between particles. The form of the potential energy term results from the assumptions that Φ is weakly repulsive and short-ranged so that it may be approximated by a δ-function.

The function Ψ also assumes a variety of identities (we use the symbol Ψ here to include our earlier notation $\langle\psi(r)\rangle$—see for example, Sections 5.1.4a and 7.3.4). Since equation (8.14) resembles the ordinary time-dependent Schrödinger equation with some modification [29], Ψ may be thought of as the superfluid or condensate wave function. However, equation (8.14) may be derived from field theory as the equation of motion of the boson wave field [30], in which case Ψ is the mean value of the field operator. Still another derivation [31] of the equation starts from an expansion of the thermodynamic potential as in the Landau–Lifshitz theory of second-order phase transitions (see

Section 7.1.2), so that Ψ is often referred to as the "order parameter" or "effective wave function." Nevertheless, common to all definitions of Ψ are the following characteristics which are significant for the present discussion:

1. Ψ is a function of position and time; thus, $\Psi = \Psi(x, t)$.
2. Ψ is normalized so that it is in some way related to ρ_s. For example, Ginzburg and Pitaevskii [31], who follow Abrikosov's [32] analysis of vortex states in superconductors, apply the Landau–Lifshitz theory to the He II region just below the λ-point to obtain

$$\rho_s \equiv m|\Psi|^2 \tag{8.15}$$

where m is the mass of the helium atom. However, see also Section 7.3.4.

3. At a solid wall, $\Psi \to 0$. This boundary condition has important consequences for the nature of superfluidity. It was imposed phenomenologically by Ginzburg and Pitaevskii [31] based upon experiments [33] indicating the absence of interaction between the superfluid and the wall. Consequently, it was concluded that this absence was due to ρ_s, but not $\mathbf{v}_s$, becoming zero at the wall. Gross [34] has extended this notion in his time-dependent self-consistent field treatment of an imperfect boson gas, which is not restricted to temperatures near T_λ. He finds that the distance a_0, over which $|\Psi|^2$ changes its values from zero at the wall to the (approximately) constant value proportional to ρ_s in the bulk fluid, is given by

$$a_0 = \hbar/(2mE)^{1/2} \tag{8.16}$$

This is a de Broglie wavelength of a few angstroms in which $E = \rho_s\Phi$. Gross calls a_0 the "healing length." a_0 is also equivalent to the correlation length ξ of equation (7.43).

4. The general solution to equation (8.14) is complex and has the form

$$\Psi(x, t) = g(x, t)\exp[i\phi(x, t)] \tag{8.17}$$

This bears considerable resemblance to Feynman's wave function, equation (8.8), and similarly admits of a relation for $\mathbf{v}_s$ equivalent to equation (8.9).

5. When solutions of cylindrical symmetry are sought, the function

$$\Psi(r, \theta, z, t) = f(r)e^{in\theta}\exp[-iE_nt/\hbar] \tag{8.18}$$

where r, θ, z are the cylindrical coordinates and n is an integer, satisfies equation (8.14). This result has been achieved for liquid helium by both Gross [35] and Pitaevskii [36] and has been interpreted by them as describing the stationary states for quantized rectilinear vortices in the superfluid. The quantum vortex is distinguishable from its classical counterpart not only through the quantization conditions, but also because relation (8.18) completely specifies the quantum vortex structure by defining the core dimension. The logarithmic energy term in the classical case must be arbitrarily specified by cutoffs at the core dimension and at R, the latter determined either by the container size or the distance between neighboring vortices. For the quantum vortex, the relevant core radius, as we might expect, is the healing length as determined by the behavior of the radial function $f(r) \propto \rho_s^{1/2}$, with $\Psi \to 0$ as $r \to 0$. Thus, the vanishing of Ψ in the core provides the nonsuperfluid obstruction necessary for the quantization condition. Furthermore, ϵ_l, the energy per unit length of vortex, obtained from equation (8.18) was found ([35]) to be

$$\epsilon_l = (\hbar^2/2m)\rho_s \ln(1.46\, R/a_0) \qquad (8.19)$$

which is numerically a close approximation to the classical formula. Equation (8.19) describes ϵ_l for a singly quantized vortex, i.e., $n = 1$; it was found that twice this energy is less than that of one vortex with $n = 2$; etc. By the same method, Amit and Gross ([37]) have found ϵ for a free quantum vortex ring to be given by equation (8.11) with the constants κ and a_0 specified to be 1.67 and 0.47×10^{-8} cm, respectively.

8.1.2d. The Connection between Vortex Lines and $v_{s,c}$. The existence of quantized vorticity in superfluid He appears to be well established. We must now inquire concerning the possible connection between the critical superfluid velocity and the appearance of vorticity. It has been customary to exploit the $\epsilon/\mathbf{p}$ criterion to make this association, but in doing so, it is well that we should first clarify the notion of a vortex line as an "excitation."

In the sense of equation (8.13), vortex lines may be considered as excitations, but they are not to be thought of, nor associated with, the normal fluid, because they are not thermal excitations. Vinen ([26]) has pointed out that vortices, unlike phonons and rotons, cannot "acquire an arbitrary steady drift velocity relative to the superfluid." In addition, although details are lacking about the lifetimes of vortices under various conditions, it is probable that for the liquid at rest, there is no thermalized equilibrium population of vortices, the stability of vorticity being many orders of magnitude less than that of the thermal excitations. On the other hand, for the liquid in steady motion, vortex states appear to be stable and even required ([38]) to minimize the free energy of the liquid, thereby providing the equilibrium condition—all of which tends to confirm that these excitations are essentially mechanical. As we might expect, the mechanical energy of vortex states will under suitable conditions be degraded into thermal energy; a group at Leiden ([39]) has experimentally verified this (see p. 296).

Fetter ([40]) has extended the analysis of rectilinear quantum vortices, beginning with equations (8.14) and (8.18), to derive the effects of a wall upon the energy of a vortex pair. Near the wall, the energy becomes small, but does not go to zero. Using these results and assuming that the Landau criterion is a necessary condition for a critical velocity, he then found the dimensional dependence of $v_{s,c}$ for He II flowing in a tube with diameter d to be

$$v_{s,c} = c(\hbar/md) \tag{8.20}$$

where c is a constant of the order unity. As seen from Fig. 8.1, this result provides an even poorer d-dependence fit to the experimental data than does equation (8.13) and is numerically much too low. Amit and Gross ([37]) have made the same calculation for vortex rings, including the effects upon ϵ arising from the proximity of the core to the wall, and the conclusions are not significantly different from equation (8.20). A similar result for the critical velocity due to vorticity production has also been obtained by Anderson ([20]), although his approach to the problem is quite different.

We point out that relations of the form of equation (8.20) had been proposed by several authors ([41]) for $v_{s,c}$ as early as 1941. The arguments for this were based on various mechanisms, all without reference to quantized vorticity. In addition, Mott ([43]) and also, later, Ginzburg ([33]) and Dash ([42]) had considered schemes leading to a $d^{-1/2}$ variation of $v_{s,c}$, which conforms somewhat better to the experimental findings. While it might therefore seem that in a quarter of a century the theoretical treatment of critical velocities has made little headway, the introduction and development of the vortex-line model must be considered as a most significant advance. Nevertheless, we are still left with an unsatisfied feeling, since the microscopic theories have not yet been able to reproduce either the experimental d-dependence or the observed magnitude of $v_{s,c}$; also, the mechanism for vortex nucleation remains incompletely defined and entirely obscure.

Several conjectures have been advanced as to how vortices might be produced. The crucial question is: what is the origin of the energy necessary to form vortices as v_s exceeds $v_{s,c}$? Vinen ([26,44]), through crude but plausible arguments, excluded several possible mechanisms. Collisions between thermal excitations could possibly produce vortices, but Vinen has argued that the transition probability for this process is exceedingly low. Alternatively, vortices could result from acceleration of the fluid flowing past protuberances from the channel wall (since any experimental channel is not ideally smooth) or from a discontinuity in the velocity profile near the wall (this is equivalent to a vortex sheet, which classically is unstable and degenerates into vortex lines); however, these processes are not energetically favorable, and numerical estimates of $v_{s,c}$ deduced from these mechanisms are not very convincing.

Vinen regards as most likely the possibility that small bits of vortex lines are always present (in metastable, not thermal, equilibrium) even for He II at rest, and that these are attached or pinned at energetically favorable sites, such as protuberances, forming nucleation centers for production of new lengths of line once $v_{s,c}$ is reached. This idea appeared attractive to Vinen as a result of his observations in the vibrating-wire experiment, where he always could detect the presence of vorticity even without rotating the system.

Glaberson and Donnelly ([45]) have amplified Vinen's hypothesis by describing how such a "primordial" vortex line, with its two ends pinned to the wall of a circular tube, might behave as a "vortex mill" in supercritical flow. They considered a balance between the forces acting on a length of vortex line. The velocity components associated with these forces are: (1) v_f, the net superfluid velocity past the line; this induces a lift or *Magnus force*, $F_m = \rho_s v_f \times K$, in a direction perpendicular to the plane containing the velocity and circulation vectors, the latter being directed along the vortex core. (2) v_i, due to the *image force*, $F_i = -\rho_s K^2/4\pi b$, where b is the distance between the line and its image in the wall; F_i is attractive, tending to pull the line towards the wall. (3) v_0, the velocity induced on one element of the line by all the other elements; v_0 is zero for a straight line and has its maximum for a circular line—this is given by equation (8.13). The balance of forces then takes the form

$$(v_f + v_0 + v_i) \times K = 0 \tag{8.21}$$

When $v_f = 0$, the vortex line is stretched as an arc across the tube; but with increasing v_f, the line bows away from the wall, retaining a stable configuration under the conditions of equation (8.21). The critical velocity is reached when the line becomes a semicircle, and here the analysis leads to $v_{s,c}$ as given by equation (8.13). For $v_f > v_{s,c}$, the Magnus force predominates and pulls the line out away from the wall. Then the line may grow and thread down the tube as a free vortex, but still with two ends pinned. At a constant subcritical v_f, the length of the line is constant, requiring no energy to maintain the configuration; but when v_f exceeds $v_{s,c}$, the line grows at the expense of energy extracted from the flow.

A second point of view, developed by Peshkov ([46]), follows more from Landau's and Feynman's original concepts and requires that the energy to form a stable excitation at $v_s = v_{s,c}$ be gathered from the kinetic energy of a certain volume of flowing fluid during some short time interval τ ($\sim 10^{-4}$ sec). Hence, as d decreases, the length l' of the channel over which the gathering process occurs becomes extended and the probability for vortex formation decreases. For tubes with $d < 10^{-3}$ cm, l' becomes considerably larger than d. Peshkov's expression for the d vs. $v_{s,c}$ relation was derived by equating the energy of vortex ring formation to the kinetic energy in the appropriate volume of superfluid. Several constants are available for fitting, and the results conform nicely to the experimental behavior for $d < 10^{-3}$ cm but not for larger d (see Section 8.1.3a).

More recently, Craig ([47]) has extended Peshkov's argument by including the effect of image forces on the energy needed to form a ring with radius approximately that of the tube. His resulting expression for $v_{s,c}$ has the form

$$v_{s,c}^3 d = B \ln(1 + C/v_{s,c}) \qquad (8.22)$$

which, with suitably chosen constants B and C, fits the experimental curve in Fig. 8.1 exceedingly well. These constants were determined to fit the recent experimental data (see next section) but they cannot be calculated *a priori* and are even difficult to estimate. Hence, we hesitate to use the success of equation (8.22) as evidence that the physical argument leading to it should be preferred over the Vinen–Glaberson–Donnelly model. (See also Section 8.1.3b.)

8.1.3. Experimental Determination of $v_{s,c}$

8.1.3a. The Dependence of $v_{s,c}$ on Flow Geometry. The selection of superfluid critical velocities from the experimental flow data has not been without ambiguities. Until quite recently, $v_{s,c}$ was considered to be merely that value of v_s at which departures from the linear behavior prescribed by equations (8.1) and (8.2) began to appear in the flow observations. With this criterion, equation (8.13) closely approximated the experimental results for channels with $d > 10^{-3}$ cm, but became increasingly too large for smaller channels. So convincing was the agreement for $d > 10^{-3}$ cm ([46,48]) that the prevailing viewpoint considered the behavior for smaller channels to be anomalous, ascribing the deviations to special effects, perhaps associated with interactions between vortices and the wall, or, as discussed above, with kinetic energy collection. In fact, Peshkov's analysis ([46]) was tailored to fit those data then believed to represent $v_{s,c}$, and it did so very well.

The work of van Alphen *et al.* ([49]), however, has reversed this sentiment by suggesting that the previously observed departures from the linear equations where $d > 10^{-3}$ cm could in most cases be ascribed to the onset of turbulence in the *normal* fluid rather than to v_s exceeding

$v_{s,c}$. When the normal fluid motion has been suppressed in these larger channels, $v_{s,c}$ has in recent experiments been found at significantly larger velocities than previously designated, forming an extension of the $v_{s,c}$ vs. d relation found for smaller channels. Thus, the geometrical dependence of $v_{s,c}$ is now generally believed to be approximately proportional to $d^{-1/4}$, with $v_{s,c}d^{1/4} \approx 1$, over the whole range of d's investigated. Here, d is the smallest dimension of the flow channel in a direction perpendicular to the flow. Some experimental points which best support the $d^{-1/4}$ representation are listed in Table 8.I. Specifically excluded from these are a number of experiments cited earlier ([46,48,49]) for establishing the $v_{s,c}$ vs. d relation, on the grounds that either normal fluid turbulence was present or the velocity reported was temperature dependent (see Section 8.1.3b). Even so, we see that some of the observed values of $v_{s,c}$ surviving this discrimination still differ by as much as a factor of two from the calculated values.

In the following, we first mention some of the experimental problems met in finding $v_{s,c}$ and then discuss briefly the various methods used to obtain the values in Table 8.I.

Table 8.I. Experimental Values of $v_{s,c}$ vs. d Compared with Calculations Made from the Relation $v_{s,c}d^{1/4} = 1$

Method	Reference	d (cm)	$v_{s,c}$(obs) (cm/sec)	$v_{s,c}$(calc) (cm/sec)
Superfluid wind tunnel	([55])	~3	0.6	0.76
Calorimeter	([39])	0.44	0.95	1.23
Rotating persistent current	([10])	0.22	0.81	1.47
Calorimeter	([39])	0.13	1.7	1.66
Adiabatic flow	([61])	1.74×10^{-2}	2	2.75
Calorimeter	([39])	1.5×10^{-2}	3.0	2.85
Adiabatic flow	([61])	8.2×10^{-3}	4	3.32
Calorimeter	([39])	1.5×10^{-3}	6.0	5.08
Heat flow	([57,58])	3.4×10^{-4}	3.0	7.35
Isothermal channel flow	([51])	2.3×10^{-4}	5.8	8.13
Isothermal channel flow	([68])	1.2×10^{-4}	4.5	9.55
Isothermal channel flow	([51])	3.1×10^{-5}	18	13.4
Isothermal channel flow	([68])	1.2×10^{-5}	11	17.0
Isothermal channel flow	([68])	5.0×10^{-6}	12	21.2
Saturated film, $H = 1$ cm	*	3.0×10^{-6}	~25	24
Saturated film, $H = 1$ cm	([56])	3.0×10^{-6}	25	24
Saturated film, $H = 10$ cm	([56])	1.4×10^{-6}	35	29
Unsaturated film	([60])	1×10^{-7}	30	56
From the following experiments, $v_{s,c}$ depends upon d^{-1}				
Isothermal channel flow	([63])	0.11	0.10–0.14	1.74
Isothermal channel flow	([64])	2.9×10^{-2}	0.40–0.55	2.42
Isothermal channel flow	([64])	1.2×10^{-2}	1.15	3.02

* Value obtained from many film flow experiments.

The difficulties associated with obtaining narrow channels of well-defined and uniform geometry are apparent, and if d is not relatively constant, ambiguity arises as to what d an observed $v_{s,c}$ corresponds. A large variety of schemes has been tried to obtain "good" narrow channels—powder-packed tubes, Millipore filters, optical flats, wire-filled tubes, wires embedded in glass, etc. For most channels that have been used, there is a wide spread in the size of a given channel, and some average d has then to be taken. Since $v_{s,c}$ depends monotonically and rather weakly on d, this may not be too serious, but quantitative requirements for channel uniformity cannot as yet be established.

Still another difficulty in interpreting various superfluid flow experiments is associated with the hysteresis effects observed for the onset of dissipation processes. This is a very complicated matter and probably depends a great deal upon the history of the sample as well as upon the manner in which the flow is initiated. Hysteresis effects have been discussed by several authors ([26,44,50,51]).

An equally delicate question concerns the length-dependence of $v_{s,c}$ for a given channel cross section. There is some indication ([51]) that so long as the length of the channel L is large compared with d, $v_{s,c}$ does not vary with L; but when L and d become comparable, $v_{s,c}$ probably increases ([52]). Further investigation of this point should be most fruitful, but here we will consider $v_{s,c}$ to be determined from experiments in which L/d is large.

Reliable values of $v_{s,c}$ have in the main been derived from either isothermal or heat flow experiments. In the former case, the usual procedure has been to establish a pressure head ΔP across the channel and then measure the flow velocity as the head relaxes to zero. An arrangement for studying such gravitational flow is shown schematically in Fig. 8.4a. This method will work for narrow channels ($d < 10^{-3}$ cm) and small ΔP, conditions which tend to make the volume flow of normal fluid negligible compared with that of the superfluid; it will also work for wider channels at very low temperatures ($T \lesssim 1.0°K$), where $\rho_n \ll \rho_s$. Beginning in 1939 with the pioneering work of Allen and Misener ([53]), it has been used often, but with results showing wide discrepancies, many even indicating no critical velocity at all. The source of these variations can be traced in part to the nonuniformity of the flow channels used, but more importantly to nonisothermal conditions. Keller and Hammel ([54]) have indicated how a temperature difference across the ends of a narrow channel of only a few micro-degrees, arising from the filtering of normal fluid, corresponds to a fountain pressure which if neglected may insidiously distort the measurements. Figure 8.5 plots ∇P vs. v_s for a typical "isothermal" flow experiment. The solid curve represents the behavior in the absence of a temperature difference and indicates how $v_{s,c}$ may be properly

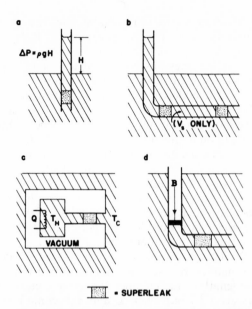

Fig. 8.4. Various experimental methods for observing superfluid flow: (a) gravitational flow (GF) through superleak; (b) superfluid wind tunnel for studying wide channel between two superleaks; (c) heat flow across a superleak; $T_H > T_C$; Q is heater; (d) forced flow (FF) through a superleak; B is an externally driven plunger (in practice, a bellows).

determined from the intersection of the curve with the v_s axis. The dotted line shows the measurements under nonisothermal conditions. By measuring the temperature difference between the ends of the channel, one may correct for the thermomechanical effect to obtain the solid curve; but without this information, an erroneous conclusion would be drawn that $v_{s,c} = 0$. Keller and Hammel [51] have used this method to obtain values of $v_{s,c}$ in uniform, well-defined parallel-sided slits with $d = 3.1 \times 10^{-5}, 2.1 \times 10^{-4}$, and 3.4×10^{-4} cm.

A successful technique for immobilizing the normal fluid in large geometries has been devised by Craig and Pellam [55] in their "superfluid wind tunnel" experiments. Here (see Fig. 8.4b), the channel is plugged at two places by superleaks; when flow of He II is initiated by either a thermal or a mechanical force, ideally only superfluid may move in the section of channel between these plugs. Craig and Pellam suspended light airfoils or wings in this space and observed the lift on them as a function of v_s. Since at subcritical velocities, the wings

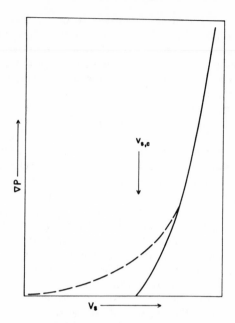

Fig. 8.5. Pressure gradient *vs.* superfluid
velocity in absence of temperature difference
across superleak (solid curve) and in presence
of small ΔT (broken curve) [Keller and
Hammel ([54])].

should experience zero lift, $v_{s,c}$ was designated as the velocity at which
positive lift values were first observed.

In another approach using wide channels, Bendt ([10]) has observed
the critical velocity for bringing the superfluid into rotation in an
annular ring 0.22 cm wide. After the annulus had been rotated at a
velocity ω and then stopped, a thin foil was slowly immersed into the
annulus at an angle of 45° to the flow. If ω was subcritical, no flow
persisted, as indicated by lack of torque on the foil; but if ω exceeded
the critical velocity, the foil responded as a Rayleigh disk and tended
to orient perpendicular to the flow.

If we consider the mobile helium film as an extension of channel
flow, observations of the transfer rate R in film flow provide opportunities for determining $v_{s,c}$ in extremely small geometries. Since we
may represent R as

$$R = (\rho_s/\rho)v_{s,c}d \qquad (8.23)$$

if d can be determined independently, we may readily obtain $v_{s,c}$. For the saturated film, $d = 3H^{-1/3} \times 10^{-6}$ cm is a fair approximation for the variation of thickness with distance H above bulk liquid. Although studies of the transfer rate have been abundant, the results unfortunately lack quantitative consistency. We will return to this problem in Section 8.1.4c.

From investigations on third sound, Atkins and Pickar [56] have recently indicated how $v_{s,c}$ in the film may be found without requiring that d be known. The propagation velocity of the third-sound mode, u_3, is expected to depend upon the relative motion of the film. If u_3^0 is the velocity for the film at rest and the film moves with velocity $(v_s)_f$ in the direction of the sound propagation, then in the first approximation, $u_3 = u_3^0 + (v_s)_f$; similarly, when the sound wave opposes the film flow, $u_3 = u_3^0 - (v_s)_f$. Experimental results for u_3 in the two moving cases are compared with u_3^0 as a function of H in Fig. 8.6. The observed differences $|u_3 - u_3^0|$ are roughly symmetrical about u_3 and indicate for each H the value of $v_{s,c}$ in the film. These substantially agree with the generally accepted data obtained in film transfer rate experiments.

In stationary thermal counterflow experiments, as described by equations (1.14)–(1.18), the entire resistance to heat flow at low fluid velocities arises from the normal fluid viscosity, and under these conditions the flow of ρ_n remains laminar. The associated pressure gradient is the fountain pressure, P_f, which, so long as the system remains linear, is related to the temperature gradient by H. London's

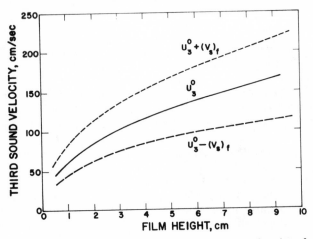

Fig. 8.6. Third-sound velocity in the moving film as a function of film height; u_3^0 is for static film; $(v_s)_f$ is velocity of film [smoothed curves from data of Atkins and Pickar [56]].

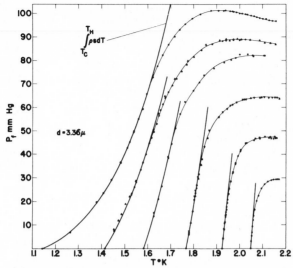

Fig. 8.7. Fountain pressures observed in a narrow channel ($d = 3.36\,\mu$) for several fixed "cold" cell temperatures T_C. Solid curves show integrated linear fountain pressure relation (H. London [from Hammel and Keller [58]].

equation (for a parallel-sided channel)

$$\nabla P = -12\eta_n v_n/d^2 = \rho s\,\nabla T = P_f \qquad (8.24)$$

With increasing heat current, depending on the channel geometry and the temperature, either the normal fluid flow will become turbulent or the superfluid will exceed its critical velocity with respect to the walls. Only in the latter case can $v_{s,c}$ be determined unambiguously from the observed changes in flow regimes. Workers at Leiden ([49,111]) have proposed that the Reynolds number for the normal fluid

$$\mathscr{R}(v_n) = |d\rho v_n/\eta_n| \qquad (8.25)$$

must be less than its classical value of ~ 1200 to permit meaningful values of $v_{s,c}$ to be extracted from heat flow data. On the basis of this criterion, almost all the heat flow data that have been obtained using wide channels do not properly give $v_{s,c}$.

The situation is better defined for smaller channels, in which v_n must become very large before normal fluid turbulence appears. For example, Hammel and Keller have studied heat flow ([57]) and fountain pressure ([58]) in the same slits as used for their isothermal flow experiments. Figure 8.4c schematically depicts the method, and Fig. 8.7

indicates how the observed P_f departs from linear behavior. The latter shows P_f for several reference temperatures T_C ("cold" cell) as the "hot" cell is incrementally heated. At each steady value of $\bar{q}$, P_f is measured and related to the heat current $\bar{q}$ through equations (1.17) and (8.24). Because the experimental temperature differences are large, these equations must be integrated with respect to T. The points of initial deviation of the observations from the integrated linear fountain pressure expression correspond to the critical heat current $\bar{q}_c$, and thus to $v_{s,c}$. Values of $v_{s,c}$ found in this way agree well with those of the isothermal flow measurements in the same slits.

In still smaller geometries, studies of heat flow in the unsaturated film ([59,60]) have established the $d^{-1/4}$ law to thicknesses of the order 5×10^{-8} cm.

Two novel approaches to determining $v_{s,c}$ figured prominently in leading the Leiden group to propose the $d^{-1/4}$ law. van Alphen et al. ([61]) have studied adiabatic gravitational flow in which the hydrostatic pressure head was just balanced by P_f, allowing pure superfluid to flow in the absence of a driving force at the critical velocity. Channels with $d = 8.2 \times 10^{-3}$ and 1.74×10^{-2} cm were investigated. Another ingenious experiment ([39,62]) determined the critical velocity calorimetrically. Superflow through a capillary discharged into a thermally isolated reservoir fitted with a thermometer and a heater. For flows in which $v_{s,c}$ was exceeded, it was assumed that vorticity produced in the channel was swept out into the reservoir and there decayed into thermal excitations. The temperature rise thus observed in the reservoir and ascribed to the energy dissipation in the flow could be analyzed by comparison with the temperature history of the reservoir following delivery of a known amount of power to the heater. Here, $v_{s,c}$ was determined as the largest v_s for which no dissipation could be detected for four different channels with d between 4.4×10^{-1} and 1.5×10^{-3} cm.

We finally consider several isothermal flow experiments which do not fit in with the $d^{-1/4}$ law but which nevertheless cannot be easily discredited for $v_{s,c}$ determination. Kidder and Fairbank ([63]) used a resonant microwave-cavity technique to detect pressure gradients as small as 3×10^{-4} dyn/cm^3 in superfluid flow in a wind tunnel ($d = 0.11$ cm). Their results for $v_{s,c}$ are about 0.1 cm/sec, or an order of magnitude lower than predicted by the $d^{-1/4}$ law. Since the superfluid flow was generated by a heater outside the wind tunnel, it is conceivable that the temperature gradient was not entirely eliminated from the section where measurements were made. However, the $v_{s,c}$ values obtained are consistent with more recent experiments of Kidder and Blackstead ([64]), to which this objection cannot be raised. These authors have studied mechanically induced flow in capillaries with

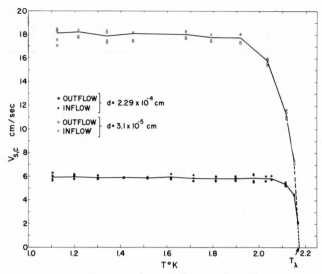

Fig. 8.8. Temperature variation of the superfluid critical velocity as measured from isothermal flow through two narrow slits [from Keller and Hammel ([51])].

$d = 0.012$ and 0.029 cm at $0.45°K$, where, since $\rho_n/\rho_s \approx 10^{-6}$, normal fluid motion and thermomechanical effects are negligible. Values of $v_{s,c}$ obtained by Kidder *et al.* are also listed in Table 8.I. Over the decade of channel sizes investigated, $v_{s,c}$ is closely proportional to d^{-1} rather than to $d^{-1/4}$.

8.1.3b. The Temperature Dependence of $v_{s,c}$. In the past, considerable confusion has existed over the temperature dependence of $v_{s,c}$. Experiments, particularly with the wider channels, appeared quite sensitive to T, some showing $v_{s,c}$ to increase with T, some to decrease with T, and still others exhibiting a pronounced maximum in the $v_{s,c}$ vs. T relation. The best available evidence now indicates that $v_{s,c}$ is essentially temperature-independent except very near the λ-point and for narrow geometries. This behavior is in accord with current theoretical belief.

Figure 8.8 shows the temperature variation of $v_{s,c}$ as deduced ([51]) from isothermal flow measurements in two slits with $d = 2.29 \times 10^{-4}$ and 3.1×10^{-5} cm. The constancy of $v_{s,c}$ for each slit over a wide temperature interval is evident, except above $T \approx 2.0°K$, where $v_{s,c}$ drops rapidly to zero at T_λ.

Clow and Reppy ([65]) have examined the region near T_λ with considerably more resolution using their superfluid gyroscope

technique ([14,15]). Persistent currents were prepared at some temperature T_s well below T_λ in an annular space stuffed with fibrous material
(three separate fillings were made so as to provide channels with
average d values of 150×10^{-4}, 10×10^{-4}, and 0.2×10^{-4} cm). The
temperature was then raised to some T_i and subsequently lowered to T_s,
at which point the system's angular momentum $\mathbf{L}_p$ was compared
with what it was before the temperature cycle. If the original angular
velocity ω was low enough to be subcritical at T_i, then $\mathbf{L}_p$ remained
unchanged according to the previously found ([15]) reversibility of
persistent current angular momentum; but if ω was supercritical at T_i,
then a reduction of $\mathbf{L}_p$ occurred when remeasured at T_s. The amount of
this reduction could be directly related to the critical angular velocity
ω_c at T_i. Results of these experiments appear in Fig. 8.9 plotted as
ω_c vs. $(T_\lambda - T)$. When ω_c is translated into linear velocity for the
$0.2\text{-}\mu$ channels,

$$\mathbf{v}_{s,c} = u_c(1 - T/T_\lambda)^{0.68 \pm 0.03} \quad \text{cm/sec} \qquad (8.26)$$

for $(T_\lambda - T) < 0.025°\text{K}$ and with $u_c = 380$ cm/sec. The curves shown
in Fig. 8.8 are compatible with the findings of Clow and Reppy.

Langer and Fisher ([66]) have theorized that near T_λ there should be
an *intrinsic critical velocity* independent of the shape and size of the
flow channel but proportional to the superfluid density. [We recall
from Section 7.3.4 that $\rho_s(T)$ has just the temperature dependence of

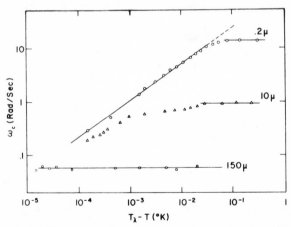

Fig. 8.9. Temperature dependence near T_λ of the critical angular
velocity ω_c observed for flow through porous materials with
average d of 0.2, 10, and 150 μ [from Clow and Reppy ([65])].

equation (8.26).] The argument proceeds from the realization that for $0 < v_s < v_{s,c}$ the superflow is a metastable state of the system. Through fluctuations there should be a finite probability of nucleating the stable state, presumably via vortex creation; but at low v_s the time scale of experiments is too small to detect this. As v_s increases to $v_{s,c}$ the probability for nucleation increases and becomes observable at $v_{s,c}$. The result that $v_{s,c} \propto \rho_s(T)$ follows from a consideration of the free energy for the critical fluctuation when the classical vortex ring energy [equation (8.11) with $\rho = \rho_s$] is used in the calculation. Near T_λ the critical condition requires that the diameter of the critical vortex ring, d_c, depends upon T as $[1 - T/T_\lambda]^{-2/3}$, while the core radius a_0, equal to the correlation length $\xi(T)$, has the same behavior. Hence near T_λ the ratio d/a_0 in equation (8.11) should be nearly a constant. From this, together with an estimate of the critical fluctuation frequency, the constant u_c in equation (8.26) was calculated. The result turns out to be larger by about a factor of four than the observed value; but considering the uncertain geometry of the experiment and the approximations made in the model calculation, this agreement is quite encouraging.

These results suggest that there are two limiting cases for observing $v_{s,c}$—the "dirty" case, in which many primordial vortex lines are present in the static situation, and the "clean" case, where there are none. Thus experiments which conform to the $d^{-1/4}$ law might represent the former, where $v_{s,c}$ signals the onset of fully developed production of additional vortex line, perhaps as described by the vortex-mill model. This should generally occur for velocities below those for which vortex creation takes place through fluctuations in the clean case. But near T_λ the ρ_s dependence of the intrinsic critical velocity provides a limiting critical condition for smaller v_s, even in the dirty case. It is therefore of extreme interest to look for evidence of the intrinsic $v_{s,c}$ in clean systems well below T_λ.

A very puzzling feature remains concerning the temperature dependence of film flow. When the observed transfer by the film is normalized by the factor (ρ/ρ_s) as in equation (8.23), R should become temperature independent. This is roughly so for $1.2° < T < 2.1°K$. Above 2.1°K, the effects represented by equation (8.26) should be relevant, but have so far gone undetected. However, below 1.2°K, R has been found ([67]) to increase by about 30%, as indicated in Fig. 1.7. No satisfactory explanation has been given for this anomalous behavior.

8.1.4. The Superfluid Dissipation Function, F_s

8.1.4a. Some Remarks on Superfluidity by Anderson. Three papers ([16,20,69]) presented at the Sussex Symposium on Quantum Fluids (1965) are of special importance in bringing into focus the close analogy between superconductivity in metals and superfluidity in He II through an exploration of those properties of the wave function Ψ (field operator, order parameter, etc.) shared by these two systems. In both cases, the form of Ψ given by equation (8.17) is appropriate, with the phase ϕ assuming an extraordinary significance. We shall extract here several points about Ψ and ϕ made by Anderson [20] which are directly related to dissipative processes in the superfluid.

The starting point of Anderson's treatment is the assumption that Ψ "has a mean value in the thermodynamic, quasiequilibrium sense" when averaged over large distances and times for the He II system. This differs from ordinary systems, where Ψ becomes negligible over very short distances and times. It is through the peculiar properties of the phase, which is everywhere definable or measurable, that Ψ achieves its long-range properties, i.e., its coherence. Hence, in the general relation (8.17), emphasis is shifted from $g(x, t)$, which is an internal order parameter defining structural properties of the liquid, to $\phi(x, t)$, which is both a dynamical and a thermodynamic variable and which can respond to external forces.

In quantum mechanics, the particle number N and the phase ϕ are canonically conjugate variables which may be related through two equations of motion, one of which is

$$\hbar(\partial \phi / \partial t) = (\partial E / \partial N) \equiv \mu \qquad (8.27)$$

defining the chemical potential. [We recall from Section 5.1.4a that Ψ as obtained by Beliaev contained the phase factor $\exp(-i\mu t/\hbar)$.] Equation (8.27) together with equation (8.9) relate $\mathbf{v}_s$, ϕ, and μ and thereby establish the dynamic properties of the superfluid.

Anderson's important contribution lies in his recognition of how vorticity production may be related to changes in μ and hence in ϕ. He considered an isolated vortex line with $n = 1$ and noted that the integral of $\nabla\phi$ in equation (8.10) passing around one side (from 0 to π) of the vortex core differs by 2π from the integral around the opposite side (0 to $-\pi$). Now, if at some distance from the vortex core there are in the fluid two points 1 and 2 at different potentials μ_1 and μ_2 and with corresponding phases $\phi_1 = \epsilon$ and $\phi_2 = -\epsilon$, Anderson argued that should the core cross an arbitrary line joining 1 and 2 the phases at these points should be changed to $\phi_1 = \pi - \epsilon$ and $\phi_2 = -\pi + \epsilon$. In other words, there will be a "phase slippage" of 2π between the points. And thus, if many vortices crossed this line at an average rate $\langle dn/dt \rangle$, from equation (8.27) we should find

$$\hbar \, d\langle \phi_1 - \phi_2 \rangle / dt = (2\pi)\hbar \langle dn/dt \rangle = \langle \mu_1 - \mu_2 \rangle \qquad (8.28)$$

Relation (8.28) tells us that whenever there is no potential difference between points 1 and 2 there will be no phase slippage, and, conversely, that a finite potential difference implies a transport of vorticity. It follows that $v_{s,c}$ is that value of v_s at which vorticity begins to be transported under steady-state conditions.

Suppose, now, we have a system composed of two reservoirs I and II filled with He II and connected by a channel also containing liquid. Starting with equilibrium conditions, i.e., $\mu_I = \mu_{II}$, $\phi_I = \phi_{II}$ (arbitrarily), and $v_s = 0$, we wish to describe in terms of the above development the general processes for the appearance of dissipation in the flow. In this connection, we also appreciate that the macroscopic superfluid equation of motion (8.1) may be written as [Landau ([17])]:

$$\partial v_s/\partial t + \nabla(\tfrac{1}{2}v_s^2 + \bar{\mu}) = 0 \qquad (8.29)$$

(where $\bar{\mu}$ is the chemical potential per gram) indicating that for steady subcritical superfluid flow, $\nabla\bar{\mu} = 0$. Next, we apply a force to move the fluid through the channel, leaving it with some steady nonzero but subcritical velocity. Then ϕ_I and ϕ_{II} will each be constant and will differ by an amount according to equation (8.9), and in principle this need not be an integral multiple of 2π. To achieve this state, no phase slippage will occur, since the applied force will produce acceleration of the fluid rather than vorticity. Thus at steady $v_s < v_{s,c}$, $\nabla\mu$ is zero—no vortex transfer occurs and maintenance of the flow requires no additional driving force. Then if the fluid is further accelerated to reach some steady velocity for which v_s exceeds $v_{s,c}$, it becomes necessary to provide a driving force, i.e., $\mu_I \neq \mu_{II}$. In this situation, vorticity is created and transported at a frequency $\omega = \Delta\mu/\hbar$, accounting for the dissipation energy.

8.1.4b. The Chemical Potential and the Superfluid Equation of Motion. In the above discussion, we have suggested that the chemical potential is the crucial quantity in determining the nature of dissipative processes in the superfluid. For equations (8.1) and (8.29) to be compatible, we must have

$$\nabla\bar{\mu} = (1/\rho)\,\nabla P - s\,\nabla T \equiv \nabla\bar{\mu}_0 \qquad (8.30)$$

which also follows from the thermodynamic definition of μ for a system at rest and in the absence of external forces. At equilibrium, $\nabla\bar{\mu} = 0$ and we immediately recover the H. London fountain-pressure equation. Experimentally, we find the gradient of the gravitational potential, $\rho g H$, due to a head H of liquid, is balanced by the gradient of the thermomechanical pressure, $\rho s \nabla T$. If, however, $\Delta T = 0$ but H is not, as in an isothermal flow experiment, then $\Delta\bar{\mu} = gH$, and the superfluid equation can no longer be satisfied unless a term $\mathbf{F}_s$ related to $\Delta\bar{\mu}$ is included. In this *ad hoc* way, we may associate $\mathbf{F}_s$ with the superfluid dissipative processes.

Bekarevich and Khalatnikov ([70]) have generalized equation (8.30) through a phenomenological derivation which takes into account the presence of vorticity and is especially useful for rotating systems. Their result is

$$\nabla\bar{\mu} = \nabla\bar{\mu}_0 + (\lambda/\rho)\,\nabla\omega - (\rho_n/\rho)\,\nabla(\mathbf{v}_n - \mathbf{v}_s)^2 \qquad (8.31)$$

Here, the term in $\omega = |\nabla \times \mathbf{v}_s|$, accounting for dissipation processes when the superfluid motion is no longer curl-free, is determined by the manner in which the internal energy of the liquid depends upon the presence of vorticity; from the phenomenological theory [cf. equation (8.19)] the coefficient λ is taken to be $\rho_s K \ln(R/a_0)$. The last term on the right of equation (8.31) arises from the interactions occurring between vortex lines and thermal excitations (mutual friction, to be discussed in Section 8.2.1). A result similar to equation (8.31) has also been obtained by Hall ([27]).

Again, when $\nabla\bar{\mu} = 0$, the superfluid equation is satisfied and no dissipation occurs; and it is interesting to note that equation (8.31) opens up quite a variety of processes in addition to the fountain effect which can occur in the superfluid while potential flow is maintained. Donnelly ([71]) has discussed some of the ways in which the equilibrium condition can be attained and has also provided experimental data ([72]) which are numerically consistent with expression (8.31).

For some time, considerable controversy existed over the exact form of the chemical potential of the flowing film, $\bar{\mu}(\mathbf{v})$, compared with that of the static film, $\bar{\mu}(0)$. In the latter case, agreement is general that in the first approximation, $\Delta\bar{\mu} = 0$ when the van der Waals potential, $-k/d^3$, balances the gravitational potential, $\rho g H$, giving the familiar thickness vs. height profile of film as $d = (k/\rho g)H^{-1/3}$. Franchetti ([73]) has argued that when the film flows, $\bar{\mu}(\mathbf{v})$ involves the superfluid kinetic energy leading to a term $(\rho_s/2\rho)v_s^2$, which would indicate that the moving film is thicker than the static film. On the other hand, Kontorovich ([74]) has contended that this term should be negative and should cause the film to thin down for $0 < \mathbf{v}_s < \mathbf{v}_{s,c}$.

An experimental investigation of this situation was first made by Gribbon and Jackson ([75]) using the optical method developed by Jackson and co-workers ([76]). While the results showed a great deal of scatter and only a small difference ($\sim 3\%$) in d between the static and the flowing cases, they did indicate a definite preference for the viewpoint of Kontorovich. The third-sound experiments ([56]) mentioned earlier have independently confirmed that d is relatively insensitive to the motion of the film. In addition, a careful analysis of the chemical potential by Tilley ([77]) appears to have put an end to the controversy, also in favor of Kontorovich. Tilley traced the error in Franchetti's derivation to an assumption that the kinetic energy of the superfluid contributes to $\bar{\mu}(\mathbf{v})$. This is inconsistent with the well-established principle that the superfluid by itself, having no entropy, cannot influence the thermodynamic properties of the liquid.

8.1.4c. Experimental Determination of Superfluid Dissipation. Because of the experimental difficulties mentioned earlier (Section 8.1.3a), the form of the superfluid dissipation function $\mathbf{F}_s$ has not often been reliably measured. Perhaps the first reliable data were obtained from the wind tunnel experiments of Craig and Pellam [55]. These were followed by the studies of Kidder and co-workers [63,64] and more recently by van Alphen and co-workers [39,62], all for essentially wide channels $(d > 10^{-3}$ cm). For narrow channels $(d < 10^{-3}$ cm), the measurements of Keller and Hammel [51] have given clearly defined results.

We may easily obtain the relationship between ∇P and $\mathbf{F}_s$ for these essentially isothermal flow measurements under steady-state conditions. Thus, in equation (8.4), the acceleration term and the term in ∇T may be omitted; also, as will be shown subsequently, $\mathbf{F}_{sn}$ is negligible under these conditions, so that equation (8.4) reduces to

$$\mathbf{F}_s = -(\rho_s/\rho)\,\nabla P \qquad (8.32)$$

For wide channels, several forms have been suggested to represent the observed dependence of ∇P upon $\mathbf{v}_s$, including

$$\nabla P = a_1 \mathbf{v}_s \tilde{\mathbf{v}} \qquad (8.33)$$

and

$$\nabla P = a_2 \tilde{\mathbf{v}}^n \qquad (8.34)$$

where $\tilde{\mathbf{v}} \equiv (\mathbf{v}_s - \mathbf{v}_{s,c})$ and n ranges between 1.7 and 2. There is not a great deal of difference between these representations, and considerable experimental accuracy is required to distinguish between them. Craig and Pellam found that expression (8.33) provided a good fit to their data (actually, the torque on the airfoil was measured here and not ∇P) at the single temperature of 1.3°K, while Kidder and Fairbank have reported that their measurements of ∇P were consistent with either equation (8.33) or (8.34) with $n = 1.7$ for $1.26° < T < 1.57°$K. However, van Alphen and co-workers have interpreted their results as showing that ∇P depends directly upon $\mathbf{v}_{s,c}^2$, independent of the temperature. In all of these cases, the shape of the dissipation curves resembles the solid curve in Fig. 8.5 displaying finite slopes and nonzero $\mathbf{v}_s$ as ∇P vanishes. However, as yet, the data are not sufficiently consistent to provide a common interpretation of the coefficient a.

For isothermal flow in narrow channels, Keller and Hammel found that their observations of the superfluid dissipation function

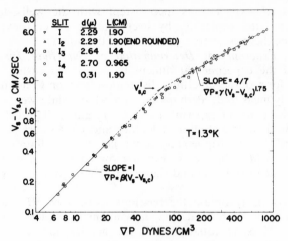

Fig. 8.10. Pressure gradient as a function of $(v_s - v_{s,c}) = \tilde{v}$ for five different narrow channel geometries at $T = 1.3°K$ [from Keller and Hammel ([51])].

could be best exhibited on a log–log plot of ∇P vs. $\tilde{v}$ as shown in Fig. 8.10. Data are plotted here for five different slit geometries which vary in length L by a factor of two and in width d by a factor of 10, all at the same temperature of 1.3°K. The following points emerge: (1) the observed dissipation is seen to be reproducible and to depend upon the pressure gradient (until now this has been an assumption), indicating that the process takes place uniformly (in a statistical sense) over the entire length of the slit; (2) the dissipation force is independent of slit width; (3) there are two well-defined flow regimes (in addition to that for which $\nabla P = 0$ for $v_s < v_{s,c}$):

$$\nabla P = \beta \tilde{v} \qquad v_{s.c} < v_s < v'_{s.c} \qquad (8.35)$$

and

$$\nabla P = \gamma \tilde{v}^{1.75} \qquad v_s > v'_{s,c} \qquad (8.36)$$

determined by a second critical velocity $v'_{s,c} \approx (v_{s,c} + 1)$ cm/sec; (4) the coefficients β and γ are of the same order of magnitude and are both unaffected by the changes in geometry investigated.

When the temperature was varied between 1.1° and 2.1°K, the character of the plot shown in Fig. 8.10 persisted, including the value of $v'_{s,c}$. The entire dependence on T is contained in β and γ, both of which are very nearly proportional to ρ_s below 1.9°K.

The two regimes defined by equations (8.35) and (8.36) have on a few occasions ([64]) also been observed for flow in wide channels.

Classical hydrodynamics predicts similar results, that is, $\nabla P = \mathbf{v}^n$, where $n = 0$, 1, and 2 for perfect fluid, laminar, and turbulent flows, respectively; however, for turbulent flows, the empirical Blasius law assigns $n = 1.75$. For $n = 0$, ∇P is a constant, and the flow, having a plane velocity profile, is considered to be one-dimensional; for $n = 1$, the streamlines are parallel, but the velocity profile is parabolic, so the flow is two-dimensional; and for $n = 2$, the streamlines are no longer parallel, rendering the flow three-dimensional. We cannot carry the analogy between superfluid and classical hydrodynamics too far, because the latter depends upon the existence of a shear viscosity. This would imply for the superfluid case that β, for example, should vary as d^{-2}, and it does not.

We can, however, modify our argument for the superfluid in conformity with the notion of vortex line production. For $\mathbf{v}_s < \mathbf{v}_{s,c}$, clearly we have ∇P constant (zero). Then as $\mathbf{v}_{s,c}$ is exceeded, vortex lines, which at lower velocities were either latent or formed and held close to the channel walls, begin to move into the mainstream of flow along with the superfluid. At low $\bar{\mathbf{v}}$, the vortices are far apart relative to d and do not interact with one another, resulting in the low-order dissipation. As $\bar{\mathbf{v}}$ increases, the vortex production rate increases and the average spacing between lines decreases, so that as $\mathbf{v}_s$ exceeds $\mathbf{v}'_{s,c}$, the lines become tangled with one another, whence the orderly flow of the separated lines gives way to a three-dimensional turbulent-like flow. If we assume that the dissipation energy all goes into making vortices, we may see by the following argument how this energy depends primarily on the frequency v of vortex production and not on d. Consider a flow channel with fixed length and breadth, but with width d which we may vary. We assume that the work against friction is given by ϵv, where ϵ is the energy of the vortex line, and that vortex lines are produced with characteristic length d—either as rings with diameter $\sim d$, or as lines stretched across the channel. In either case, the energy required to form a vortex is roughly proportional to d; however, at the same time, the energy available from the flow is also proportional to d. Consequently, the d-dependence of the work done to create a vortex cancels and leaves the dissipation proportional to the number of vortices produced per unit time.

The above results are for gravitational flow (GF) in narrow channels in which the fluid always decelerated, approaching $\mathbf{v}_{s,c}$ from higher velocities. Keller and Hammel ([51]) have studied $\mathbf{v}_{s,c}$ and superfluid dissipation in a narrow slit ($d = 3.36\mu$, but otherwise similar to slits used in GF) in the apparatus shown in Fig. 8.4d. Here fluid may be forced through the slit at a variety of constant speeds both subcritical and supercritical. We call this forced flow (FF). Typical results of ∇P vs. $\mathbf{v}_s$ are shown in Fig. 8.11, where nearly every point represents an

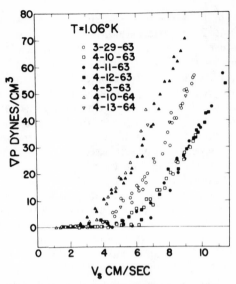

Fig. 8.11. Superfluid dissipation in forced flow.

experiment in which the fluid is initially at rest and is subsequently brought up to the indicated constant linear velocity. In all instances, the FF data show that for a given v_s, the ∇P is less than, or at most equal to, that which would be observed in the corresponding GF. This is interpreted as an indication that whereas in GF, the vorticity production sites are uniformly distributed over the length of the slit, in FF, the production is generally not fully developed and takes place at a relatively few favored sites which are somewhat reproducible (data in the figure were taken over the space of a year, and though several distinct curves are defined, each was reproduced on different occasions). Thus here we seem to have a situation intermediate between the "clean" and "dirty" cases mentioned in Section 8.1.3b; and indeed Fig. 8.11 shows that $v_{s,c}$ is variable and up to several times larger than observed for GF in the same slit. Although in Fig. 8.11 we have plotted $\nabla P = \Delta P/L$, (L is the length of the slit), if the dissipation occurs over only a portion of the slit, we really do not know what the "effective" L is for calculation ∇P. Hence the plot is equivalent to one of ΔP vs. v_s with ΔP normalized by L. In this light, we see that for a given ΔP, v_s is larger when the vorticity is concentrated over some length less than L than when it is uniformly spread out along L.

We turn now to the mobile He II film, which in some ways may be considered an extension of narrow-channel flow, albeit with the added complication of variable d over the flow path. The causes for the notorious nonreproducibility of the observed film transfer rate R have been long sought but not altogether successfully uncovered. It is well known that R for a clean surface is lower than for one contaminated with dirt or condensed gases; that R depends upon the composition of the substrate; and that R is affected by such external conditions as mechanical agitation and stray heat sources. Some authors [78,79] have measured consistently different transfer rates from the same vessel, depending upon whether the vessel was initially filled by complete immersion in the helium bath or filled only by film flow. The explanation offered [79,80] for this behavior considered that the film thickness at the vessel rim is different in the two cases.

During a given transfer process, discrete and spontaneous changes in R have also been observed [79,81,82]. Mate et al. [81] have produced histograms showing the distribution in transfer rates observed for a number of beaker-emptyings at 0.65° and 1.35°K. The overall rates varied from ~ 7 to 14×10^{-5} cm^2/sec but displayed strikingly sharp preferences for values of R at distinct intervals $\Delta R = 0.57 \times 10^{-5}$ cm^2/sec, the same for both temperatures. In a given emptying process, the rate would progressively decrease in several such steps.

To define the transfer process in terms of R, with units "cm^3 of liquid/sec/cm perimeter," we need to know what perimeter limits the flow. In the past, this has been universally taken [83] as the "smallest perimeter of the vessel lying above the highest liquid level." In a cylindrical beaker, this would simply be the inside diameter, but for more complicated geometries, the situation is not so clear-cut as this statement would imply.

There has also been some question about the dependence of R upon the various heights in the problem. Consider the outflow process pictured in Fig. 8.12. Many experiments have indicated that except when the inside level is very near the rim, the emptying rate of the beaker is practically independent of both H_1 and H_2. On the other hand, careful measurements by Allen and Armitage [82] strongly suggest that R is limited by d at the inside rim, which in turn is determined by H_1; i.e., $R = (\rho_s/\rho)\mathbf{v}_{s,c}d = 6.5\ (\rho_s/\rho)H_1^{-1/4} \times 10^{-5}$ cm^2/sec when d is given by $3H_1^{-1/3} \times 10^{-6}$ cm and $\mathbf{v}_{s,c}$ by $Ad^{-1/4} \approx d^{-1/4}$ cm/sec. In addition, we may be fairly certain that the quantity $mg(H_2 - H_1) = (\mu_1 - \mu_2) = \Delta\mu$ provides the driving force (per particle) for the film flow.

It seems possible that at least some of the nonreproducibility of R measurements has arisen from effects similar to those observed in the FF experiments in narrow channels—namely, that for a given $\Delta P = \rho g(H_2 - H_1)$, the flow rate depends upon ∇P, or $\nabla\mu$, and therefore on the specific distribution of vorticity production sites. On this basis, Keller and Hammel [84] have used a simple level-sensing technique to probe the variation of $\mu(s)$ along the film flow path s. The

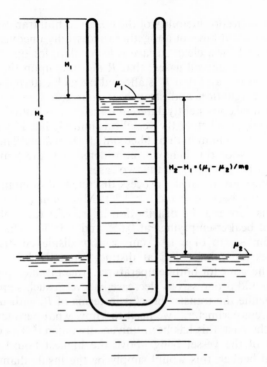

Fig. 8.12. Relevant heights in a film outflow experiment, showing the relationship with the chemical
potential difference.

device, as shown in Fig. 8.13, is a small tube inserted into the beaker
wall, with the level in the tube, h_t, indicating μ at the point of insertion
relative to μ at either h_i or h_0. In case A with $h_t = h_i$, the probe tells us
that $\Delta\mu = 0$ along the path from h_i to the tube opening; whereas in case
B, h_t is between h_i and h_0, indicating that a definite fraction of the total
$\Delta\mu$, namely, $(h_i - h_t)/(h_i - h_0)$ takes place between h_i and the tube
opening.

Through a number of observations using this type of probe in a
variety of geometries and in conjunction with simultaneously measured
flow rates, the following characteristics for outflow emerged: (1) In
some instances, $\mu(s)$ was found to be a step-function, indicating that the
entire $\Delta\mu$, and therefore all the dissipation, occurred at a highly
localized point on the path (e.g., at the inside rim of the beaker); in other
cases, $\mu(s)$ was distributed along the *inside* wall over a considerable
distance. (2) Flow rates were quite sensitive to the distribution of
dissipation, R being larger when $\Delta\mu$ was localized than when $\Delta\mu$ was

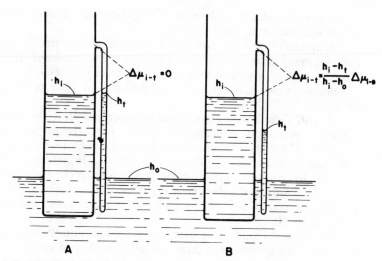

Fig. 8.13. Beaker fitted with probe tube for sensing the relative chemical potential at the tube opening during a film flow process.

spread out, similar to the interpretation of the FF results for narrow channels. (3) A spreading-out of $\Delta\mu$ was always accompanied by a decrease in R; but for a given distribution, R remained constant even though the total $\Delta\mu$ was changing. (4) Changes in R and $\mu(s)$ occurred either spontaneously or as a consequence of some applied perturbation, suggesting a metastable character of the flow. These last two remarks bear upon the results of Mate et al. ([81]). (5) The dissipation limiting R was found to occur in the vicinity of the smallest *cross-sectional area* of the film, i.e., $A_f = p \times d$ (p is the perimeter and d is inferred from the static height *vs.* d relation) rather than at the smallest p above the highest level. Often, these two conditions do not coincide.

Now consider again the arrangement shown in Fig. 8.12, bearing in mind the $H_1^{-1/3}$ dependence of d near the inside rim. For any constant R, the volume flow rate, $v_s A_f$, will through continuity also be constant along the flow path. Hence if A_f is a minimum at the inside rim, then v_s will be a maximum and it is easy to see how the dissipation may be localized there. Such a condition obtains when H_1 is small, less than about 2 cm. But when H_1 is larger than this, the d vs. H profile along the inside wall becomes rather flat near the rim; i.e., proceeding downward from the rim, A_f increases only slowly at first and then more rapidly. It is quite likely that in the film the ∇P vs. v_s relation is shaped similarly to the solid curve in Fig. 8.5, so that for a given ΔP there will be a range of values of $v_s > v_{s,c}$. Since $v_s A_f =$ constant, there is then also a range of A_f in which dissipation may take place. In this way we may understand how the dissipation may spread down the inside wall, becoming nonlocalized.

It appears that these potential probes do indeed provide explanations for many of the anomalous flow experiments previously reported. However, for a complete description of these processes we require simultaneous measurements of d, $\mu(s)$, and R; and these we do not yet have.

8.1.4d. Interference Phenomena in Superfluid He. The similarity between superconductivity and superfluidity in He II expressed through the phase of the wave function and the associated long-range correlations has elicited a variety of exciting prospects. In particular, predictions by Josephson [85] concerning phase interference phenomena in superconductors and subsequent experimental confirmation of these predictions have stimulated a search for the appearance of like effects in liquid He II.

In the superconducting case, the wave function Ψ describes the collective and coordinated center-of-mass motion of bound pairs of conduction electrons (Cooper pairs). Consider two separated chunks of superconductors, I and II, for which the phases ϕ_I and ϕ_{II} of Ψ are arbitrary. Since Ψ does not go to zero at the metal surface, but decays exponentially outside it, if I and II are brought together to within ~ 10 Å, these tails of the wave functions will overlap in the insulating region between I and II. Under these conditions, the probability for quantum-mechanical tunneling of Cooper pairs is enhanced, resulting in a transfer of these pairs across the insulator and a current, $\mathbf{j} = \mathbf{j}_{max}$ $\sin(\phi_I - \phi_{II})$, tending to produce the equilibrium situation defined by $\phi_I = \phi_{II}$. Conversely, by imposition of a small constant current $\mathbf{j}$ across this sandwich, tunneling of pairs is enforced and a phase difference $\Delta\phi$ is established between I and II. The current $\mathbf{j}$ is called the *Josephson current*. The important point here is that $\mathbf{j}$ may be imposed across the sandwich without a corresponding voltage drop, so that the entire assembly acts as if it were an integral superconducting sample. This is the *dc Josephson effect* and the sandwich in which it occurs is known as a *Josephson tunnel junction*.

If we now impose a voltage V across the junction, $\Delta\phi$ will no longer remain constant but will vary with time, and the current should then oscillate at a frequency $\nu = 2eV/h$ (e is the electron charge). This is the *ac Josephson effect* and ν is the *Josephson frequency*.

For the dc effect, Josephson predicted a particular relation between $\mathbf{j}$, an external magnetic field $\mathbf{H}$ applied parallel to the sandwich plane, and the vector potential $\mathbf{A}$. Through this relation, Anderson and Rowell [86] experimentally detected the phase difference associated with $\mathbf{j}$, thereby confirming Josephson's theory. The ac effect has proved more difficult to observe. However, this has been accomplished in the

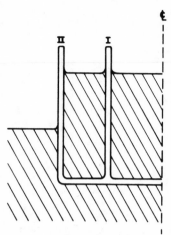

Fig. 8.14. The double-beaker film-
flow experiment.

elegant experiments by Yanson *et al.* ([87]), who first measured the
characteristic photons ($\lambda \approx 1$ cm) emitted from the oscillating electromagnetic field in the junction.†

Between a superconductor and superfluid helium we may recog-
nize the following analogies: (1) the persistent electron current i corresponds to the superfluid velocity v_s, both quantities being associated
with dissipation-free flow up to some critical value, i_c and $v_{s,c}$ respectively; (2) the voltage V and the chemical potential μ are analogous;
(3) the application of an external magnetic field H corresponds to a
rotation of the He II system, though the interaction between H and
the vector potential A does not appear to have a helium counterpart;
(4) the quantization of circulation in liquid He II has as its analog in
superconductivity the quantization of the fluxoid ([88]) in units of $2e/hc$
(c is the velocity of light). The intimacy of these interrelations suggests
that the Josephson effects should also be observed in He II.

Donnelly ([86]) has suggested that the Daunt and Mendelssohn ([90])
double-beaker experiment (Fig. 8.14) represents a clear-cut demonstration of the dc Josephson effect in liquid He. Here, the film flows
from the inner to the outer beaker over rim I at a subcritical velocity,
while the flow over rim II proceeds as in an ordinary emptying process.
Thus levels in the two beakers should drop together with no height
difference between them—as observed within experimental error—and
over rim I, a current of superfluid flows in the absence of a potential
difference. However, the film differs from the superconducting
Josephson junction in that the superfluid is continuous throughout.

† For a useful exposition of Josephson phenomena, see Feynman *et al.* ([141]).

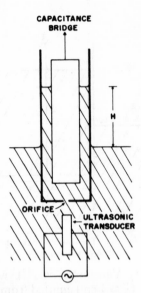

Fig. 8.15. The Richards–Anderson experiment (schematic) for detecting the ac Josephson effect in He II.

If the analogy is to be strictly drawn, then in liquid He, the Josephson tunneling junction must be geometrically comparable with the healing length, $a_0 \approx 10^{-8}$ cm, if the necessary overlap in Ψ's is to be achieved (for T near T_λ, a_0 becomes larger). Mamaladze and Cheishvili [91] have discussed the theory of this problem for geometries with extremely narrow pores or gaps.

On the other hand, a very clever experiment by Richards and Anderson [52] has provided evidence that phase phenomena in He may be more readily detected in the ac analog—the reverse of the case for superconductors. Figure 8.15 shows the apparatus schematically. The beaker forms one arm of a capacitance bridge, which measures changes in level difference H of the liquid inside and outside the beaker. The bottom of the beaker is a metal foil $\sim 2.5 \times 10^{-3}$ cm thick perforated by one orifice with $d \approx 1.5 \times 10^{-3}$ cm. Placed near the orifice in the bath is a quartz crystal oscillator. With the oscillator turned off, displacement of the inside level by either raising or lowering the beaker was followed by the usual rapid, smooth approach to equilibrium. But with the oscillator turned on, the flow was more or less arrested, showing steps at values of H satisfying the relation

$$n_1 mgH = n_2 hv'$$ (8.37)

where n_1 and n_2 are integers and v' is the sound frequency generated by the oscillator. The interpretation of these results assumes the formation of vortices through phase slippage at the orifice at the rate given by equation (8.28), or $v = \Delta\mu/h$. When $v = v'$, the sound field is synchronized with the vortex production, which, it is believed, causes a vortex (or vortices) in the orifice to oscillate back and forth, thus stopping the flow. In this condition, coherence of the phases of the liquid in the two reservoirs is enforced and is maintained until the system is perturbed by fluctuations. This measurement of v represents the detection of the Josephson frequency for liquid He.

The experiment has been repeated with several refinements by Khorana and Chandrasekhar ([92]), who achieved considerably more clear-cut results than did Richards and Anderson. Figure 8.16 graphs

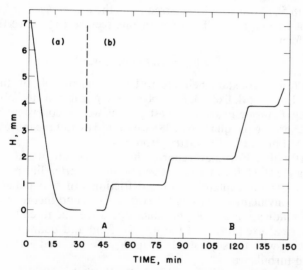

Fig. 8.16. The ac Josephson effect in He II. (a) shows the time history of the level difference H for flow through the orifice when the sound is turned off (see Fig. 8.15). (b) is the H vs. time behavior with the sound turned on. (The sound field may either arrest the level equilibration at distinct steps following a displacement H, or, as shown here, may "pump" the inside level starting from the $H = 0$ condition.) Transducer switched on at A produces $H = 1.01$ mm, equivalent to the Josephson frequency $\Delta\mu/h = 99.722$ kc/sec, which is also the frequency of the sound. At B, sound intensity momentarily increased to perturb the system results in a jump of twice the Josephson frequency. [Drawn after recorder traces of Khorana and Chandrasekhar ([92]).]

some of the new data taken with $2\pi\nu' = \omega = 99.722$ kc/sec, which corresponds to $\Delta H = 1.01$ mm. We see from the figure that the step separations are very nearly this value of ΔH and that a given step is stable for a considerable time—the authors report such stability for as long as 45 min.

8.2. MUTUAL FRICTION

At sufficiently large relative velocities $\mathbf{v}_r = (\mathbf{v}_s - \mathbf{v}_n)$, we expect that the independence of the normal fluid and superfluid velocity fields described by equations (8.1) and (8.2) should be destroyed. From the results of thermal conduction experiments, Gorter and Mellink [93] were led to introduce into these relations a force $\mathbf{F}_{sn}$ to account for the mutual interaction between the velocity fields. This force appears with equal magnitude but opposite sign in the two equations of motion (8.4) and (8.5), and is usually referred to as the *mutual friction force*, or simply the *mutual force*. The experiments seemed to require that $\mathbf{F}_{sn}$ have the form

$$\mathbf{F}_{sn} = A(T)\rho_s\rho_n(v_r^2)\mathbf{v}_r \tag{8.38}$$

where $A(T)$ is a constant believed to be dependent only on the temperature. Early work fixed $A(T) \approx 50$ cm-sec/gm, increasing somewhat with rising T, though various investigations were inconsistent on this point. According to equation (8.38), we should expect the mutual force to be turned on gradually starting from $\mathbf{v}_r = 0$.

Shortly after Feynman reported his ideas on quantized vorticity in flowing He II, Hall and Vinen seized upon the vortex-line model as a physical basis for explaining mutual friction. In two papers, they produced convincing experimental evidence [94] and theoretical arguments [38] indicating that $\mathbf{F}_{sn}$ becomes operative due to collisions between thermal excitations of the normal fluid and quantized vortex lines moving with the superfluid. Thus, $\mathbf{F}_{sn}$ is associated with a sort of superfluid turbulence.

Hall and Vinen [94] experimentally studied mutual friction by investigating the attenuation of second sound in rotating systems. The mutual force was found to be given by

$$\mathbf{F}_{sn} = B(T)\rho^{-1}\rho_s\rho_n|\boldsymbol{\omega}|\mathbf{v}_r \tag{8.39}$$

where $\boldsymbol{\omega}$ is the angular rotational velocity and $B(T)$ is a temperature-dependent constant of order unity. The connection between equations (8.38) and (8.39)—that is, between mutual friction in a heat current and in rotating systems, was provided by the heat-flow experiments of Vinen [95–98]. This work demonstrated that both types of mutual friction do indeed have a common origin and that $A(T)$ and $B(T)$ are simply related by

$$A(T)/B(T) = 4\pi^2\alpha^2/3K\rho \tag{8.40}$$

in terms of the circulation K and an empirical constant α.

We shall not repeat the lengthy arguments leading to these results, but refer the reader to the original papers as well as to pertinent review articles by Hall ([27]) and Vinen ([26]). Nevertheless, in the following, we shall draw freely upon the ideas and conclusions contained in these important works.

According to Hall and Vinen, in order for a fully-developed mutual friction to be operative in a flow process, the following conditions must be fulfilled: (1) vorticity must be present and (2) vorticity must be homogeneously distributed through the flowing superfluid. The first of these implies that v_s must be supercritical and that below $v_{s,c}$, F_{sn} should be zero. The effects of this cutoff of F_{sn} are not included in equation (8.38). As we shall see, experiments in wide channels are not very sensitive to whether the cutoff is specified; however, in general, we should include it, and the results of flows in narrow channels provide an indication of how this should be done.

The condition that vorticity be homogeneously distributed is based upon an analogy with ordinary fluid turbulence and may be expressed by requiring that $l < d$, where l is the average spacing of vortex lines in the system. In terms of the parameter α appearing in equation (8.40), Vinen ([97]) has on dimensional grounds found the relationship between l and the average relative velocity $\bar{v}_r$, namely

$$l|\bar{v}_r| = \hbar/m\alpha \tag{8.41}$$

Unfortunately, we cannot calculate α independently; but Vinen has obtained $\alpha(T)$ from the experimental values of $A(T)$ and $B(T)$ and plotted $l|\bar{v}_r|$ vs. T. This, shown in Fig. 8.17, allows us to estimate l knowing just T and v_r, subject to the assumptions made by Vinen in the derivation of equation (8.41). Using Fig. 8.17, we may determine how well the $l < d$ criterion is fulfilled in wide channels. An unfavorable situation would be one in which $v_n = 0$, so that vorticity first appears at $\bar{v}_r = v_{s,c}$. Taking an average value of $l|\bar{v}_r| = 6 \times 10^{-3}$ cm^2/sec $= lv_{s,c}$, we find that $l < d$ so long as $v_{s,c}d > 6 \times 10^{-3}$/sec. From Fig. 8.1, this will be true for $d > 10^{-3}$ cm, independent of whether the Feynman or the $d^{-1/4}$ rule correctly describes the $v_{s,c}$ vs. d relation. Hence, for wide geometries, whenever $\bar{v}_r$ exceeds $v_{s,c}$, we expect the mutual force to be fully operative. For $d < 10^{-3}$ cm, this is not necessarily the case.

Because of the foregoing remarks, we will again find it convenient to distinguish between flows in narrow and wide channels, not because

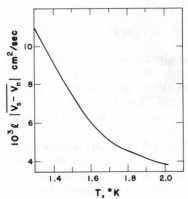

Fig. 8.17. Plot of $l|\bar{v}_r|$ vs. temperature [after Vinen ([97])].

the equations of motion are different, but because some of the assumptions we make for simplifying these equations are valid for one case and not the other.

8.2.1. F_{sn} in Wide Channels

By inserting expression (8.38) into equation (8.4) for the superfluid under stationary conditions and with the approximation that $\mathbf{F}_s$ is negligible, we obtain

$$(\rho_s/\rho)\nabla P + \rho_s s \, \nabla T - A(T)\rho_s\rho_n(v_r^2)\mathbf{v}_r = 0 \tag{8.42}$$

Then, using $\bar{q} = \rho sT v_n$ together with equation (8.24) for ∇P, we may solve equation (8.42) for the temperature gradient,

$$\nabla T = -\frac{12\eta}{\rho^2 s^2 T d}\bar{\mathbf{q}} + \frac{A(T)\rho_n}{\rho_s^4 s^4 T^3}\bar{\mathbf{q}}^3 \tag{8.43}$$

(for a parallel-sided channel). The term in $\bar{q}^3$ was first introduced by Gorter and Mellink ([93]).

Vinen ([95]) has made careful measurements of the heat flow in rectangular tubes with $d = 0.24$ and 0.40 cm. At all but the smallest gradients, the results could be represented accurately by

$$\nabla T = D\bar{q}^3 \tag{8.44}$$

When we compare equations (8.44) and (8.43), we see that in these experiments, the term linear in $\bar{q}$ is completely dominated by the cubic term, and therefore

$$A(T) = \rho_s^4 s^4 T^3 D/\rho_n \tag{8.45}$$

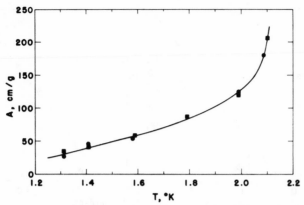

Fig. 8.18. Vinen's determination of the Gorter–Mellink mutual friction parameter $A(T)$: ■ from heat-flow measurements; ● from second sound attenuation across a heat current [after Vinen ([95])].

From the measured values of D, Vinen found $A(T)$ as plotted in Fig. 8.18, independent of d. Also, the same values of $A(T)$ were obtained by Vinen ([95]) from observations of the attenuation of second sound propagated at 90° to the heat current. Taken together, these determinations have provided the most generally acceptable geometry-independent values for $A(T)$.

Vinen ([96–98]) has also discussed the transient effects leading to the establishment and the decay of fully-developed mutual friction in terms of competing processes accounting for the generation and destruction of vorticity. At equilibrium, the two processes balance. It is assumed that under these conditions, there is a steady-state length of line, $L = L_0$ per cm³, and $dL/dt = 0$. Vinen has deduced, using dimensional analysis, empirical results, and analogies with classical hydrodynamics, the following relation between L_0 and $\mathbf{v}_r$ in a steady heat current:

$$\chi_1 \frac{B\rho_n}{2\rho} \mathbf{v}_r L_0^{3/2} + \gamma \mathbf{v}_r^{5/2} - \chi_2 \frac{\hbar}{m} L_0^2 - \chi_3 \frac{B\rho_n}{2\rho} \mathbf{v}_r \frac{L_0}{d} = 0 \qquad (8.46)$$

Here, χ_1, χ_2, and χ_3 are slightly temperature-dependent parameters of the order unity and γ is another empirical quantity which varies rapidly with T.

The first two terms of equation (8.46) describe the growth of vorticity assuming that some remnant lines are present in the static situation. The term in γ is generally small but is important in determining the time scale for the buildup of mutual friction. The third term accounts for the decay of vorticity, and the last includes effects due to the channel walls. Figure 8.19a plots $L_0^{1/2}$ vs. $\mathbf{v}_r$.

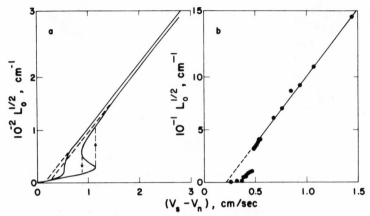

Fig. 8.19. $L_0^{1/2}$ vs. relative velocity: (a) Calculated from equation (8.46) at $T = 1.4°$K, upper curve for $d = 0.1325$ cm, lower curve for $d = 0.0875$ cm. Arrows show direction of hysteresis. (b) Experimental results at $T = 1.4°$K for $d = 0.40$ cm. Note changes in scales. [After Vinen ([98]).]

At high $\mathbf{v}_r$, we may approximate $L_0^{1/2}$ as

$$L_0^{1/2} = \frac{\chi_1}{\chi_2} \frac{B\rho_n}{2\rho} \frac{m}{\hbar} \mathbf{v}_r \qquad (8.47)$$

The ratio (χ_1/χ_2) cannot be calculated directly, but it can be shown ([97]) to be proportional to $[A(T)/B(T)^3]^{1/2}$ and therefore determinable from experiment. The ratio varies somewhat for different geometries. At low $\mathbf{v}_r$, all the effects described by equation (8.46) become important, and, in particular, the wall term is responsible for the hysteresis shown in the figure. Vinen has argued that this arises because of either or both of the following processes: (1) annihilation of vorticity at the walls as a result of a Magnus force on the moving lines; and (2) interference by the wall with the production and decay processes associated with superfluid turbulence.

The development leading to equation (8.46) is admittedly rather crude, so that while we do not expect quantitative agreement with experiment, in some respects it turns out to be very good. In Fig. 8.19b we plot some of Vinen's experimental results ([98]), which are qualitatively similar to the theoretical curves. One important failing of the theory seems to be that it inadequately accounts for the critical velocity for the onset of mutual friction.

Brewer and Edwards ([99]) have made careful measurements of heat flow in capillaries ($d = 5.2 \times 10^{-3}$, 1.07×10^{-2}, and 3.66×10^{-2} cm) and have also analyzed their results using equation (8.46). Agreement with theory at large v_r is good; but at low v_r, l became comparable with d, at which point the theory is no longer valid. Brewer and Edwards did find, however, that all their data fell on nearly a single curve when plotted as the dimensionless quantities $(DL_0^{1/2})$ vs. $(mv_r D/h)$, with D the ratio of the area to the perimeter of the channel. They also observed $A(T)$ to be independent of channel geometry, to vary with T similarly to Vinen's results, but to be about 50% larger than Vinen's values. We note in this respect that $A(T)$ as determined from a variety of experiments has assumed a wide range of values [see, for example, Kramers [100]], among which some† agree with Vinen's. Brewer and Edwards suggested that $A(T)$ might be sensitive to the particular apparatus and details of experimental procedure.

Vincentini-Missoni and Cunsolo [102] have pointed out a source of error attendant to measurements of large heat currents in wide geometries. Using negative ions as "tracers" for following the counter-flow processes, they have found that the jet of normal fluid extends appreciably into the "cold" reservoir past the tube orifice, thereby altering the temperature distribution along the tube. Such effects could also be involved in the difficulties associated with obtaining consistent values of $A(T)$.

A number of interesting heat flow experiments [103] have been carried out in long tubes (1 to 8 m). By probing the time variation of the temperature profile along a tube, it has been possible to demonstrate that vorticity does not develop homogeneously throughout the liquid, but instead propagates initially in well-defined fronts. When a heat current is switched on at one end of the tube in which the liquid has been allowed to remain undisturbed for some time (~ 30 min), two fronts, one from the "cold" end and one from the "hot" end, propagate toward one another, each moving with a characteristic steady velocity, v_C or v_H. If successive heatings are performed at intervals sufficiently short that the vorticity cannot substantially decay, then fronts may originate in the middle section of the tube. Attempts at describing the behavior of v_H and v_C within the framework of Vinen's equations for vortex generation have not as yet been quantitatively successful.

8.2.2. F_{sn} in Narrow Channels

When d of the experimental flow channel is less than $\sim 10^{-3}$ cm, some of the approximations made for wide-channel flow are no longer valid and questions concerning the wall interactions become appreciably more acute. In particular, the neglect of a low-velocity cutoff for F_{sn} cannot be ignored; nor can the omission of the linear $\bar{q}$ term in

† See, for example, Wiarda and Kramers [101].

equation (8.43). Also, since $A(T)$ may possibly be geometry-dependent in wide channels, we must inquire whether $A(T)$ has significance in small channels, and, if so, what.

Some light has been shed on these problems by the heat-flow and fountain-pressure measurements of Hammel and Keller ([57,58]) using slits with $d = 2.12 \times 10^{-4}$ and 3.36×10^{-4} cm. Figure 8.20 shows the results of heat flow measurements for the 3.36 μ slit and for temperature differences $\Delta T = (T_H - T_C)$ ranging up to 1°K. Each curve in the figure represents measurements in which T_C (the "cold" temperature) is held constant while successive small increments of heat are added to the "hot" side, which equilibrates at the temperature T_H. The hot side communicates thermally with the rest of the system only through the slit.

A family of heating curves appropriate for this slit has been calculated ([104]) using $\mathbf{F}_{sn}$ in the form of equation (8.38) which leads to expression (8.43) for the temperature gradient. Here we must retain the term linear in $\bar{\mathbf{q}}$. For the large values of ΔT encompassed by these experiments, it is not possible (as it was, for example, in Vinen's cases) to approximate ∇T by $\Delta T/Z$ [Z is the slit length; also, see equation (8.70)]. Both terms in the equation are strong functions of the temperature, and we must therefore integrate equation (8.43) over the tempera-

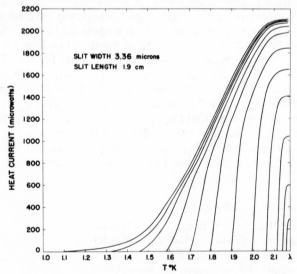

Fig. 8.20. Measurements of heat flow through a narrow channel for several reference temperatures [from Keller and Hammel ([57])].

ture interval. We wish to solve for $\overline{q}$, with the result

$$\overline{q} = \frac{d^2}{Z} \int_{T_C}^{T_H} \frac{\Lambda \, dT}{1 + ad^2\overline{q}^2} \tag{8.48}$$

where

$$\Lambda = (\rho s)^2 T/12\eta_n \tag{8.49}$$

and

$$a = \frac{A(T)(\rho_n/\rho)}{12\eta_n(\rho_s/\rho)^3 s^2 T^2} \tag{8.50}$$

Since $\overline{q}$ appears in the integrand of equation (8.48), the solutions must be obtained numerically. When Vinen's values of $A(T)$ were used, the heating curves in Fig. 8.21 were obtained ($d = 3.36 \, \mu$). The initial part of each curve is essentially due to the linear part of equation (8.48), which, if extended to larger values, would indicate tremendous heat currents. Instead, $\mathbf{F}_{sn}$ becomes important and limits the heat flow.

In the present model, the corresponding expression for the fountain pressure is

$$P_f = \int_{T_C}^{T_H} \frac{\rho s \, dT}{1 + ad^2\overline{q}^2} \tag{8.51}$$

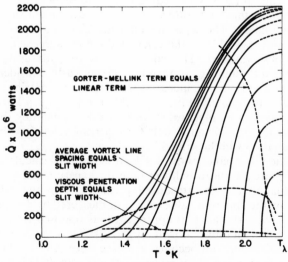

Fig. 8.21. Calculations of heat flow through the 3.36-μ slit as obtained using equation (8.48) with Vinen's values for $A(T)$ [from Craig et al. ([104])].

and, as seen in Fig. 8.7, the diminution of P_f below the ideal fountain pressure is considerable for this slit ($d = 3.36 \mu$) at the higher velocities. For the 0.31-μ slit, the ideal P_f is observed to nearly T_λ and becomes as large as ~ 490 mm Hg.

From an overall comparison of the curves in Figs. 8.20 and 8.21, it is evident that the Gorter–Mellink–Vinen model for $\mathbf{F}_{sn}$ in heat flow gives a remarkably good account of the experiments even in narrow channels. A more detailed analysis ([104]) has indicated in addition that Vinen's $A(T)$ values provide the best overall agreement with experiment, suggesting that the geometrical dependence of $A(T)$ has been overstated by some authors.

The dashed lines cutting the heating curves in Fig. 8.21 indicate several regions useful in interpreting the vortex-line model. Three of these indicate the separate criteria either for the validity of the model or for the appearance of a fully developed mutual force. We have already discussed the conditions that $\mathbf{F}_{sn} = 0$ unless $\mathbf{v}_s \geqslant \mathbf{v}_{s,c}$ and that l should be less than d for the vorticity to be homogeneous. Still another criterion ([97]) is that the effective viscous penetration depth, $\lambda_p = \rho_n|\bar{\mathbf{v}}_r|/2\eta_n$, should be small compared with d. All three conditions must be met for $\mathbf{F}_{sn}$ to become operative, so that as $\mathbf{v}_r$ increases for any given flow situation, the last of these to be satisfied should determine the onset of mutual friction.

For the particular case of the 3.36-μ slit, the calculations predict that below about 1.9°K, $\mathbf{v}_s$ exceeding $\mathbf{v}_{s,c}$ should be the critical condition, whereas above this temperature, the $l < d$ requirement should be the last to be fulfilled. The experimental evidence is consistent with these notions. For $T_C < 1.9$°K, the calculated curves agree extremely well with the observations. [The calculations were made using equation (8.38), and although $\mathbf{F}_{sn}$ is therefore erroneously considered to be gradually turned on as $\mathbf{v}_r$ increases from zero, the contribution to the heat flow is fortunately quite negligible for $\mathbf{v}_s < \mathbf{v}_{s,c}$.] Furthermore, in this temperature range, values of $\mathbf{v}_{s,c}$ as determined by the method illustrated in Fig. 8.7 agree well with critical velocities observed in gravitational flow in the same slit.

On the other hand, above 1.9°K, the heat flow calculations using the full $\mathbf{F}_{sn}$ are significantly lower than the experimental $\bar{\mathbf{q}}$, suggesting that mutual friction is introduced prematurely in the calculations. In addition, the apparent values of $\mathbf{v}_{s,c}$, as measured by deviations from linear behavior, rise as T_λ is approached, as opposed to the decrease observed in gravitational flow (cf. Fig. 8.8). Thus, it seems that here, mutual friction does not become operative when $\mathbf{v}_s = \mathbf{v}_{s,c}$, but at some larger value of $\mathbf{v}_s$ when l becomes comparable with d. This is consistent with the temperature variation of $\mathbf{v}_r$ at $\mathbf{v}_s = \mathbf{v}_{s,c}$: if we consider $\mathbf{v}_{s,c}$ to be independent of T, the corresponding $\mathbf{v}_r$ is much smaller at high temperature than it is at low temperature. Thus, the homogeneity condition is more easily satisfied at low T than at high T. Figure 8.17 is useful for estimating when $l \approx d$ in these cases.

It is clear that equation (8.38) incompletely describes $\mathbf{F}_{sn}$ and that some cutoff condition at low velocities must be imposed. Vinen [97] and others have suggested that (v_r^2) in equation (8.38) be replaced by $(|\mathbf{v}_s - \mathbf{v}_n| - \mathbf{v}_0)^2$, where $\mathbf{v}_0$ is some critical velocity. Experiments in wide channels are not sensitive to $\mathbf{v}_0$, and, in general, this quantity has not been adequately specified. It appears from the above discussion of narrow-channel flow that an appropriate way of modifying equation (8.38) would be to write

$$\mathbf{F}_{sn} = 0 \qquad\qquad \mathbf{v}_r < \mathbf{v}_{r,c}$$
$$\mathbf{F}_{sn} = A(T)\rho_s\rho_n(v_r^2)\mathbf{v}_r \qquad \mathbf{v}_r > \mathbf{v}_{r,c} \tag{8.52}$$

with the understanding that $\mathbf{v}_r = \mathbf{v}_{r,c}$ is the smallest value of $\mathbf{v}_r$ for which both conditions, $\mathbf{v}_s \geqslant \mathbf{v}_{s,c}$ and $l < d$, are satisfied. This expression suggests that at $\mathbf{v}_{r,c}$, the full mutual force should suddenly be switched on, causing the flow characteristics to change discontinuously. It seems likely that such a discontinuity is smeared out for heat flow in slits: for given $\bar{\mathbf{q}}$, $\mathbf{v}_r$ at the hot end is smaller than $\mathbf{v}_r$ at the cold end; $\mathbf{F}_{sn}$ probably first becomes operative where $\mathbf{v}_r$ is largest, and with increasing $\bar{\mathbf{q}}$, the dissipation process moves down the slit. The curves in Figs. 8.7 and 8.20 exhibit no discontinuities; instead, the departures from linear behavior are smooth but marked by inflection points.

A complete account of the forces determining the heat flow in the experiments discussed above should also include the effects of $\mathbf{F}_s$. However, from the velocity dependences of the forces, we may easily verify that $\mathbf{F}_{sn}$ completely swamps $\mathbf{F}_s$ in these situations, so that the latter may quite properly be neglected.

We have examined the above particular flow situations in some detail here in order to demonstrate how various subtle effects enter into the observations and to emphasize the caution that must be exercised in interpreting apparent changes in flow regimes. Overall, we may conclude that the vortex-line model is in excellent accord with the results and we may confidently expect it to apply to a wide range of geometries once the limitations of the model are fully appreciated for each case. The model is also capable of predicting some effects in considerable detail. As an example, consider the experimental curves in Fig. 8.7 for $T_C = 1.15°$ and $1.42°$K. For these curves, and not others at higher T_C, the P_f vs. T relations pass through maxima, which at first sight seems highly unlikely. Nevertheless, the calculations [105] using the Gorter–Mellink–Vinen model properly predict the conditions and the magnitude of these observed features.

8.3. THE FLOW OF NORMAL FLUID

8.3.1. Laminar Flow of Normal Fluid

In the absence of a mutual force, we may consider the flow of the normal fluid alone. At sufficiently low velocities, we expect such flows to be laminar and thus governed entirely by viscous forces. Since this is the behavior expected of ordinary fluids, our interest in these flows is nominal, except for perhaps two observations which serve to confirm quite dramatically the independent velocity-field aspect of the two-fluid model for He II as well as the correctness of the linear formalism.

The first of these concerns the determination of η_n from measurements of the thermal resistance at velocities such that $\mathbf{v}_n$ is laminar and both the mutual force and the superfluid force are inoperative. The most accurate values of η_n obtained in this way are due to Brewer and Edwards([106]) using capillaries with $d = 5.2 \times 10^{-3}$ and 1.08×10^{-2} cm. Their results as a function of temperature are shown in Fig. 8.22 compared with data from oscillating disks ([107]) and rotating viscometers ([108]) as well as from the attenuation of second sound ([109]). It is seen that the heat flow measurements agree exceptionally well with those from the latter two sources.

Also shown in Fig. 8.22 are the measurements of η_n derived from the heat flow data of Keller and Hammel ([57]) for micron-size slits.

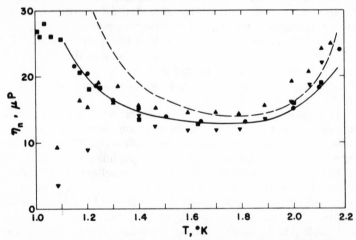

Fig. 8.22. Normal fluid viscosity as a function of temperature determined from heat flow measurements [solid line, Brewer and Edwards([106]), $d = 1.08 \times 10^{-2}$ and 5.2×10^{-3} cm; ▲ Keller and Hammel ([57]), $d = 3.36 \times 10^{-4}$ cm; ▼ Keller and Hammel ([57]), $d = 2.12 \times 10^{-4}$ cm] as compared with oscillating-disk data [dashed line, Dash and Taylor ([107])], rotating viscometers [●, Heikkila and Hallett([108])], and second-sound attenuation [■, Zinov'eva([109])].

Again the agreement with other experiments is good, except at $T < 1.3°K$. The drop in η_n in this region is quite suggestive of the behavior predicted by Atkins ([110]) for instances when the mean free paths of the thermal excitations (which increase as T decreases) become comparable with the channel width and the system resembles a Knudsen gas.

The second point we wish to mention for the laminar region concerns the range of validity of the separate linear two-fluid equations of motion. In his book ([4]), London cautioned that these relations should be reliable only in the limit as ∇P and ∇T approach zero, whereas more recent experiments with narrow slits ([57,58]) indicate this estimate to be much too conservative. Measurements of the heat conduction and the fountain pressure conform precisely to the linear equations (within the experimental errors of the thermal data) over temperature differences greater than 0.5°K, though, as already mentioned, the equations must be integrated with respect to T in these cases. For a 3.36-μ slit, the P_f curves in Fig. 8.7 illustrate the extent of the agreement, whereas for a 0.276-μ slit, P_f measurements ([58]) starting with $T_C = 1.50°K$ conform to linear behavior to within a few millidegrees of the λ-point. Particularly striking in the former example is the fact that the normal fluid velocity in the channel may become larger than 100 cm/sec (for $T_C = 1.15°K$) while the system retains its linear character.

8.3.2. Normal Fluid Turbulence

At sufficiently large velocities, the laminar flow of the normal fluid should become unstable and develop turbulence. We have already mentioned the criterion for this transition as being the critical Reynolds number $\mathscr{R}_c = \mathscr{R}_c(\mathbf{v}_n) \approx 1200$, with $\mathscr{R}(\mathbf{v}_n)$ defined by equation (8.25). Here we examine further the justification and applicability of this condition.

Staas et al. ([111]) were among the first to emphasize the necessity of considering turbulence in the normal fluid for the interpretation of certain He II flow measurements. Their own heat-conduction experiments were cleverly designed to study the normal fluid isolated from the complicating features of mutual friction; the apparatus could be arranged to provide high normal fluid velocities while $\mathbf{v}_r$ was maintained negligibly small. In analyzing the results, the authors assumed $\mathbf{F}_s = 0$ and combined the two equations of motion (8.4) and (8.5) using the hydrodynamic principle of dynamic similarity to obtain equation (8.25) and its counterpart $\mathscr{R}(P)$ in terms of the pressure gradient:

$$\mathscr{R}(P) = (\rho d^3 / 4\eta_n^2) \nabla P \qquad (8.53)$$

Then, for laminar flows, it follows that

$$\mathscr{R}(P) = \mathscr{R}(\mathbf{v}_n) \tag{8.54}$$

and, in analogy with the empirical Blasius rule for classical turbulence, Staas *et al.* wrote for turbulent normal fluid flow,

$$\mathscr{R}(P) = 4.94 \times 10^{-3}[\mathscr{R}(\mathbf{v}_n)]^{1.75} \tag{8.55}$$

Figure 8.23 presents a sampling of the experimental results obtained using a capillary tube with $d = 8.2 \times 10^{-3}$ cm and plotted as $\mathscr{R}(P)$ *vs.* $\mathscr{R}(\mathbf{v}_n)$. Both the linear and 1.75-power regimes clearly emerge, with the transition occurring at the critical value $\mathscr{R}_c \approx 1200$ independent of temperature, $1.29° < T < 2.13°$K. Similar conclusions apply to data for tubes with $d = 1.735 \times 10^{-2}$ and 2.55×10^{-2} cm.

What is surprising about equation (8.25) is that the density enters as ρ and not as ρ_n, the latter being what one might ordinarily expect. The assumption that $\mathbf{v}_r \ll \mathbf{v}_n$ allows this substitution, so that it is appropriate to question the validity of equation (8.25) when $\mathbf{v}_r$ is not

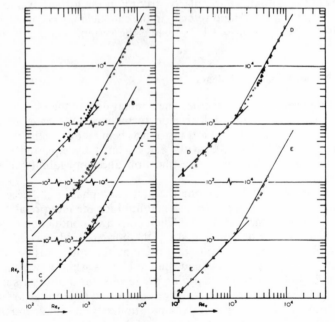

Fig. 8.23. Flow properties of an 82μ capillary plotted as $\mathscr{R}(P)$ *vs.* $\mathscr{R}(\mathbf{v}_n)$. From A to E, temperature increases from $1.292°$ to $2.135°$K. [From Staas *et al.* ([111]).]

small. Experimentally, Staas *et al.* found the same behavior as shown in Fig. 8.23 when v_r was allowed to be larger. It is still not clear why relations (8.53) and (8.54) should be valid independent of the magnitude of v_r, since their derivation specifically excludes this condition.

Chase ([112]) has taken exception to the above criterion for the turbulent transition, since his extensive thermal counterflow measurements ([113]) were not consistent with $\mathcal{R}_c \approx 1200$ and independent of T. Instead, he found $\mathcal{R}_c$ nearly constant only below about 1.5°K at a value more than twice that claimed by Staas *et al.* Above 1.5°K, Chase's observations of $\mathcal{R}_c$ in wide channels decrease steadily to zero at T_λ. He has cited other variations in $\mathcal{R}_c$ [e.g., from the data of Brewer and Edwards ([50]) and of Cornelisson and Kramers ([114])] ranging from 2900 to 700 at temperatures between 0.6° and 1.8°K, and concluded that these may be accounted for by geometrical differences between flow channels and other experimental conditions. From empirical evidence, he proposed that another dimensionless quantity be used as a criterion for the onset of turbulence in these experiments, namely

$$\mathcal{R}_{ns} = \rho d \left[\frac{v_n}{\eta_n} + \frac{v_s}{\eta_E} \right] \tag{8.56}$$

with a critical value of ~ 3000. This relation introduces another parameter, η_E, the so-called "eddy" viscosity or "effective superfluid" viscosity. This is presumed to be analogous to the eddy viscosity found in ordinary fluids and to be associated with the radial transfer of momentum arising from the interaction between vortex lines. On dimensional grounds, η_E is assumed proportional to $L_0^{1/2}$ and to the channel cross-section geometry. Brewer and Edwards ([115]) as well as Chase ([112]) have discussed the evidence for this type of dissipation process; however, a theory for η_E is lacking. Chase found empirically that η_E is of the order of 4 μP and nearly independent of temperature and channel diameter. With these results, the criterion provided by equation (8.56) holds well for his experiments over the range $0.080 < d < 0.402$ cm, $1.2° < T < 2.15°$K.

A somewhat different approach to this problem has been taken by Tough ([116]) who has proposed a phenomenological theory indicating how the presence of the mutual force may reduce $\mathcal{R}_c$ in counterflow situations in wide channels. From an analysis of the flow stability in the presence of perturbations accounting for turbulence in both the normal fluid and superfluid, the deviations of $\mathcal{R}_c$ from its classical value due to coupling with $\mathbf{F}_{sn}$ are given in terms of the dimensionless quantity

$$g = \rho d \bar{v}_r A(T) / [1 + \rho d \bar{v}_r A(T)] \tag{8.57}$$

where $\bar{v}_r$ is the mean (turbulent) relative velocity.

Tough deduced that there should be a function $\mathscr{R}(g)$ with a general critical value $\mathscr{R}_c(g)$ determining the onset of normal fluid turbulence. Thus, when the effects of mutual friction are negligible ($\bar{v}_r$ small), g is also small and the $v_r = 0$ results of Staas et al. ([111]) are recovered. For the data of Chase ([113]) and of Brewer and Edwards ([50]), Tough found a nearly common relationship between $\mathscr{R}_c$ and the coupling constant g, with g approaching ~ 0.6 as $\mathscr{R}_c$ decreases. The large v_r results of Staas et al. do not fit in with this picture and remain unexplained.

Figure 8.24 illustrates some of the ramifications of Tough's treatment and as well demonstrates how the various dissipation processes occurring in thermal counterflow in wide channels may be distinguished. In the region of low heat flow, the only frictional processes are due to normal fluid viscosity, so that the linear equations should apply, making $\nabla T/q$ vs. q nearly constant. A second flow regime is entered as q increases to q_0, at which point vorticity presumably appears so that both F_s and F_{sn} become operative. Tough has considered F_s in the form of equation (8.34) with $n = 2$. At still larger heat flows, a third regime becomes evident beginning at q_c, where an additional dissipation, associated with F_n, takes place in the normal fluid. In ordinary fluid hydrodynamics, the region of Reynolds numbers $\mathscr{R}_c < \mathscr{R} < 2\mathscr{R}_c$ is considered a transitional one in which

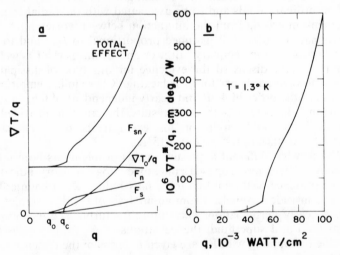

Fig. 8.24. Thermal resistance, $\nabla T/q$, vs. q: (a) theoretical (schematic) decomposition of the total effect into contributions from $\nabla T_0/q$ (the linear term), F_s, F_n, and F_{sn}; (b) the data of Chase ([113]) showing the excess thermal resistance $\nabla T^*/q = \nabla T/q - \nabla T_0/q$; $d = 0.08$ cm [after Tough ([116])].

fluctuations of ∇P are large. According to Landau and Lifshitz ([117]), for $\mathcal{R}$ near $\mathcal{R}_c$, the amplitude of these disturbances is proportional to $(\mathcal{R} - \mathcal{R}_c)^{1/2}$ and increases until fully developed turbulence is established (Blasius region). On this basis, the pressure gradient associated with $\mathbf{F}_n$ has been accounted for by an eddy viscosity in the *normal* fluid, η_{nE}; thus

$$\eta_{nE} = \beta(\mathcal{R} - \mathcal{R}_c)^{1/2} \tag{8.58}$$

where β is a geometry- and temperature-dependent constant. In support of equation (8.58), Tough et al. ([118]) have observed the effects of a heat current on the damping of a vibrating wire stretched across the flow channel; above $\mathbf{q}_c$, the damping could be expressed in terms of η_n plus a force $\mathbf{F}_n$ proportional to $(\mathcal{R} - \mathcal{R}_c)^{1/2}$.

Using the above arguments, Tough ([116]) has analyzed the thermal-flow data of Chase ([113]) and the pressure-gradient data of Brewer and Edwards ([115]), finding a satisfactory fit to the measurements, clearly indicating the various flow regimes. The close relationship of Chase's data and theory is shown in Fig. 8.24. The occurrence of three distinct hydrodynamic regions had been indicated earlier by Allen et al. ([120]), who studied the response of a fiber suspended across a channel through which either a steady heat current or a heat pulse was transmitted. While their data do not unambiguously and quantitatively characterize the turbulent regions, they nevertheless provide qualitative evidence in support of Tough's treatment.

These results present significant consequences for the choice of a critical velocity $\mathbf{v}_{s,c}$ and especially for the critique of the $d^{-1/4}$ law discussed in Section 8.1.3a. For example, the data of Brewer and Edwards just mentioned do not fit this law. Yet, when $\mathbf{v}_{s,c}$ is taken to correspond to their $\mathbf{q}_0$, it would seem that the onset of superfluid vorticity is being signaled; and the data therefore cannot be rejected on the basis that the appearance of normal fluid turbulence is masking the effect. Further work is required in order to develop a completely consistent picture for counterflow processes in wide channels. Finally, we emphasize that these complications do not arise for small channels ($d < 10^{-3}$ cm). In narrow-channel heat flows, Keller and Hammel ([57]) observed no evidence of normal fluid turbulence, nor should any have been expected on the basis of criteria such as $\mathcal{R}_c \approx 1200$. Furthermore, there was no indication for any sort of eddy viscosity.

At temperatures below $\sim 1°K$, the mean free paths of the thermal excitations become comparable with d; the system resembles a Knudsen gas; and the heat conductivity decreases. For $T \lesssim 0.6°K$, phonons are overwhelmingly the dominant carriers of heat and the heat conduction process in the liquid resembles that of the solid. The latter subject will be discussed in Section 9.3.4. Fairbank and Wilks ([119]) and

Whitworth (^{121}) have measured the thermal conductivity of the liquid in this region and discussed the results in relation to the theory.

8.4. DISSIPATION FUNCTIONS FOR LIQUID He II

8.4.1. Dissipation Associated with F_s, F_{sn}, and F_n

In the previous sections, we mentioned dissipation in qualitative terms. We wish now to be more specific. To describe ideal hydrodynamics, the conservation of entropy is generally taken as one of the specifying equations; and in the case of the ideal, inviscid, incompressible hydrodynamics this is expressed as

$$\partial \rho s / \partial t + \rho s \, \nabla \cdot \mathbf{v} = 0 \qquad (8.59)$$

When irreversible processes are present, the entropy is no longer conserved, and we must consider an entropy balance for the rate of entropy production, i.e., $\dot{s}$. A general expression for $\dot{s}$ occurring in the flow of ordinary fluids may be given for the system in a volume V defined by a surface $\mathscr{S}$, $\dot{s}$ being the sum of the entropy flux through the surface plus the entropy generated in the volume:

$$\frac{\partial}{\partial t} \int_V \rho s \, dV = - \int_{\mathscr{S}} (\rho s \mathbf{v} + \mathbf{q}/T) \cdot \mathbf{n} \, d\mathscr{A} + \int_V (\Phi/T - \mathbf{q} \cdot \nabla T/T^2) \, dV$$

$$(8.60)$$

Here, $d\mathscr{A}$ is an element of $\mathscr{S}$ with $\mathbf{n}$ the unit vector normal to $\mathscr{S}$ at $d\mathscr{A}$; $\mathbf{q}$ is the heat flux; and Φ is called the "dissipation function," the rate at which the kinetic energy of the fluid is degraded into heat. For each type of frictional process, Φ assumes a characteristic form. In particular, for ordinary viscous interactions for an incompressible fluid, we have the well-known Rayleigh dissipation function, Φ_η:

$$\Phi_\eta = \frac{\eta}{2} \sum_{i,k} \left(\frac{\partial v_i}{\partial x_k} + \frac{\partial v_k}{\partial x_i} \right)^2 \qquad (8.61)$$

Several interesting features emerge when equation (8.61) is applied to liquid He II flowing in a channel, for which the heat flux may be represented as

$$\mathbf{q} = \rho s T \mathbf{v}_n - \lambda_n \nabla T \qquad (8.62)$$

The first term on the right describes the heat current associated with the drift velocity of the thermal excitations, while the second term is the contribution from the analog of the ordinary diffusive heat-flow mechanism with λ_n being the heat conduction coefficient. Above about 1°K, the former completely dominates the latter; below this temperature, λ_n increases rapidly (as will be discussed in Section 8.4.2) and thermal counterflow becomes less significant. Also at low temperatures, mean-free-path effects complicate the treatment. Hence, the following discussion applies only to the region $T \gtrsim 1°K$.

We then find that the entropy flux is simply $\mathbf{q}/T = \rho s \mathbf{v}_n$. This states the equivalence in He II between the transport of matter and the transport of heat, whereas ordinarily these involve two distinct dissipation processes. From this it can be shown [122] that for steady flow conditions, the rate of total entropy change for the system may be given equivalently by any one of the four integrals on the right-hand side in equation (8.60); that is,

$$\dot{s} = -\int_V \frac{\mathbf{q} \cdot \nabla T}{T^2}\, dV = \int_V \frac{\Phi}{T}\, dV = \int_{\mathscr{S}} \left(\frac{\mathbf{q}}{T}\right) \cdot \mathbf{n}\, d\mathscr{A} = \int_{\mathscr{S}} \rho s \mathbf{v}_n \cdot \mathbf{n}\, d\mathscr{A}$$

$$(8.63)$$

In the laminar region of thermal counterflow, viscous shear in the normal fluid is the only dissipative mechanism. From equation (8.61) we may obtain the normal-fluid viscous-dissipation function, one form of which is (for a parallel-sided channel)

$$\Phi_{\eta_n} = q^2/T\Lambda d^2 \qquad (8.64)$$

Here, Λ is defined by equation (8.49). Then, the total entropy production of the system takes place in the slit (of length Z and breadth W), and we find from equation (8.63) that

$$\dot{s}_{\eta_n} = \int_0^d \int_0^W \int_0^Z \frac{\Phi_{\eta_n}}{T}\, dx\, dy\, dz = Wd \int_{T_C}^{T_H} \left(\frac{\Phi_{\eta_n}}{T}\right) \frac{dz}{dT}\, dT$$

$$= \mathbf{q}Wd\left(\frac{1}{T_C} - \frac{1}{T_H}\right) \qquad (8.65)$$

since dz/dT is given by $-d^2 \Lambda/\mathbf{q}$. We may rewrite this last expression in the alternate forms

$$\dot{s}_{\eta_n} = Wd[(\rho s \mathbf{v}_n)_{T_C} - (\rho s \mathbf{v}_n)_{T_H}]$$

$$\approx Wds_0[(\rho_n \mathbf{v}_n)_{T_C} - (\rho_n \mathbf{v}_n)_{T_H}] \qquad (8.66)$$

where in the second line, we have used the approximation $\rho s \approx \rho_n s_0$, with s_0 the entropy per gram of normal fluid.

We have already noted for steady-state heat flow that $(\mathbf{v}_n)_{T_C} > (\mathbf{v}_n)_{T_H}$, requiring the thermal excitations to accelerate on passage from the hot end of the slit to the cold end. Equation (8.66) tells us in addition that a greater *number* of excitations per unit time emerges from the cold end than enters the hot end. In other words, excitations must be created in the channel as a result of viscous dissipation.

We next consider the form of Φ appropriate for the situation when at larger fluid velocities $\mathbf{F}_s$, $\mathbf{F}_{sn}$, and $\mathbf{F}_n$ must be included in the equations of motion. In the steady state and with the assumption that both $\nabla \cdot \mathbf{v}_n$ and the $(\mathbf{v} \cdot \nabla)\mathbf{v}$ terms in the substantial derivatives are zero, we may manipulate equations (8.4) and (8.5) to find

$$\rho s T \mathbf{v}_n \cdot (\nabla T/T) = \mathbf{v}_n \cdot (\eta \nabla^2 \mathbf{v}_n) - \mathbf{v}_s \cdot \mathbf{F}_s - \mathbf{v}_n \cdot \mathbf{F}_n - (\mathbf{v}_s - \mathbf{v}_n) \cdot \mathbf{F}_{sn} \quad (8.67)$$

or

$$\mathbf{q} \cdot (\nabla T/T) = \Phi_{\eta_n} + \Phi_s + \Phi_n + \Phi_{sn} = \Phi_{\text{total}} \quad (8.68)$$

Thus, each component of the total dissipation function involves a separate type of frictional force multiplied by the relevant velocity. (This derivation is due to Professors M. Cohen and E. Huggins, private communication.)

It is worthwhile to point out that when viscous forces and mutual forces together account for substantially all the dissipation—as in the case of heat transport through narrow channels—the magnitude of the total entropy production for a given heat current is identical to what it would be if viscous forces were acting alone. This can be seen if we insert Φ_{total} as

$$\Phi_{\text{total}} = \Phi_{\eta_n} + \Phi_{sn} = -\frac{q^2}{T \Lambda d^2}(1 + ad^2 q^2) \quad (8.69)$$

together with the proper expression for the temperature gradient, i.e.,

$$dz/dT = -\Lambda d^2 \mathbf{q}^{-1}(1 + ad^2 q^2)^{-1} \quad (8.70)$$

into equation (8.63) [a is given by equation (8.50)]. The result is again just equation (8.65), showing that each process contributes to $\dot{s}$ but that Φ_{η_n} contributes less than if Φ_{sn} were absent. Oliphant[123] has derived expressions indicating how $\dot{s} = \dot{s}_{\eta_n} + \dot{s}_{sn}$ may be partitioned:

$$\dot{s}_{\eta_n} = Wd \int_{T_C}^{T_H} \frac{\mathbf{q}\, dT}{T^2(1 + ad^2 q^2)} \quad (8.71)$$

and

$$\dot{s}_{sn} = Wd \int_{T_C}^{T_H} \frac{ad^2 \mathbf{q}^3\, dT}{T^2(1 + ad^2 q^2)} \quad (8.72)$$

Calculations of these quantities for a narrow channel ($d = 3.36\,\mu$) have been made[122], with the results shown in Fig. 8.25. For the larger values of $(T_H - T_C)$, entropy production via mutual friction eventually dominates that arising from viscosity.

With respect to superfluid dissipation, Φ_s may be obtained from equation (8.32) when a suitable expression for the pressure gradient is employed; and of course, ∇P may be related to the production of

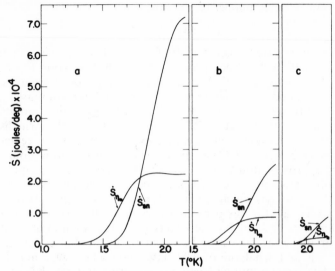

Fig. 8.25. Entropy production in narrow channel ($d = 3.36\ \mu$) thermal flow due to viscous forces and the mutual force calculated from equations (8.71) and (8.72): (a) $T_C = 1.08°K$; (b) $T_C = 1.46°K$, (c) $T_C = 1.9°K$. [From Hammel and Keller ([122]).]

vorticity. We have already concluded that vortex lines are not to be thought of as thermal excitations, but as mechanical states which ultimately decay into thermal energy.

8.4.2. The Landau–Khalatnikov Formulation of Dissipation in He II

We shall not review here the entire Landau–Khalatnikov (LK) theory of superfluidity, since this has been done with thorough and extensive elegance by Khalatnikov ([5]). On the other hand, it is important that we be aware of some of the more powerful capabilities of this point of view, which, being a phenomenological treatment based on the kinetic quasiparticle interactions, is quite different from that considered so far. In particular, we are interested in the specific form of the dissipation function derived through the LK hydrodynamic equations for liquid He II. This is:

$$\Phi_{LK} = \zeta_2 (\nabla \cdot \mathbf{v}_n)^2 + \zeta_3 (\nabla \cdot \mathbf{j} - \rho \mathbf{v}_n)^2 + 2\zeta_1 \nabla \cdot \mathbf{v}_n \nabla \cdot (\mathbf{j} - \rho \mathbf{v}_n)$$
$$+ \frac{\eta_n}{2} \sum_{i,k,l} \left(\frac{\partial \mathbf{v}_{ni}}{\partial x_k} + \frac{\partial \mathbf{v}_{nk}}{\partial x_i} - \frac{2}{3} \delta_{ik} \frac{\partial \mathbf{v}_{nl}}{\partial x_l} \right)^2 + \lambda_n \frac{(\nabla T)^2}{T} \qquad (8.73)$$

Here, $\mathbf{j}$ is the momentum per unit volume

$$\mathbf{j} = \rho_s \mathbf{v}_s + \rho_n \mathbf{v}_n \tag{8.74}$$

and ζ_1, ζ_2, and ζ_3 are the coefficients of second viscosity. The summed terms in equation (8.73) comprise the Rayleigh dissipation function, which, when compared with Φ_η as given by equation (8.60) includes an extra contribution. This arises because here the fluid is not assumed to be incompressible (i.e., $\nabla \cdot \mathbf{v}_n \neq 0$ and $\nabla \cdot \mathbf{v}_s \neq 0$), a generalization which also introduces the coefficients of second viscosity into the formalism.

Generally speaking, Φ_{LK} complements rather than replaces Φ_{total} as given by equation (8.68). In processes such as thermal counterflow, the approximation $\nabla \cdot \mathbf{v} = 0$ is usually a good one, and equation (6.68) quite satisfactorily describes the heat generation due to those irreversible processes which are important in this situation. However, Φ_{LK} is inadequate for this particular task, since the form of equation (8.73) does not account for the effects of mutual friction and other nonlinear processes known to be operative in thermal counterflow. [Bekarevich and Khalatnikov ([70]) have shown how Φ_{LK} might be amended to include mutual friction for rotating systems; but as yet, an extension to heat flow situations has not been provided.] On the other hand, Φ_{LK} is especially well-suited for describing energy losses accompanying the several types of wave propagation in liquid He II. The linear equations of motion in the LK hydrodynamic formulation lead to the following expressions for the attenuation coefficients of first and second sound, respectively:

$$\alpha_1 = \frac{\omega^2}{2\rho u_1^3}\left[\frac{4}{3}\eta + \zeta_2 + \rho \frac{\lambda_n}{c_P}\left(\frac{c_P}{c_V} - 1\right)\right] \tag{8.75}$$

and

$$\alpha_2 = \frac{\omega^2}{2\rho u_2^3}\frac{\rho_s}{\rho_n}\left[\frac{4}{3}\eta + (\zeta_2 + \rho^2\zeta_3 - 2\rho\zeta_1) + \frac{\rho_n}{\rho_s}\frac{\lambda_n}{c_P}\right] \tag{8.76}$$

ω is the frequency of the sound wave. Equation (8.75) was originally given by Kirchhoff and Lord Rayleigh to describe sound attenuation in classical fluids.

8.4.2a. The Kinetic Coefficients. The five kinetic coefficients appearing in equation (8.73) have all been derived in the LK theory from considerations of the scattering processes between the elementary excitations of the liquid, with η_n and λ_n depending primarily upon elastic collisions and. the second viscosity coefficients determined by inelastic collisions.

Both η_n and λ_n are obtained from a Boltzmann-like equation satisfied by the quasiparticle distribution function, with rotons and phonons treated as if they were particles of independent gases so that both coefficients may be separated into two parts, i.e.,

$$\lambda_n = \lambda_\phi + \lambda_r \tag{8.77}$$

and

$$\eta_n = \lambda_\phi + \lambda_r \tag{8.78}$$

where the subscripts ϕ and r refer to phonons and rotons, respectively. Above about 1.8°K, the independent-gas approximation breaks down because of interactions between the components, and thus, these partitions are no longer valid approximations.

For heat conduction and viscosity, the equilibrium distribution function may be used in the Boltzmann equation, since thermal equilibrium is achieved in times short compared with the relaxation times characterizing the scattering processes important for these transport coefficients. The processes we must consider, according to Khalatnikov [5] are: (1) roton–roton elastic scattering, for which the interaction energy V_0 cannot be explicitly calculated; (2) phonon–phonon elastic scattering (also called the "four-phonon" process); (3) inelastic phonon–phonon processes (also called the "five-phonon" process, since a phonon is created—or destroyed—in the collision, i.e., 2 phonons $\rightleftharpoons$ 3 phonons) which are responsible for restoring the number of phonons in the system to its equilibrium value after a disturbance; and (4) elastic phonon–roton scattering, in which the magnitude of the phonon momentum and the direction of the roton momentum remain substantially unchanged, since the collision resembles a small ball bouncing off a large one.

The roton part of λ_n depends almost entirely upon roton–roton scattering and increases with decreasing temperature as T^{-1}. On the other hand, the most important contribution to λ_ϕ comes from phonon–roton processes; λ_ϕ also rises as the temperature is lowered, but as $\exp(\Delta/k_B T)$, where Δ is the energy of the roton minimum. At high temperatures, λ_r dominates λ_ϕ, the two contributions becoming equal near 1.4°K; below 0.9°K, $\lambda_\phi \gg \lambda_r$, so that to a good approximation, $\lambda_n = \lambda_\phi$. Again we stress that λ_n is completely divorced from the counterflow mechanism of heat flow but is the analog to the coefficient of thermal conductivity in ordinary fluids. There are, however, important differences between λ_n and this latter quantity which are due to the unusual features of the quasiparticle spectrum for He II. In particular, λ_n calculated by the LK method for a pure phonon gas would be zero, whereas for liquid helium, the presence of even a very low concentration of rotons critically alters the situation.

The roton contribution to η_n depends only upon the spectral para-meters $\mathbf{p}_0$ and μ and upon V_0 and is therefore not a function of temperature. The η_r cannot be calculated *a priori*, but must be estimated from experimental data. The calculations for η_ϕ are somewhat different from those of λ_ϕ. In addition to the phonon–roton interactions, the four-phonon process here makes a sizeable contribution, especially below $0.7°K$, where η_ϕ is expected to be proportional to T^{-5}. At higher temperatures, the dependence is more like $\exp(\Delta/k_B T)$. Above $T = 1.4°K$, η_r provides the major part of η_n, whereas at lower temperatures, η_r becomes completely swamped by η_ϕ. The final expression for the first viscosity coefficient has a very complicated temperature dependence.

In ordinary fluids, the second (or bulk) viscosity η' describes the energy dissipation accompanying changes in the system which occur too rapidly for thermodynamic equilibrium to be maintained during the course of the process. In such cases, η' is related to the mechanisms responsible for restoring equilibrium in the disturbed system. Usually, the disturbance is compressional, so that η' may become important when $\nabla \mathbf{v} \neq 0$. Formally, η and η' correspond to the shear and bulk moduli familiar from the theory of deformable bodies. Because in liquid He II there are two types of thermal excitations, four coefficients are required. These may be considered in a rough way to be associated with the three generic collision processes—phonon–phonon, phonon–roton, and roton–roton—although there is by no means a simple one-to-one correspondence between these and the ζ's. Similarly, phonon–roton collisions are equivalent to roton–phonon collisions, so that only three of the ζ's are independent. We find $\zeta_1 = \zeta_4$.

In a liquid He II system disturbed from the equilibrium condition, N_r and N_ϕ (the number of rotons and phonons per unit volume) deviate from their respective equilibrium numbers, N_{r0} and $N_{\phi 0}$. Similarly, the corresponding *relative* chemical potentials, μ_r and μ_ϕ, depart from the equilibrium value of zero. When these departures are small and not too rapid, the rate at which the roton and phonon numbers approach N_{r0} and $N_{\phi 0}$, respectively may be related to the chemical potentials by equations having the same form as the conservation laws; for example,

$$dN_r/dT + \nabla \cdot (N_r \mathbf{v}_n) = -\mu_r(\Gamma_r + \Gamma_{r\phi}) + \mu_\phi \Gamma_{r\phi} \qquad (8.79)$$

A similar equation exists for dN_ϕ/dT and introduces Γ_ϕ. The coefficients Γ are determined from the appropriate quasiparticle collision integrals in which the five-phonon processes figure prominently. It is found that

$$\Gamma_\phi = aT^{11} \qquad (8.80)$$

and

$$\Gamma_{r\phi} = b \exp(-2\Delta/T) \tag{8.81}$$

with a and b temperature-independent constants. Γ_r, being small, is neglected in the treatment. The LK theory relates the second viscosity coefficients to these parameters as follows:

$$\zeta_1 = -\frac{1}{\Gamma_\phi}\frac{\partial N_t}{\partial \rho}Q_t - \frac{1}{\Gamma_{r\phi}}\frac{\partial N_r}{\partial \rho}Q_r \tag{8.82}$$

$$\zeta_2 = \frac{1}{\Gamma_\phi}Q_t^2 + \frac{1}{\Gamma_{r\phi}}Q_r^2 \tag{8.83}$$

and

$$\zeta_3 = \frac{1}{\Gamma_\phi}\left(\frac{\partial N_t}{\partial \rho}\right)^2 + \frac{1}{\Gamma_{r\phi}}\left(\frac{\partial N_r}{\partial \rho}\right)^2 \tag{8.84}$$

with

$$N_t = N_r + N_\phi \tag{8.85}$$

and

$$Q_i = N_i - \frac{\partial N_i}{\partial s}s - \frac{\partial N_i}{\partial \rho}\rho, \quad i = r \text{ or } t \tag{8.86}$$

8.4.2b. Experimental Determination of the Kinetic Coefficients.

From measurements of the attenuation of second–sound waves at frequencies from 200 to 4000 c/sec, Zinov'eva ([109]) has investigated equation (8.76) over the temperature range 0.83° to 1.31°K. The dominant dissipation mechanism for the bulk of the sample was found to be due to thermal conduction, but losses which occurred at the surface of the second sound resonator were ascribed primarily to the effects of first viscosity. These two processes have different frequency dependencies and hence may be separated, allowing λ_n and η_n to be obtained once estimates were made for the contribution of the second viscosity coefficients (which should be small, since low frequencies were used). The results for η_n and λ_n below 1.01°K are shown in Table 8.II as a function of temperature. We see that λ_n rises sharply as T decreases, and numerically, the values are consistent with the LK theory ([124]). Measurements of this quantity at still lower temperatures would be of considerable interest, since we expect some as yet undescribed relaxation phenomenon to limit the rise of λ_n.

The values of η_n found by Zinov'eva from second-sound absorption agree rather well with the results obtained by other methods for $T > 1.0°K$. More recently, Woods and Hallett ([125]), using a rotating coaxial-cylinder viscometer, have measured η_n down to $0.79°K$ and observed systematic deviations from Zinov'eva's data below $1°K$, as indicated in Table 8.II. At the lowest temperatures, the data points of Woods and Hallett lie nearly a factor of two above those of the earlier work. The viscometer data can be exceedingly well fitted by the function

$$\eta_n(\mu P) = 12.6 + 3.5 \times 10^{-2} T^{-1/2} \exp(\Delta/k_B T) f(\theta_{\phi r}/\theta_\phi) \quad (8.87)$$

This is the form given by the LK theory, where the constant term is η_r and $f(\theta_{\phi r}/\theta_\phi)$ involves relaxation times characterizing phonon–roton collisions and the five-phonon process. Again, an investigation of η_n to still lower temperatures would be of extreme interest.

Table 8.II. Viscosity and Thermal Conductivity Coefficients below 1.01°K

$T(°K)$	$\eta_n(\mu P)$ ([109])	$\eta_n(\mu P)$ ([125])	λ_n (cal/deg-cm-sec) ([109])
1.01	25	37	1.72×10^{-3}
1.00	26.1	—	1.39×10^{-3}
0.98	29.6	—	1.59×10^{-3}
0.95	33.8	—	1.63×10^{-3}
0.94	37.2	—	2.2×10^{-3}
0.925	—	55	—
0.90	34.8	—	3.2×10^{-3}
0.89	36.6	—	5.5×10^{-3}
0.86	37	—	7.4×10^{-3}
0.855	56	85	5.05×10^{-3}
0.85	55	—	6.9×10^{-3}
0.83	67	—	1.21×10^{-2}
0.815	—	131	—
0.804	—	162	—
0.800	—	158	—
0.790	—	173	—

We see from equation (8.75) that there are two sources of attenuation of an ordinary sound wave, viscous processes and heat conduction processes. Above about $1°K$, the latter contribute a negligible amount of dissipation, since both λ_n and $[(c_P/c_V) - 1]$ for liquid helium are small. Below this temperature, the heat conduction term may become quite important. But for high-frequency sound waves ($\omega \gtrsim 1$ Mc/sec), the period of the wave is comparable with the relaxation times associated with λ_n and η_n, so that the corresponding processes are highly damped, and the entire sound absorption may be associated with ζ_2. Figure 8.27 shows the general temperature-dependent features of α_1.

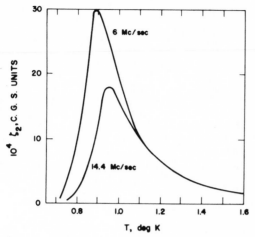

Fig. 8.26. Temperature variation of the He II second viscosity coefficient ζ_2 calculated from the absorption of ordinary sound at two frequencies [after Dransfeld *et al.* ([127])].

The coefficient ζ_2 is a complicated function of temperature, pressure, and frequency. Archipov ([126]) has shown how the LK formalism may be used to compute these dependencies, an example being given in Fig. 8.26, where ζ_2 is plotted against T for two different frequencies. We note that the magnitude of ζ_2 can be considerably larger than η_n at the same temperature. The calculations also indicate that at constant ω and increasing pressure, ζ_2 decreases rapidly, with the maximum shifting to higher temperatures. Dransfeld *et al.* ([127]) have investigated the absorption of sound at 6.0 and 14.4 Mc/sec at pressures up to 25 atm and over the temperature range 0.4° to 1.6°K. Their results provide qualitative verification for the substance of the theory as well as quantitative estimates for various parameters entering into ζ_2. In particular, they find for a and b of equations (8.80) and (8.81), $a = 1.9 \times 10^{43}$ and $b = 3.4 \times 10^{50}$ at saturated vapor pressure; both quantities decrease with increasing P.

As early as 1955, Chase and Herlin ([128]) had observed that below about 0.8°K, the measured attenuation, α_1, became considerably larger then predicted theoretically, and in the interval $0.1° < T < 0.6°$K, the data could be well fitted by a function proportional to ωT^4. Now, the LK theory of α_1 is based on the assumption that the four-phonon process is the lowest order collision process compatible with the assumed dispersion relation for low-momentum phonons:

$$\epsilon(p) = u_1 p(1 - \gamma p^2) \tag{8.88}$$

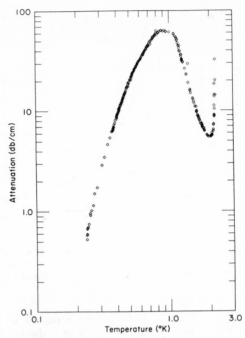

Fig. 8.27. Attenuation of 30 Mc/sec sound in He II as
a function of temperature [from Abraham *et al.* ([139])].

where γ has been taken as 3×10^{37} sec^2/g^2-cm^2. From this, Khalatnikov ([129]) has calculated a contribution to α_1 proportional to ωT^6.
However, Woodruff ([130]), Dransfeld ([131]), and Kawasaki and Mori
([132]), each in different ways, have considered how the three-phonon
process may be possible. In the treatment by Dransfeld, for example,
a thermal phonon may interact with an acoustical phonon of the im-
pressed sound wave, thereby transferring an amount of energy $\hbar\omega$ to
the thermal phonon. All of these analyses have led to the ωT^4 dependence of α_1.

While the difficulties in explaining α_1 at low temperatures were
apparently dispelled when the three-phonon process was taken into
account, the question was reopened by new experiments. Jeffers and
Whitney ([133]) remeasured α_1 at six frequencies between 1.0 and
11.7 Mc/sec for temperatures as low as 0.2°K. For $T < 0.6$°K, they
found the attenuation could be best fitted by the relation $\alpha_1 = 0.11$
$\omega^{3/2} T^3$, which is inconsistent with what had been predicted from the
three-phonon process studies.

The original LK theory for sound absorption assumed that equilibrium in the separate phonon and roton gases was attained slowly. More recently, Khalatnikov and Chernikova ([134]) have reexamined this assumption, finding it to hold only above 1.2°K. At lower temperatures, the times characterizing the relaxation for the phonon gas (via the five-phonon process) and the roton gas (via roton–roton collisions) were both found to become shorter than the time required for establishing equilibrium between the two gases (via roton–phonon collisions); and for $T < 0.6$°K, only phonon interactions are important. On this basis, Khalatnikov and Chernikova derived new—and quite complicated—expressions for the kinetic coefficients as well as the dispersion and attenuation of first and second sound in both the collisionless ($\omega\tau > 1$) and hydrodynamic ($\omega\tau < 1$) regimes (τ is some relaxation time). They also found that the term γp^2 in equation (8.88) could be neglected, suggesting that γ should be much smaller than 3×10^{37} sec^2/g^2 cm^2. For $T < 0.6$°K, Disatnik ([135]) has more recently reported an alternate, simplified derivation which reproduces the results of Khalatnikov and Chernikova. Others ([136,137]) have specifically treated the problem of first sound and the three-phonon process, arriving at expressions similar to those of the more general treatment mentioned above.

The attenuation measurements by Jeffers and Whitney ([133]) are quite consistent with the predictions of these newer theories, as are the more recent data obtained by Whitney and Chase ([138]) on the dependence of u_1 upon ω and T for frequencies between 1 and 12 Mc/sec and $0.15° < T < 1.8$°K. However, at frequencies greater than 12 Mc/sec and up to 204 Mc/sec, Abraham et al. ([139,140]) have reported that observations of both α_1 and the dispersion are in serious disagreement with the three-phonon process theories. A proper explanation of the experiments has not yet been offered.

REFERENCES

1. C. C. Lin, in *Liquid Helium* (G. Careri, ed.), p. 93, Academic Press, New York (1963).
2. R. B. Dingle, *Advances in Physics* (*Phil. Mag. Suppl.*), **1**, 111 (1952).
3. J. G. Daunt and R. S. Smith, *Rev. Mod. Phys.*, **26**, 172 (1954).
4. F. London, *Superfluids*, Vol. II, John Wiley, New York (1954).
5. I. M. Khalatnikov, *An Introduction to the Theory of Superfluidity*, Benjamin, New York (1965).
6. E. L. Andronikashvili and Yu. G. Mamaladze, *Rev. Mod. Phys.*, **38**, 567 (1966); **39**, 494 (1967); in *Progress in Low Temperature Physics* (C. J. Gorter, ed.), Vol. V, p. 79, Interscience Publishers, Amsterdam, New York (1967).
7. P. L. Kapitza, *J. Phys.* (*USSR*), **5**, 59 (1941); *Phys. Rev.*, **60**, 354 (1941).
8. H. E. Hall, *Phil. Trans. Roy. Soc. London*, **A250**, 980 (1957).
9. W. F. Vinen, *Proc. Roy. Soc.* (*London*), **A260**, 218 (1961).

10. P. J. Bendt, *Phys. Rev.*, **127**, 1441 (1962).
11. J. D. Reppy and D. Depatie, *Phys. Rev. Letters*, **12**, 187 (1964).
12. S. C. Whitmore and W. Zimmermann, Jr., *Phys. Rev. Letters*, **15**, 389 (1965); *Phys. Rev.*, **166**, 181 (1968).
13. J. B. Mehl and W. Zimmermann, Jr., *Phys. Rev. Letters*, **14**, 815 (1965); *Phys. Rev.*, **167**, 214 (1968).
14. J. Clow, J. C. Weaver, D. Depatie, and J. D. Reppy, in *Low Temperature Physics LT-9* (J. G. Daunt, D. O. Edwards, F. J. Milford, and M. Yaqub, eds.), p. 328, Plenum Press, New York (1965).
15. J. D. Reppy, *Phys. Rev. Letters*, **14**, 733 (1965).
16. P. Nozières, in *Quantum Fluids* (D. F. Brewer, ed.), p. 1, North Holland, Amsterdam (1966).
17. L. D. Landau, *J. Phys. (USSR)* **5**, 71 (1941); **11**, 91 (1947).
18. L. Onsager, *Nuovo Cimento Suppl.*, **6**, 2249 (1949).
19. R. P. Feynman, in *Progress in Low Temperature Physics* (C. J. Gorter, ed.), Vol. I, p. 17, North Holland, Amsterdam (1955).
20. P. W. Anderson, *Rev. Mod. Phys.*, **38**, 298 (1966); *Quantum Fluids* (D. F. Brewer, ed.), p. 146, North Holland, Amsterdam (1966).
21. J. C. Fineman and C. E. Chase, *Phys. Rev.*, **129**, 1 (1963).
22. E. S. Raja Gopal, *Ann. Phys. (N.Y.)*, **25**, 196 (1963).
23. E. Huggins, *Phys. Rev. Letters*, **17**, 1283 (1966).
24. G. W. Rayfield and F. Reif, *Phys. Rev. Letters*, **11**, 305 (1963); *Phys. Rev.*, **136**, A 1194 (1964).
25. H. Lamb, *Hydrodynamics*, 6th ed., p. 241, Dover, New York (1945).
26. W. F. Vinen, in *Progress in Low Temperature Physics* (C. J. Gorter, ed.), Vol. III, p. 1, North Holland, Amsterdam (1961).
27. H. E. Hall, Advances in Physics (*Phil. Mag. Suppl.*) **9**, 89 (1960).
28. R. J. Donnelly, *Experimental Superfluidity*, University of Chicago Press (1967).
29. T. T. Wu, *J. Math. Phys.*, **2**, 105 (1961).
30. E. P. Gross, *Ann. Phys. (N.Y.)*, **4**, 57 (1958); **9**, 292 (1961).
31. V. L. Ginzburg and L. P. Pitaevskii, *Zh. Eksperim. i Teor. Fiz.*, **34**, 1240 (1958) [English translation, *Soviet Phys.—JETP*. **7**, 858 (1958)].
32. A. A. Abrikosov, *Zh. Eksperim. i Teor. Fiz.*, **32**, 1442 (1957) [English translation, *Soviet Phys.—JETP*, **5**, 1174 (1957)].
33. V. L. Ginzburg, *Zh. Eksperim. i Teor. Fiz.*, **29**, 244 (1955) [English translation, *Soviet Phys.—JETP*, **2**, 170 (1956)].
34. E. P. Gross, *J. Math. Phys.*, **4**, 195 (1963).
35. E. P. Gross, *Nuovo Cimento*, **20**, 454 (1961).
36. L. P. Pitaevskii, *Zh. Eksperim. i Teor. Fiz.*, **40**, 646 (1961) [English translation, *Soviet Phys.—JETP*, **13**, 451 (1961)].
37. D. Amit and E. P. Gross, *Phys. Rev.*, **145**, 130 (1966).
38. H. E. Hall and W. F. Vinen, *Proc. Roy. Soc. (London)*, **A238**, 215 (1956).
39. R. De Bruyn Ouboter, K. W. Taconis, and W. M. van Alphen, in *Progress in Low Temperature Physics* (C. J. Gorter, ed.), Vol. V, p. 44, Interscience Publishers, Amsterdam, New York (1967). This article contains references to recent Leiden work on superfluid flow.
40. A. L. Fetter, *Phys. Rev.*, **138A**, 429 (1965); see also, M. P. Kawatra and R. K. Pathria, *Phys. Rev.*, **151**, 132 (1966).
41. A. Bijl, J. de Boer, and A. Michels, *Physica*, **8**, 655 (1941); F. London, *Rev. Mod. Phys.*, **17**, 310 (1945); V. L. Ginzburg, *Dokl. Akad. Nauk SSSR*, **69**, 161 (1949).
42. J. G. Dash, *Phys. Rev.*, **94**, 825 (1954).
43. N. F. Mott, *Phil. Mag.*, **40**, 61 (1949).

44. W. F. Vinen, in *Liquid Helium* (G. Careri, ed.), p. 336, Academic Press, New York (1963); also in *Quantum Fluids* (D. F. Brewer, ed.), p. 74, North Holland, Amsterdam (1966).
45. W. I. Glaberson and R. J. Donnelly, *Phys. Rev.,* **141**, 208 (1966).
46. V. P. Peshkov, *Proceedings of the VII International Conference on Low Temperature Physics* (G. M. Graham and A. C. H. Hallett, eds.), p. 555, University of Toronto Press (1961); *Progress in Low Temperature Physics* (C. J. Gorter, ed.), Vol. IV, p. 1, North Holland, Amsterdam (1966).
47. P. P. Craig, *Physics Letters,* **21**, 385 (1966).
48. See K. R. Atkins, *Liquid Helium,* p. 198, Cambridge University Press (1959).
49. W. M. van Alphen, G. J. van Haasteren, R. De Bruyn Ouboter, and K. W. Taconis, *Physics Letters,* **20**, 474 (1966).
50. D. F. Brewer and D. O. Edwards, *Phil. Mag.,* **6**, 775 (1961).
51. W. E. Keller and E. F. Hammel, *Physics,* **2**, 221 (1966).
52. P. L. Richards and P. W. Anderson, *Phys. Rev. Letters,* **14**, 540 (1965).
53. J. F. Allen and A. D. Misener, *Proc. Roy. Soc. (London),* **A172**, 467 (1939).
54. W. E. Keller and E. F. Hammel, *Cryogenics,* **5**, 245 (1965).
55. P. P. Craig and J. R. Pellam, *Phys. Rev.,* **108**, 1109 (1957).
56. K. R. Atkins and K. Pickar, in *Superfluid Helium* (J. F. Allen, ed.), p. 271, Academic Press, London (1966): LT-10, Vol. I, p. 313, Academic Press, London (1967).
57. W. E. Keller and E. F. Hammel, *Ann. Phys. (N.Y.).* **10**, 202 (1960).
58. E. F. Hammel and W. E. Keller, *Phys. Rev.,* **124**, 1641 (1961).
59. E. Long and L. Meyer, *Phys. Rev.,* **98**, 1616 (1955).
60. K. Fokkens, K. W. Taconis, and R. De Bruyn Ouboter, *Physica,* **32**, 2129 (1966).
61. W. M. van Alphen, W. Vermeer, K. W. Taconis, and R. De Bruyn Ouboter, in *Low Temperature Physics LT-9* (J. G. Daunt, D. O. Edwards, F. J. Milford, and M. Yaqub, eds.), p. 323, Plenum Press, New York (1965).
62. W. Vermeer, W. M. van Alphen, J. F. Olijhoek, K. W. Taconis, and R. De Bruyn Ouboter, *Physics Letters,* **18**, 265 (1965); W. M. van Alphen, J. F. Olijhoek, R. De Bruyn Ouboter, and K. W. Taconis, *Physica,* **32**, 1901 (1966).
63. J. N. Kidder and W. M. Fairbank, *Phys. Rev.,* **127**, 987 (1962).
64. J. N. Kidder and H. A. Blackstead, in *Low Temperature Physics LT-9* (J. G. Daunt, D. O. Edwards, F. J. Milford, and M. Yaqub, eds.), p. 331, Plenum Press, New York (1965).
65. J. R. Clow and J. D. Reppy, *Phys. Rev. Letters,* **19**, 91 (1967).
66. J. S. Langer and M. E. Fisher, *Phys. Rev. Letters,* **19**, 560 (1967); also see S. V. Iordanskii, *Zh. Eksperim. i Teor. Fiz.,* **48**, 708 (1965) [English translation, *Soviet Phys.—JETP,* **21**, 467 (1965)].
67. E. Ambler and N. Kurti, *Phil. Mag.,* **43**, 260 (1952).
68. J. F. Allen and J. D. Watmough, in *Low Temperature Physics LT-9* (J. G. Daunt, D. O. Edwards, F. J. Milford, M. Yaqub, eds.), p. 304, Plenum Press, New York (1965).
69. P. C. Martin, in *Quantum Fluids* (D. F. Brewer, ed.), p. 232, North Holland, Amsterdam (1966).
70. I. L. Bekarevich and I. M. Khalatnikov, *Zh. Eksperim. i Teor. Fiz.,* **40**, 920 (1961); [English translation, *Soviet Phys.—JETP,* **13**, 643 (1961)].
71. R. J. Donnelly, *Physics Letters,* **17**, 109 (1965).
72. H. A. Snyder and R. J. Donnelly, *Phys. Fluids,* **2**, 408 (1959).
73. S. Franchetti, *Nuovo Cimento,* **4**, 1504 (1956); **5**, 183 (1957); **5**, 1266 (1957); **10**, 622 (1958); **16**, 1158 (1960); **33**, 3424 (1964).
74. V. M. Kontorovich, *Zh. Eksperim. i Teor. Fiz.,* **30**, 805 (1956) [English translation, *Soviet Phys.—JETP,* **3**, 770 (1956)].
75. P. W. F. Gribbon and L. C. Jackson, *Can. J. Phys.,* **41**, 1047 (1963).

76. A. C. Ham and L. C. Jackson, *Proc. Roy. Soc. (London)*, **A240**, 243 (1957); L. G. Grimes and L. C. Jackson, *Phil. Mag.*, **48**, 1346 (1959).
77. J. Tilley, *Proc. Phys. Soc. (London)*, **84**, 77 (1964).
78. B. N. Eselson and B. G. Lazarev, *Dokl. Akad. Nauk SSSR*, **81**, 537 (1951); *Zh. Eksperim. i Teor. Fiz.*, **23**, 552 (1952).
79. J. F. Allen and C. C. Matheson, *Proc. Roy. Soc. (London)*, **A290**, 1 (1966).
80. J. Tilley and C. G. Kuper, *Proc. Roy. Soc. (London)*, **A290**, 14 (1966).
81. C. F. Mate, R. F. B. Harris-Lowe, and K. L. McCloud, in *Superfluid Helium* (J. F. Allen, ed.), p. 279, Academic Press, London (1966).
82. J. F. Allen and J. G. M. Armitage, *Physics Letters*, **22**, 121 (1966).
83. K. R. Atkins, *Liquid Helium*, Chapter 7, Cambridge University Press (1959).
84. W. E. Keller and E. F. Hammel, *Phys. Rev. Letters*, **17**, 998 (1966); LT-10, Vol. I, p. 447, Moscow (1967).
85. B. D. Josephson, *Physics Letters* **1**, 251 (1962).
86. P. W. Anderson and J. M. Rowell, *Phys. Rev. Letters*, **10**, 230 (1963); J. M. Rowell, *Phys. Rev. Letters*, **11**, 200 (1963).
87. I. K. Yanson, V. M. Svistunov, and I. M. Dmitrenko, *Zh. Eksperim. i Teor. Fiz.*, **48**, 796 (1965) [English translation, *Soviet Phys.—JETP*, **21**, 650 (1965)].
88. B. S. Deaver, Jr. and W. M. Fairbank, *Phys. Rev. Letters*, **7**, 41 (1961); and following articles by N. Byers and C. N. Yang, by L. Onsager, and by R. Doll and M. Näbauer in the same journal.
89. R. J. Donnelly, *Phys. Rev. Letters*, **14**, 939 (1965).
90. J. Daunt and K. Mendelssohn, *Phys. Rev.*, **69**, 126 (1946); B. S. Chandrasekhar and K. Mendelssohn, *Proc. Phys. Soc. (London)*, **A68**, 857 (1955).
91. Yu. G. Mamaladze and O. D. Cheishvili, *Zh. Eksperim. i Teor. Fiz.*, **52**, 182 (1967) [English translation, *Soviet Phys.—JETP*, **25**, 117 (1967)]. References to the authors' earlier work on the subject may be found here.
92. B. M. Khorana and B. S. Chandrasekhar, *Phys. Rev. Letters*, **18**, 230 (1967).
93. C. J. Gorter and J. H. Mellink, *Physica*, **15**, 285 (1949).
94. H. E. Hall and W. F. Vinen, *Proc. Roy. Soc. (London)*, **A238**, 204 (1956).
95. W. F. Vinen, *Proc. Roy. Soc. (London)*, **A240**, 114 (1957).
96. W. F. Vinen, *Proc. Roy. Soc. (London)*, **A240**, 128 (1957).
97. W. F. Vinen, *Proc. Roy. Soc. (London)*, **A242**, 493 (1957).
98. W. F. Vinen, *Proc. Roy. Soc. (London)*, **A243**, 400 (1957).
99. D. F. Brewer and D. O. Edwards, *Phil. Mag.*, **7**, 721 (1962).
100. H. C. Kramers, *Physica*, **26**, S81 (1960).
101. T. M. Wiarda and H. C. Kramers, in *Low Temperature Physics LT-8* (R. O. Davies, ed.), p. 98, Butterworth, Washington (1963).
102. M. Vincentini-Missoni and S. Cunsolo, *Phys. Rev.*, **144**, 196 (1966).
103. K. Mendelssohn and W. A. Steele, *Proc. Phys. Soc. (London)*, **73**, 144 (1959); S. M. Bhagat, P. R. Critchlow, and K. Mendelssohn, *Cryogenics* **4**, 166 (1964); V. P. Peshkov and V. K. Tkachenko, *Zh. Eksperim. i Teor. Fiz.*, **41**, 1427 (1961) [English translation, *Soviet Phys. JETP*, **14**, 1019 (1962)]; S. M. Bhagat and P. R. Critchlow, *Can. J. Phys.*, **41**, 1307 (1963).
104. P. P. Craig, W. E. Keller, and E. F. Hammel, *Ann. Phys. (N.Y.)* **21**, 72 (1963).
105. E. F. Hammel and W. E. Keller, *Physica*, **31**, 89 (1965).
106. D. F. Brewer and D. O. Edwards, *Proc. Roy. Soc. (London)*, **A251**, 247 (1959).
107. J. G. Dash and R. D. Taylor, *Phys. Rev.*, **105**, 7 (1957).
108. W. J. Heikkila and A. C. Hollis Hallett, *Can. J. Phys.*, **33**, 420 (1955).
109. K. N. Zinov'eva, *Zh. Eksperim. i Teor. Fiz.*, **31**, 31 (1956) [English translation, *Soviet Phys.—JETP*, **4**, 36 (1957)].
110. K. R. Atkins, *Phys. Rev.*, **108**, 911 (1957).

111. F. A. Staas, K. W. Taconis, and W. M. van Alphen, *Physica*, **27**, 893 (1961). See also, C. E. Chase, ref. (113).

112. C. E. Chase, in *Superfluid Helium* (J. F. Allen, ed.), p. 215, Academic Press, London (1966).

113. C. E. Chase, *Phys. Rev.*, **127**, 361 (1962); **131**, 1898 (1963).

114. P. L. J. Cornelisson and H. C. Kramers, in *Low Temperature Physics LT-9* (J. G. Daunt, D. O. Edwards, F. J. Milford, and M. Yaqub, eds.), p. 316, Plenum Press, New York (1965).

115. D. F. Brewer and D. O. Edwards, *Phil. Mag.*, **6**, 1173 (1961).

116. J. T. Tough, *Phys. Rev.*, **144**, 186 (1966).

117. L. D. Landau and E. M. Lifshitz, *Statistical Physics*, Addison-Wesley, Reading, Mass. (1959).

118. J. T. Tough, W. D. McCormick, and J. G. Dash, *Phys. Rev.*, **140**, A1524 (1965).

119. H. A. Fairbank and J. Wilks, *Proc. Roy. Soc.*, **A231**, 545 (1955).

120. J. F. Allen, D. J. Griffiths, and D. V. Osborne, *Proc. Roy. Soc. (London)*, **A287**, 328 (1965).

121. R. W. Whitworth, *Proc. Roy. Soc. (London)*, **A246**, 390 (1958).

122. E. F. Hammel and W. E. Keller, LT-10, Vol. I, p. 30, Moscow (1967).

123. T. R. Oliphant, *Ann. Phys. (N.Y.)*, **23**, 38 (1963).

124. I. M. Khalatnikov, *Zh. Eksperim. i Teor. Fiz.*, **23**, 8 (1952); **23**, 21 (1952).

125. A. D. B. Woods and A. C. H. Hallett, *Can. J. Phys.*, **41**, 596 (1963).

126. R. G. Archipov, *Dokl. Akad. Nauk SSSR*, **98**, 747 (1954).

127. K. Dransfeld, J. A. Newell, and J. Wilks, *Proc. Roy. Soc. (London)*, **A243**, 500 (1958).

128. C. E. Chase and M. A. Herlin, *Phys. Rev.*, **97**, 1447 (1955).

129. I. M. Khalatnikov, *Zh. Eksperim. i Teor. Fiz.*, **44**, 769 (1963) [English translation, *Soviet Phys.—JETP*, **17**, 519 (1963)].

130. T. O. Woodruff, *Phys. Rev.* **127**, 682 (1962).

131. K. Dransfeld, *Phys. Rev.*, **127**, 17 (1962).

132. K. Kawasaki and H. Mori, *Prog. Theoret. Phys.* (Kyoto), **28**, 784 (1962).

133. W. A. Jeffers, Jr., and W. M. Whitney, *Phys. Rev.*, **139**, A1082 (1965).

134. I. M. Khalatnikov and D. M. Chernikova, *Zh. Eksperim. i Teor. Fiz.*, *Pis'ma*, **2**, 566 (1965) [English translation, *JETP Letters*, **2**, 353 (1965)]; *Zh. Eksperim. i Teor. Fiz.*, **49**, 1957 (1965) [English translation, *Soviet Phys.—JETP*, **22**, 1336 (1966)]; *Zh. Eksperim. i Teor. Fiz.*, **50**, 411 (1966) [English translation, *Soviet Phys.—JETP* **23**, 274 (1966)].

135. Y. Disatnik, *Phys. Rev.*, **158**, 162 (1967).

136. P. C. Kwok, P. C. Martin, and P. B. Miller, *Solid State Comm.*, **3**, 181 (1965).

137. C. J. Pethick and D. ter Haar, *Physica*, **32**, 1905 (1966).

138. W. M. Whitney and C. E. Chase, *Phys. Rev.*, **158**, 200 (1967).

139. B. M. Abraham, Y. Eckstein, J. B. Ketterson, and J. H. Vignos, *Phys. Rev. Letters*, **16**, 1039 (1966).

140. B. M. Abraham, Y. Eckstein, J. B. Ketterson and M. Kuchnir, *Phys. Rev. Letters*, **19**, 690 (1967).

141. R. P. Feynman, R. B. Leighton, and M. Sands, *The Feynman Lectures on Physics*, Vol. III, p. 21–14, Addison–Wesley, Reading, Mass. (1965).

Chapter 9

Compressed He^3 and He^4

Some of the more surprising aspects of both He^3 and He^4 are the exceedingly complex phase diagrams which have been mapped for these seemingly simple substances. In connection with the λ-transition of He^4, we have already seen how the $P-V-T$ and thermal properties behave anomalously, as we have also discussed some of the unusual characteristics of compressed liquid He^3 as a Fermi liquid. While these are generally understandable as direct consequences of the degeneracy conditions of nonideal quantum fluids, there are several other remarkable equilibrium features attributable to quantum effects. Principal among these are first, that the solidification curves for both liquids display a minimum in the $P-T$ plane, and second, that both isotopes have been found to exist in three different stable crystallographic modifications.

Because of the great interest in these matters, much current research has been directed toward them. Experimental difficulties associated with high pressures and low temperatures often lead to results of less than desired accuracy, especially since many manifestations of the effects being studied are extremely subtle. As a consequence, the subject has been spiced with frequent controversies. The situation up to 1965 has been summarized in two review articles, one on the compressed liquids by Sherman ([1]), the other on the solids by Dugdale ([2]). Considerable significant progress toward our understanding of compressed helium has been made since then—enough to warrant more space than can be allotted here—but by all odds the most remarkable and outstanding recent development has been the discovery by H. Fairbank's group of the propagation of second sound in solid He^4.

While a primary purpose of the present chapter is to provide an overall view of the properties of compressed helium, we do not intend to retrace too much of the ground covered by the earlier reviews.

347

Instead, our general remarks will be brief, allowing us to cover several special areas or viewpoints not fully contained in those reviews, such as proposals for the origins of the anomalous liquid properties, further discussion of the melting curves, a few brief remarks about the ground-state energy calculations for the crystals, and the second sound work in solid He^4 as it has emerged from thermal conductivity studies.

9.1. LIQUID PHASE DIAGRAMS OF THE HELIUM ISOTOPES

The schematic projections on the P–T plane shown as solid lines in Figs. 9.1 and 9.2 represent boundaries for the regions of stability of the various phases of He^3 and He^4, respectively. Dotted lines in the figures indicate the loci for the vanishing of the isobaric expansion coefficient. Table 9.I complements these graphs by supplying the (P, T) coordinates of the salient features of these phase diagrams (numbers of the phase points in the table correspond to those on the graphs). While various authors have correctly pointed out the similarities between these two diagrams as being remarkable—for we have become conditioned to expect differences between the two isotopes—we should appreciate that such common properties as the melting curve minima and the $\alpha_P = 0$ loci in the liquids have in each case diverse origins. This viewpoint will be amplified in the following sections.

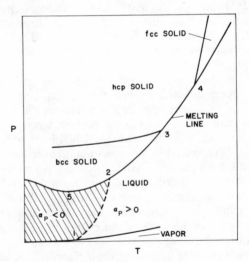

Fig. 9.1. P–T diagram for He^3 (schematic); P–T coordinates for numbered phase points appear in Table 9.I.

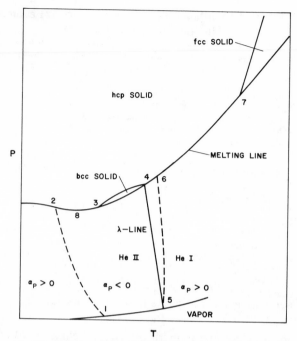

Fig. 9.2. P–T diagram for He⁴ (schematic); P–T coordinates for
numbered phase points appear in Table 9.I.

9.1.1. The P–V–T and Thermal Properties of Liquid He³

As first suggested by Goldstein ([3]), the dominant role played by
the spin system in determining the thermal properties of liquid He³ is
by straightforward thermodynamics repeated for the P–V–T properties.
In particular, for the model used by Goldstein, in which the spin and
non-spin degrees of freedom are separated through the empirically
determined nuclear paramagnetic susceptibility, the expansion coefficient may be written as

$$\alpha_P(T) = \alpha_\sigma(T) + \alpha_{n\sigma}(T) \tag{9.1}$$

[Cf. equation (6.42).] Here, $\alpha_\sigma(T)$ is defined as

$$\alpha_\sigma(T) \equiv V^{-1}(dV_\sigma/dT) = -\tfrac{2}{3}V^{-1}\beta_T(T)C_\sigma(T) \tag{9.2}$$

so that the spin part of the total expansion coefficient is always
negative. Because the non-spin part of $\alpha_P(T)$ is considered normal, and
therefore positive, Goldstein predicted a volume minimum [or
$\alpha_P(T) = 0$] at such points in the phase diagram that the spin and

Table 9.I. P–T Coordinates for Several Important Features of the He³ and He⁴ Phase Diagrams

Phase point	P (atm)	T (°K)	References
He³			
1. $\alpha_P = 0$ (SVP)	2.7×10^{-4}	0.502	[6]
2. $\alpha_P = 0$ (P_m)	47.0	1.26	[7]
3. hcp-bcc-fluid	3.138 ⟵⟶	135.44	[a]
4. hcp-fcc-fluid	~~1608~~ *1556* ✱	17.78	[b]
5. P_{min} of $P_m(T)$	28.92	0.32	[39]
He⁴			
1. $\alpha_P = 0$ (SVP)	7.0×10^{-4}	1.14	[24]
2. $\alpha_P = 0$ (P_m)	25	0.59	[21]
3. bcc-hcp-fluid	25.93	1.463	[60,102]
4. bcc-hcp-fluid	29.67	1.771	[60,102]
5. $\alpha_P = 0$ (SVP)	5.0×10^{-2}	2.178	[20]
6. $\alpha_P = 0$ (P_m)	30.9	1.80	[58]
7. hcp-fcc-fluid	~~1050~~ *1092* †	14.9	[c]
8. P_{min} of $P_m(T)$	24.96	0.775	[58]

[a] G. C. Straty and E. D. Adams, *Phys. Rev.*, **150**, 123 (1966).
[b] J. P. Franck, *Phys. Rev. Letters*, **7**, 435 (1961).
[c] J. S. Dugdale and F. E. Simon, *Proc. Roy. Soc. (London)*, **A218**, 291 (1953).

✱ *error in units: see J.S. Dugdale and J.P. Franck, Proc. Roy. Soc. (London) A257, 1076 (196*
† *miscalculated*

non-spin portions become numerically equal. While $\alpha_\sigma(T)$ could be calculated explicitly from susceptibility data, the nature of $\alpha_{n\sigma}(T)$ was quantitatively unknown, so that the P–T locus of the vanishing expansion coefficient could not be predicted numerically.

The Nernst theorem requires $\alpha_P(T) = 0$ at $T = 0°K$. Hence, at some T on an isobar between $T = 0°K$ and the $\alpha_P(T) = 0$ locus, $\alpha_P(T)$ must exhibit a minimum and approach $T = 0°K$ with a negative slope. Goldstein [3] predicted this minimum to be at $\sim 0.18°K$ at SVP and to decrease to $\sim 0.05°K$ at the melting curve. According to his theory, $\alpha_\sigma(T)$ dominates $\alpha_{n\sigma}(T)$ at very low temperatures, so that $\alpha_P(T)$ should vanish linearly as $T \to 0°K$ according to $\alpha_P(T) = -aT$. At SVP, Goldstein [4] estimated $a = 0.103(°K)^{-2}$. Using quite different arguments, based on the Brueckner–Gammel theory, Brueckner and Atkins [5] arrived at the same limiting form for $\alpha_P(T)$ with $a = 0.076(°K)^{-2}$.

The experimental results have qualitatively confirmed the above predictions for the behavior of $\alpha_P(T)$. These have come from a wide variety of sources including: pycnometric measurements at SVP [6]; conventionally obtained P–V–T data [7,8]; the temperature changes accompanying adiabatic expansion (or compression) of the liquid [9–11], since $\alpha_P = (C_P/VT)(\partial T/\partial P)_S$: and from dielectric constant measurements [12–14]. Unfortunately, the various values obtained for α_P are somewhat inconsistent, so that several of the quantitative features for this coefficient remain poorly defined. An example of the uncertainties in the results is shown in Fig. 9.3, where data are compared for α_P at or near SVP as determined by several different investigators.

The locus of the volume minima $[P(\alpha_P = 0), T(\alpha_P = 0)]$ in the liquid was first inferred from the P–V–T data of Grilly and Mills [8] taken above 1.3°K and extrapolated to lower temperatures. Soon thereafter, Kerr and Taylor [6] observed the minimum directly at SVP, and Brewer and Daunt [9] used the adiabatic expansion method to trace the locus at higher pressures. Other density measurements in this region followed. A summary of the experimental points purporting to define the locus is presented in Fig. 9.4, while the approximate intersections with the vaporization and melting curves are listed in Table 9.I.

Limiting values of the slope of α_P as $T \to 0°K$ at SVP obviously must be obtained by extrapolation of data taken at higher temperatures and therefore are quite susceptible to error. As discussed by Kerr and Taylor [6], their data as well as others suggest that a ranges between 0.08 and 0.125(°K)$^{-2}$, bracketing Goldstein's estimate. The most recent evaluation, due to Boghosian et al. [14], who measured the dielectric constant down to $T \approx 0.07°K$, favors a value near 0.08(°K)$^{-2}$ and therefore supports the prediction of Brueckner and Atkins. These distinctions, however, do not appear too meaningful; rather, we believe

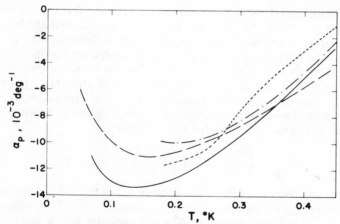

Fig. 9.3. Thermal expansion coefficient of liquid He³ as a function of temperature for pressures near P_{sat}: solid curve, Boghosian et al. [14]; dashed curve, Rives and Meyer [13]; dotted curve, Lee et al. [12]; and dashed-dotted curve, Kerr and Taylor [6]. [Drawn after Boghosian et al. [14].]

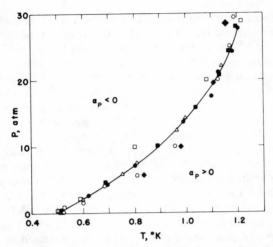

Fig. 9.4. Locus of $\alpha_P = 0$ for liquid He^3: ● Boghosian et al. ([14]); ■ Rives and Meyer ([13]); △ Brewer and Daunt ([9]); □ Lee et al. ([12]); ○ Sherman and Edeskuty ([7]); and ◆ Grilly and Mills ([8]). [Drawn after Boghosian et al. ([14]).]

the overall agreement to be quite gratifying considering the difficulties inherent in making the extrapolations.

Experimental location of the points defining the minima of α_P presents an unresolved problem. Figure 9.3 suggests that at SVP, the temperature of the minimum $T(\alpha_{min})$ should lie between 0.12°K and 0.20°K, the upper limit agreeing with Goldstein's prediction. On the other hand, the data of Boghosian et al. ([14]) support the lower value and indicate as well that at all pressures up to ~ 28 atm, $T(\alpha_{min})$ is near 0.12°K. This pressure dependence of $T(\alpha_{min})$ is at variance with both Goldstein's theory and the empirical constant-pressure specific heat ([11,15]). Through the thermodynamic relation

$$\left(\frac{\partial \alpha_P}{\partial T}\right)_P = -\frac{1}{VT}\left(\frac{\partial C_P}{\partial P}\right)_T - \alpha_P^2 \qquad (9.3)$$

the crossings of the $C_P(P)$ vs. T curves shown in Fig. 6.8 place a lower limit on $T(\alpha_{min})$, with the best estimates from the thermal data suggesting that $T(\alpha_{min})$ is higher than 0.16°K at all pressures and is possibly as high as 0.25°K in some regions. (See also Table 9.II, which gives $T(\alpha_{min}) \approx 0.18$°K at the melting curve.) Admittedly, these considerations stringently test the accuracy of the experiments, since they involve second derivatives of the density measurements and first derivatives of the heat capacity. At the same time, they emphasize the inconsistencies in the available data and indicate where more work needs to be done.

Goldstein ([16]) has designated the shaded region on the P–T diagram (Fig. 9.1) as one of anomalous thermal and state properties. He has drawn in considerable detail the thermodynamic consequences of the anomalies associated with the negative α_P and the minimum in the melting curve $P_m(T)$. Of the many anomalous properties which propagate from these features, only a few have been clearly experimentally observed. Most important among these is the behavior of the isothermal compressibility along an isobar. At low temperatures, Goldstein has indicated the abnormal positive character of the derivative $(\partial \alpha_P/\partial P)_T$. Through thermodynamics, this implies that $(\partial \beta_T/\partial T)_P$ is negative over the same region—also an abnormal condition. At some higher temperature, but less than $T(\alpha_{min})$, both coefficients revert to the normal behavior. The data of Boghosian et al. ([14]) have confirmed these expectations, suggesting that $(\partial \beta_T/\partial T)_P$ becomes zero between about 0.4 and 0.6°K. We should appreciate that these deductions by Goldstein are essentially divorced from his model for the nuclear spin contributions, but demonstrate the power of carefully applied thermodynamics.

Figure 9.5 presents a projection of the S–T–P surface of compressed He³ upon the S–T plane. Of particular interest here is the crossing

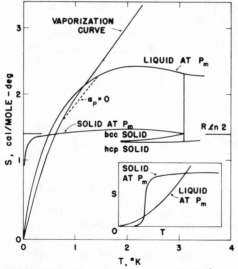

Fig. 9.5. Entropy–temperature diagram for He³; inset showing crossings of liquid and solid curves at melting is schematic.

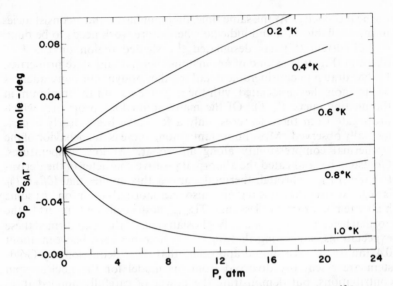

Fig. 9.6. Entropy of compression for liquid He³ [after Lee *et al.* ([12])].

of the isobars in the liquid region consistent with the anomalous behavior of α_P. An alternate way of visualizing what is happening here may be had by considering the isotherms in Fig. 9.6 representing the entropy of compression. This quantity has been evaluated both from thermal data and from P–V–T data plus the entropy at SVP using the relation

$$(s_{P_2} - s_{P_1}) = - \int_{P_1}^{P_2} (\alpha_P/\rho)\, dP \tag{9.4}$$

Regions of positive $(s_P - s_{\text{sat}})$ correspond to negative α_P. While the results from various investigations are not in complete agreement, the qualitative behavior of $(s_P - s_{\text{sat}})$ is well established.

9.1.2. The P–V–T and Thermal Properties of Liquid He⁴

In He I above the $\alpha_P = 0$ locus, the state properties are well behaved. Below this locus, the fluid displays a number of anomalies, those associated with the λ-transition having already been discussed in Chapter 7. Useful tables and graphical summaries of the P–V–T properties and of the specific heat, entropy, internal energy, and the free energy of the fluid have been published by Lounasmaa ([17]) $(1.2° < T < 2.9°\text{K}; P_{\text{sat}} < P < P_m)$ and by Hill and Lounasmaa ([18])

$(3° < T < 20°K; 5 < P < 100 \text{ atm})$. In the present section, we shall largely confine our remarks concerning the liquid to the interesting region below 1.2°K.

The 1955 paper of Atkins and Edwards ([19]) reported pycnometer measurements of He II at SVP down to 0.85°K which indicated that α_{sat} becomes positive below 1.15°K. Since then, Kerr and Taylor ([20]) have repeated these experiments and observed $\alpha_{sat} = 0$ at $T = 1.172°K$. We may obtain α_P from α_{sat} through equation (7.40), which gives $\alpha_P = 0$ at a slightly higher temperature.

The locus of $\alpha_P = 0$ was extended to higher pressures by Mills and Sydoriak ([21]), who measured α_P from 0.5 to 1.5°K and at four pressures between 3 and 24 atm using the method of adiabatic expansion. These data for α_P together with those of Kerr and Taylor ([20]) at SVP were fitted by an empirical function for an isotherm

$$\ln[2.0 - \alpha_P(10^{-3} \text{ deg}^{-1})] = a + b\ln[1.0 + P\,(\text{atm})] \tag{9.5}$$

where the constants a and b are temperature dependent. Smoothed values of α_P obtained from equation (9.5) were then used to determine such properties as the $\alpha_P = 0$ locus, β_T relative to β_T at 1.5°K, $(S_P - S_{sat})$, and $C_P = T(\partial S/\partial T)_P$. Coordinates for the terminal points of the $\alpha_P = 0$ locus are given in Table 9.I.

Over the region measured, β_T behaves normally, increasing with temperature at constant P and decreasing with pressure at constant T. But, as expected, the entropy curves cross in a complicated fashion. Figure 9.7 presents an overall view of S–T diagram for He⁴, while Fig. 9.8 shows some of the low-temperature details of the entropy of compression for the liquid as determined by using equation (9.5) in equation (9.4) together with the calorimetrically determined S_{sat} ([22]). These results as well as those for C_P are consistent with specific-heat measurements made by the authors ([23]) in the same apparatus.

More recently, Boghosian and Meyer ([24]) have taken dielectric-constant data over a similar region of the P–V–T surface and derived values for the density and the expansion and compressibility coefficients as well as the entropy of compression. Their results generally agree with those of Mills and Sydoriak ([21]), but indicate several worthwhile refinements over the earlier work, especially at the higher pressures.

According to Landau's theory, the coefficient of expansion can be separated into contributions arising from the phonons and rotons. Thus

$$\alpha_P(T) = \alpha_\phi(T) + \alpha_r(T)$$

$$= -\frac{1}{V}\left(\frac{\partial S_\phi}{\partial P}\right)_T - \frac{1}{V}\left(\frac{\partial S_r}{\partial P}\right)_T \tag{9.6}$$

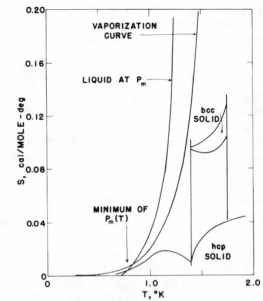

Fig. 9.7. Entropy–temperature diagram for He^4 at low
temperatures (partly schematic).

where S_ϕ and S_r are given in terms of the sound velocity and the roton
parameters Δ/k_B, μ, and p_0 [cf. equations (1.33) and (1.37)]. The phonon
part, $\alpha_\phi(T)$, involves the coefficient $\partial u_1/\partial P$ which has been evaluated by
Atkins and Edwards ([19]) from the sound-velocity measurements of
Atkins and Stasior ([25]). At SVP, $\alpha_\phi(T)$ becomes $(1.08 \pm 0.04) \times 10^{-3}$
T^3 deg^{-1}. Determination of $\alpha_r(T)$ is somewhat more complicated in
that the density derivatives of all three roton parameters are required.
Of particular importance is the quantity $(\rho/\Delta)(\partial\Delta/\partial\rho)$, which has been
found ([19,26]) to be of the order $-1/2$ and which causes the roton
expansion coefficient to become negative. Just below the λ-point, then,
where the roton contribution dominates, the theory predicts the total
expansion coefficient to be negative; but as T decreases and the phonons
become relatively more important, a point is reached at which the two
contributions become numerically equal, rendering $\alpha_P(T) = 0$. Below
about 0.6°K, the positive phonon part makes up essentially the entire
$\alpha_P(T)$.

Mills ([26]) has extracted the pressure and temperature dependence
of the Landau parameters from an analysis of the adiabatic expansion
data of Mills and Sydoriak ([21]); Boghosian and Meyer ([24]) have
followed with a similar analysis of their own data. The roton entropy,

as seen from equation (1.37), is a function of μ, p_0, and Δ/k_B: it may be readily obtained by subtracting from the observed total entropy the phonon part as calculated from data for ρ and u_1. Both investigations showed that below 1.5°K and at constant density, Δ/k_B is only slightly temperature-dependent, but is sensitive to pressure (or density), decreasing from about 8.6°K at SVP ($\rho = 0.145$ g/cm³) to about 7.4°K at 25 atm ($\rho = 0.172$ g/cm³). These results are in reasonable agreement with those obtained from neutron data at SVP ([27]) and at 25.3 atm ([28]), and with those deduced by van den Meijdenberg *et al.* ([29]) from fountain-pressure measurements in the limited region between 1.15° and 1.3°K. Once Δ/k_B and S_r are known, the quantity $p_0^2\mu^{1/2}$ can be obtained directly, though it is considerably more difficult to calculate values for p_0 and $\mu^{1/2}$ individually. Even so, there is some confusion about the best values for $p_0^2\mu^{1/2}$—this quantity also varies with ρ and but little with T. Curves of $p_0^2\mu^{1/2}$ *vs.* ρ deduced by Mills and by van den Meijdenberg *et al.* have opposite slopes, whereas the points of Boghosian and Meyer are in better agreement with the latter.

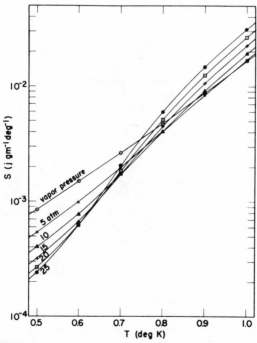

Fig. 9.8. Entropy–temperature diagram for liquid He⁴ at several pressures, showing crossings of the isobars near 0.8°K [from Mills and Sydoriak ([21])].

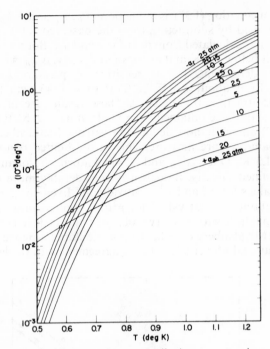

Fig. 9.9. Phonon and roton contributions to α_P at various
pressures. Circled points indicate locus for $\alpha_P = 0$ [from
Mills [26]].

In addition to the primary parameters, Mills computed the pres-
sure and temperature dependence of the quantities $(\rho/\Delta)(\partial\Delta/\partial\rho)_T$ and
$[(\rho/2\mu)(\partial\mu/\partial\rho)_T + (\rho/2p_0)(\partial p_0/\partial\rho)_T]$, both necessary for evaluating
$\alpha_r(P, T)$. From smooth values of the various coefficients, he derived the
separate roton and phonon contributions to $\alpha_P(T, P)$, shown graphi-
cally in Fig. 9.9. The crossing points of $-\alpha_r$ and α_ϕ in the figure define
the $T - P$ locus of $\alpha_P = 0$ and agree on the average with the experimental points to within $\pm 0.013°$K. Similar families of curves have
been constructed for S and C_P, with the total entropies and heat
capacities differing on the average by less than $\pm 3\%$ from the calorimetrically determined quantities at SVP. Quite recently, Wiebes and
Kramers [30] have measured C_P along several isobars between 0.1 and
25 atm temperatures down to 0.3°K. Preliminary comparisons between
these data and Mills' calculation are extremely favorable, the differences
in the entropies being no more than $\pm 2\%$.

9.2. THE MELTING PROPERTIES OF HELIUM

9.2.1. The Melting Curve of He^3

The anomalous melting properties of He^3 are directly associated with the relative magnitudes of the liquid and solid entropies, both of which are heavily dependent upon the behavior of the spin systems of the two phases. As early as 1950, Pomeranchuk ([31]) suggested that spin alignment in the solid would not take place until a temperature of the order of $10^{-7}\,°K$ was reached, and therefore the solid molar entropy, S_s,† down to this temperature should be at least as large as $R \ln 2$ due to the random spins. On the other hand, Pomeranchuk expected the spin system of the liquid in equilibrium with the solid to align at a considerably higher temperature so that for $T \gg 10^{-7}\,°K$, the liquid entropy, S_l, should become less than S_s. Providing the change in volume on melting ($\Delta V_m = V_l - V_s$) does not become negative, the condition $\Delta S_m = (S_l - S_s) < 0$ implies, via the Clapeyron equation, a minimum in the melting curve $P_m(T)$.

Pomeranchuk's arguments were based upon the assumption that the exchange effects, demanded by FD statistics and responsible for spin ordering in the liquid, should be negligible in the solid because the restriction of atoms to fixed positions in the crystal was believed to preclude the overlap of atomic wave functions located about adjacent lattice sites. Thus, the alignment temperature was predicted on essentially classical grounds to occur when $k_B T$ becomes comparable with the energy difference between nuclear spin states in the presence of the local magnetic field in the crystal. Since the latter is of the order of 1 G, Pomeranchuk arrived at the very low alignment temperature quoted above.

These ideas persisted until 1959, when a more extensive analysis by Bernardes and Primakoff ([32]) indicated that due to zero-point energy, a He^3 atom in the crystal makes large excursions about its lattice site, thereby making overlap possible. Consequently, the exchange energy for the solid near melting conditions is nontrivial and should elevate the alignment temperature considerably above Pomeranchuk's forecast. In fact, Bernardes and Primakoff calculated a paramagnetic Curie temperature $T_c \approx 0.1°K$. Although the magnitude of the exchange was overestimated here, the authors were led to the fairly accurate prediction of a minimum, $P_{\min}$, in $P_m(T)$ at 0.37°K.

In the region below $T \approx 0.4°K$, the Debye or phonon contribution to S_s is relatively small, so that when the system loses its spin entropy near T_c, the curve for S_s should drop rapidly and cross the liquid entropy

† In this chapter, we reserve the lower case subscripts s and l to identify properties of the solid and liquid along the melting curve; upper case subscripts S and L refer to these phases at other conditions. The subscript m refers to the melting process.

curve; i.e., S_s should again become less than S_l, implying a maximum in $P_m(T)$ for $T < 0.1°$K. At temperatures below the maximum, S_l is nearly linear in T and S_s is expected to be proportional to T^3, a temperature dependence characteristic of spin waves in the solid. Therefore, no further crossings of the entropy curves are expected at lower temperature. These features of the entropy are illustrated in the inset of Fig. 9.5.

He^3 was first solidified in 1951 by Osborne et al. ([33]) and $P_m(T)$ was measured by an experimental technique which precluded the observation of a minimum ([34]). Here the melting process was detected when upon isothermal compression of the liquid, the capillary leading to the sample chamber became blocked with solid. Observation of $P > P_{min}$ at $T < T_{min}$ by sensing the pressure in the capillary thus becomes impossible. The initial experimental clue for the existence of a minimum was uncovered by Fairbank and Walters ([35]) as a reversal in sign of the heat accompanying the melting process near 0.4°K. At the same time, their susceptibility data demonstrated the essential correctness of the ideas of Bernardes and Primakoff. Baum et al. ([36]) first directly detected the minimum in $P_m(T)$ using a variation of the blocked-capillary procedure. At 1.2°K, the sample chamber was filled to a pressure that would ensure the maintenance of two-phase equilibrium over the region to be investigated. Upon cooling, the capillary became plugged and thereby trapped the sample in a constant volume—provided the plug did not subsequently move. Pressure changes in the sample were related to the accompanying deformations of the chamber's thin cylindrical wall as measured by a strain gage attached externally to this wall.

A number of other investigations ([12,38,39]) employing the blocked capillary as well as different techniques have amply substantiated the minimum in $P_m(T)$. All of the data for the melting curve are in excellent quantitative agreement, except those of Baum et al. ([36]), which are uniformly higher in pressure than the rest by about 4 psi, suggesting a small systematic error in the original work. The minimum is quite accurately placed at $P_{min} = 28.9$ atm, $T_{min} = 0.32°$K. Anderson et al. ([39]) have measured $P_m(T)$ over the extended range $0.03° \leqslant T \leqslant 0.4°$K and found a least-squares fit to their results to be

$$P_m(T) = [28.92 + 33.06(0.3191 - T)^2 + 37.19(0.3191 - T^3]\quad \text{atm}$$

$$(9.7)$$

In Table 9.II, we list some of the more important anomalous properties of He^3 along the melting curve. The entries between 1.20°K and 0.33°K are due to Mills et al. ([37]), who smoothly joined their own $P–V–T$ data with those at higher temperatures of Grilly and Mills ([8]) and of Sherman and Edeskuty ([7]); entries between 0.32°K and 0.02°K

Table 9.II. Anomalous Properties of He³ along the Melting Curve

T (°K)	P_m (atm)	V_l (cm³/mole)	V_m (cm³/mole)	α_l (10^3 deg⁻¹)	β_l (10^{-3} atm⁻¹)	$(dP/dT)_m$ (atm/deg)
1.20	45.10	24.065	1.060	−0.4	3.7	−31.6
1.00	39.30	24.628	1.100	−2.9	4.2	−26.5
0.80	34.56	25.171	1.141	−5.8	4.7	−21.0
0.60	31.01	25.649	1.178	−7.4	5.2	−14.5
0.40	29.07	25.964	1.198	$\begin{bmatrix} -5.5 \\ 0 \end{bmatrix}$	5.8	−4.5
0.33	28.91	25.990	1.200		6.0	0
0.32	28.920	25.990	1.200	−7.00	5.64	0
0.28	28.977	25.998	1.204	−7.57	5.61	2.86
0.22	29.295	25.956	1.222	−8.18	5.58	7.85
0.16	29.953	25.875	1.243	−8.36	5.50	14.21
0.10	31.044	25.733	1.265	−7.69	5.39	22.50
0.06	32.079	25.600	1.274	−6.14	5.28	29.63
0.02	33.445	25.422	1.262	−2.64	5.11	39.31

are the results of a self-consistent thermodynamic analysis by Anderson *et al.* ([39]) based on specific-heat, acoustic, and melting-curve measurements by these authors plus the assumption that the entropy of the solid is $R \ln 2$ over the temperature range in question. From the table, we see that the liquid molar volume along the melting curve, V_l, passes through a maximum just below the melting curve minimum, and that the volume change on melting, ΔV_m, is indeed everywhere positive and increases with decreasing T but apparently displays a maximum near 0.06°K. Although the two sets of data for V_l and ΔV_m join well at (P_{min}, T_{min}), there are serious discrepancies in the temperature derivative of V_l, that is, α_l. It now appears likely ([14]) that the inferences by Mills *et al.* ([37]) for α_l near P_{min} are in error and that α_l does not have a zero at this point. The calculations of Anderson *et al.* ([39]) show the minimum of α_l to be near 0.18°K, as mentioned earlier. The joining of the compressibility coefficient of the liquid β_l is satisfactory and suggests that β_l displays a low broad maximum near (P_{min}, T_{min}). Finally, the values shown for $(dP/dT)_m$, the slope of the melting curve, give no indication, even at 0.02°K, of the maximum in P_m expected below 0.1°K.

The behavior of β_l and β_s has been of considerable interest. Ordinarily, we would expect $\beta_l > \beta_s$, but early direct measurements ([40]) of β_S ($P > P_m$) as well as values derived from heat capacity data ([41]) suggested the reverse. The most recent experiments ([42,43]) strongly support the near equality of β_s and β_l down to about 1.0°K. This is shown in Fig. 9.10, where on the plot of β *vs.* molar volume, the horizontal tie-lines connect β_s and β_l at the temperatures indicated.

Of even more concern is the trend of α_s at low temperatures. As we shall see in Section 9.3.2, the temperature of the magnetic transition near the melting curve has been placed at $T_c \approx 0.001°$K. Bernardes and Primakoff [32] and also Goldstein [44] have suggested that the thermal and state properties of the solid along $P_m(T)$ should reflect this transition at considerably higher temperatures. In particular, the former authors predicted α_s would become negative somewhere near 0.6°K, whereas Goldstein [45] has given ~ 200 $T_c \approx 0.2°$K as the temperature at which the expansion coefficient should vanish. Several investigations [42,43,46] of α_s in the compressed solid, as for example shown in Fig. 9.11, have hinted that α_s becomes very small at low temperatures, but direct evidence for this has finally been reported by Panczyk et al. [47]. We defer further discussion of this important work until Section 9.3.2 so that we may properly relate it to the magnetic behavior of the solid.

A number of experimental difficulties are associated with measurements on the liquid in that sliver of the liquid phase in which $P > P_{min}$, $T < T_{min}$. These arise first, because the capillary leading to the sample is plugged, making direct pressure observations impossible, and second, because of the possibility that the plug may slip, changing the amount of liquid in the sample. Undoubtedly, these problems plagued the initial investigations of sound propagation [48], magnetic properties [49], and heat capacity [38] in this region; these displayed anomalous behavior which led to an interpretation in terms of a "new" liquid phase. A

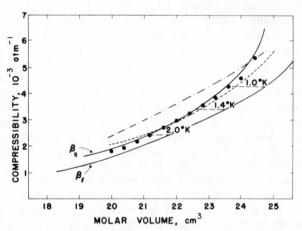

Fig. 9.10. Compressibility of He^3 vs. molar volume: solid curves show measured β_s and β_l [Straty ([42])]; ●, β_s for bcc solid at $T = 0.35°$K [Straty ([42])]; dotted-dashed curve shows calculation for bcc solid in two-body approximation [Nosanow ([67])]; dashed curve is calculation with three-body term included [Hetherington et al. ([76])].

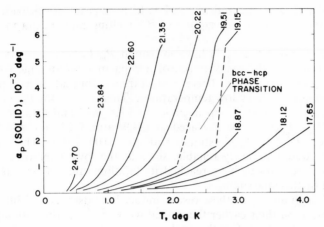

Fig. 9.11. Thermal expansion coefficient for solid He³ at several molar volumes [selected data have been smoothed, from Straty ([42])].

suggestion by Fairbank ([50]) that these results merely implied a sample consisting of a mixture of the solid and liquid phases was substantiated by the subsequent head capacity measurements of Edwards et al. ([51]) and by the further work of Wheatley's group ([39]). Thus, the idea of a new liquid phase was quickly dispelled.

9.2.2. The Melting Curve of He⁴

In 1960, Goldstein ([52]) predicted that the melting curve of He⁴ should display a shallow minimum just below 1°K. The basis for his expectations lay in a model incorporating two propositions we have already introduced, namely: anomalous thermal properties of the liquid are reflected across the phase transition line to the solid; and these anomalous properties arise when the system contains two or more distinct and competing types of excitations which contribute additively to the separate thermal properties.

Despite the subtle character of the expected minimum, indirect evidence of the effect was first reported some three years later by Wiebes and Kramers ([53]), followed shortly by a direct determination by Le Pair et al. ([54]) of P_{min} at $T_{min} = 0.75°K$. Subsequent investigations by Zimmerman ([55]) and by Sydoriak and Mills ([56]) reconfirmed the minimum but supplied significantly different parameters for $P_m(T)$ than obtained earlier. Commentary on the history and on the relative accuracy of these several determinations has been presented by Le Pair et al. ([57]). Here we should like to turn our attention to the most recent experimental and theoretical work which appears to provide an appealingly consistent description of the melting phenomena in He^4 below 1°K.

Straty and Adams ([58]) have measured $P_m(T)$ between 0.35 and 0.95°K using for the pressure sensor a capacitive strain gage with a sensitivity of $\sim 10^{-4}$ atm. This is truly a tremendous advance in pressure resolution at very low temperatures. Their results for $P_m(T)$ and $dP_m(T)/dT$ are shown as open circles in Figs. 9.12 and 9.13, respectively (P_{min}, T_{min}) has been placed at (24.96 atm, 0.775°K), with the difference $[P_m^{(0°K)} - P_{min}]$ estimated at only 0.0075 atm. This latter estimate should be fairly reliable, since at the lowest temperatures, $dP_m(T)/dT$ appears to have reached its limiting value of zero as demanded by thermodynamics.

The high quality of these results induced Goldstein and Mills ([59]) to elaborate on their earlier theoretical work ([26,52]) and to attempt a detailed explanation for the melting anomaly. Qualitatively, the minimum in $P_m(T)$ was expected on the basis that phonons are the dominant excitations in the condensed phases at low temperature. In the solid, both transverse and longitudinal phonons are possible, while in the liquid, which cannot support shear, these modes are restricted to

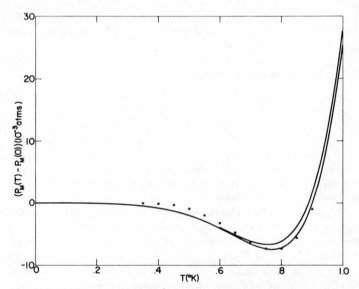

Fig. 9.12. Melting curve of He^4 showing the minimum. Pressures are referenced to P_m at $T = 0°K$. Upper curve calculated from thermodynamic data; lower curve calculated from spectral parameters; data points from smooth curve of Straty and Adams ([58]). [From Goldstein and Mills ([59]).]

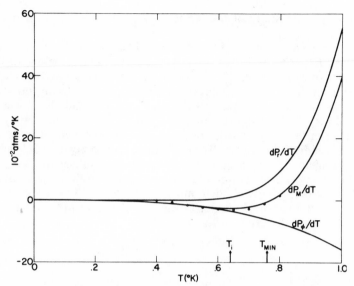

Fig. 9.13. The theoretical slope of the melting curve dP_m/dT decomposed into contributions from the phonons, dP_ϕ/dT, and from higher order excitations, dP_r/dT. Experimental points are from data of Straty and Adams [58]. [From Goldstein and Mills [59].]

the compressional branch. In terms of the characteristic (Debye) temperatures θ, we may then write for the phonon part of the molar entropy of the liquid at melting

$$S_l/R = (4\pi^4/15)(T/\theta_l)^3 \qquad (9.8)$$

and of the solid with which it is in equilibrium

$$S_s/R = 3(4\pi^4/15)(T/\theta_s)^3 \qquad (9.9)$$

The factor 3 in the last equation arises from the three directions of polarization of the phonons in the solid, and θ_s is an appropriate average over both classes of modes. If, now, θ_s is not larger than θ_l, the entropy of the solid should exceed that of the liquid in the temperature region where the phonon contributions attain preeminence in both phases— i.e., when the higher energy excitations (rotons) of the liquid cease to contribute significantly. Provided ΔV_m remains positive, $dP_m(T)/dT$ will then pass through zero and become negative, signalling the mini-mum. The objective of the paper by Goldstein and Mills [59] was to make these ideas quantitative; and this they have done in two ways, first, through a thermodynamic argument using empirically determined quantities along the melting line, and second, through a statistical thermodynamic study of the elementary excitation spectrum of the liquid near $P_m(T)$.

The essential thread of the thermodynamic argument runs as follows. Experimental data for ΔV_m are not available below 1.3°K; however, measurements ([60]) at higher temperatures suggested that ΔV_m approaches a limiting value of 2.09 cm³/mole. Goldstein and Mills have assumed this constant value for $T < 1.3$°K and thereby considered $dP_m(T)/dT$ proportional to $\Delta S_m(T) = S_l - S_s$. The S_l may be obtained in two ways which are mutually consistent: either from the previous analysis by Mills ([26]) or from the heat capacity data of Wiebes and Kramers ([30]) taken at ~ 25 atm, a pressure sufficiently close to $P_m(T)$ at low T. For the solid, S_s may be evaluated through equation (9.9) using the empirically determined value of θ_s. According to the heat capacity measurements of Edwards and Pandorf ([61]), Goldstein and Mills have derived

$$\theta_s = \theta_s^{(0°\mathrm{K})} - \tau T^2$$

$$= (27.08 - 1.755\, T^2)\quad °\mathrm{K} \tag{9.10}$$

We point out in passing that from sound-velocity measurements ([62]), $\theta_l = 32.3$°K, larger than θ_s by a comfortable margin. Next, $dP_m(T)/dT$ was considered in two temperature ranges, $0°\mathrm{K} < T < 0.3°\mathrm{K}$ and $0.3°\mathrm{K} < T < 1.2°\mathrm{K}$. In the former, the phonons contribute exclusively in both the liquid and the solid; here, $dP_m(T)/dT = dP_\phi/dT$ is a function of ΔV_m, θ_s, and θ_l and is negative, thereby showing that the phonons are responsible for the melting anomaly. Above 0.3°K, additional excitations enter the picture with a normal or positive contribution, dP_r/dT, and these ultimately produce the net positive $dP_m(T)/dT$. The extent of this latter contribution was obtained numerically by subtracting the phonon part from the empirical heat capacity data. Below $T_{\min}$, $P_m(T)$ exhibits an inflection point at T_i, as required by the Nernst theorem, and it is of interest to note that this implies a crossing of the specific heat curves $C_s(T)$ and $C_l(T)$.

The second part of the calculations by Goldstein and Mills ([59]) consists of an extension of the earlier analysis by Mills ([26]) to obtain more refined values of the Landau spectrum parameters for the liquid along the melting curve. Again $dP_m(T)/dT$ was decomposed into a roton and a phonon part and evaluated in terms of these parameters. Superimposed upon the experimental data in Fig. 9.13 are these results together with their sum, which closely approximates the measurements. In Fig. 9.12, the upper solid curve of $[P_m(T) - P_m(0)]$ vs. T has been obtained from the thermodynamic calculations and the lower one from the spectrum analysis. The overall consistency between theory and experiment is extremely gratifying.

9.3. SOLID HELIUM

The first X-ray determination ([63]) of the crystal structure of solid He⁴ revealed a lattice symmetry consistent with the hexagonal close packing (hcp) of spheres. This in itself was considered surprising, for the other chemically inert gases, Ne, Ar, Kr, and Xe, were known to solidify into cubic close packed (fcc) structures. If one computes the lattice energies for hcp and ccp purely on the basis of two-body inter-actions summed over all possible pairs of atoms, it turns out that the hexagonal structure should actually be energetically more stable than the cubic by just a very slight margin. It is not difficult to understand, then, that other considerations, even very subtle ones, might tip the delicate balance to favor one structure over another, and that such effects as the zero-point energy, which is tremendous in the case of the heliums, could weigh most heavily.

But the case of the heliums is more complicated still. As can be seen from Figs. 9.1 and 9.2, both isotopes do crystallize into a fcc phase at high temperatures, in conformity with the other rare gases; both form stable hcp phases over extended regions; and, in addition, both may exist in a non-close-packed structure, a body-centered cubic (bcc) lattice. The structural parameters for each of these modifications have been determined through X-ray diffraction techniques by Schuch and co-workers as summarized in the articles by Schuch and Mills ([64,65]). Table 9.III presents their results at a representative point of the phase diagram for each crystal form. Also shown in the table are the molar volumes obtained from the X-ray work, which are in general good agreement with those calculated from $P-V-T$ data ([8]) for the corresponding conditions. Values quoted in Table 9.III have been

Table 9.III.

Iso-tope	P (atm)	T (°K)	Structure	Cell dimension (Å)	Molar volume (cm³) X-ray	$P-V-T$
He³	125	2.88	bcc	$a_0 = 3.963$	18.75	19.23
	163	3.48	hcp	$\begin{cases} c_0 = 5.721 \\ a_0 = 3.501 \end{cases}$	18.29	18.19
	1690	18.76	fcc	$a_0 = 4.242$	11.50	11.54
He⁴	29	1.73	bcc	$a_0 = 4.110$	20.91	20.93
	129	3.95	hcp	$\begin{cases} c_0 = 5.540 \\ a_0 = 3.470 \end{cases}$	17.40	17.29
	1255	16.0	fcc	$a_0 = 4.240$	11.48	11.80

derived from the final analyses by the authors, in contrast to some other similar tables appearing in the earlier literature ([2,64,65]).

9.3.1. Microscopic Calculations of the Ground State of Solid Helium

In the solid, because the atoms are localized and therefore in principle distinguishable, we expect particle statistics to be of considerably less importance than in the fluid phases. Consequently, a proper microscopic approach for solid helium at $T = 0°K$ should be equally valid for both He^3 and He^4. The primary objectives of such a theory should include predictions of: E_0, the ground-state or cohesive energy at $0°K$, as a function of volume; the manner in which E_0 is apportioned among the various contributing factors, such as potential energy, zero-point energy, and, in the case of He^3, the exchange energy arising from the spin system; and, finally, the energetically most favorable structure for the crystal.

There are two essentially different approaches to the microscopic theory of solid He. The first of these begins with the single-particle picture and seeks to determine what potential the particle is seeing. Then, collective modes are built from the single-particle functions. Several authors ([66,67]) have argued for this method, contending that the harmonic approximation of "classical" lattice dynamics breaks down for "quantum crystals" because the kinetic zero-point energy is of the same order of magnitude as the potential energy. This in effect "blows up" the lattice and permits excessively large excursions of an atom from its lattice site. Figure 9.14 compares schematically the potentials seen by a particle in the classical case and in the quantum case.

The second point of view, while recognizing the extreme anharmonicity of the crystal potential, nevertheless treats this potential as if it could be approximated through a fictitious harmonic Hamiltonian. The "best" such Hamiltonian is found and then used to determine the collective modes for the system. Koehler ([68]) has applied this method to He crystals.

Both of the above approaches for He lead to similar results, with the notable exception that at large wave-vectors near the Brillouin zone boundaries, the phonon dispersion curves are significantly different. As yet, we cannot determine which is more nearly correct. In the following, we shall concentrate on the single-particle picture, if only because this has been more thoroughly explored.

Perhaps the simplest approach to the problem consists of a variational calculation using as a trial wave function a product of single-particle functions (Hartree approximation). This was attempted in some of the early work; but not until 1962 were the limitations of this

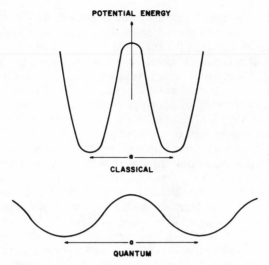

POTENTIAL ENERGY

CLASSICAL

QUANTUM

Fig. 9.14. Potential wells as seen by atoms in a classical crystal compared with a quantum crystal (schematic). In the latter, the well is broadened, the nearest-neighbor distance a is increased, and because of this, the potential barrier is decreased. Due to zero-point energy in the quantum case, there is considerable probability that the atom will be somewhere other than at the center of the well.

procedure fully appreciated. At that time, Nosanow and Shaw ([69]) discovered that an exact calculation obtained from spherically symmetric single-particle wave functions and two-body interactions described by the LJ (12-6) potential, gave surprisingly poor results for E_0, i.e., $+14$ cal/mole for He⁴ (compared with the experimental value of -12 cal/mole) and $+34$ cal/mole for He³ (compared with an estimated value of -1.6 cal/mole). On the other hand, the method was very successfully applied to Ar, Kr, and Xe, although a 5% difference in E_0 from the experimental value was obtained for Ne. The deficiencies in the theory for He—and also for Ne—undoubtedly arise from the fact that this approximation does not adequately take into account: (1) the crystal symmetry; (2) the exchange energy; and (3) the correlation effects.

Rosenwald ([70]) has reported similar calculations but for orbitals having cubic symmetry about the lattice sites to approximate the conditions for bcc He³. He found this change produced roughly a 10% improvement over the results of Nosanow and Shaw. In addition, he estimated that these calculations account for about one-third of the quantum effects which make up the difference in, for example, the enthalpy, between a "classical" crystal and the real crystal.

This latter result still neglects the importance of exchange and correlation effects, which nevertheless do not enter the problem independently. As expressed by Nosanow [67], there are two types of correlations, "structural" and "dynamic." The Hartree approximation describes the motion of one particle in a self-consistent potential averaged over the motions of all the other particles: it thereby properly places each particle in its own potential well and defines the structural aspects of the system. But completely omitted are the dynamic correlations, especially the important short-range strong couplings between the motions of two or a few nearest neighbors. Inclusion of these reduces the total energy by lowering both the kinetic and potential energies. In both the Hartree and the Hartree–Fock approximations, the atoms are constrained to individual potential wells so that no overlaps of orbitals between neighboring atoms is possible; but if the dynamic correlations, which effectively broaden the wells, are introduced, then exchange interaction can be realized through suitable symmetrization of the trial wave function.

The significance of dynamic correlations had already been appreciated by Bernardes and Primakoff [32], whose determination of E_0 for He^3 was a hybrid between a variational calculation and a phenomenological strain derived by correspondence with He^4. To introduce correlations into their trial wave function, an antisymmetrized product of orbitals of the Heitler–London type, they modified the interparticle potential, taken as LJ (12-6), by the factor $\exp(-\lambda r_{ij}^{-10})$. Here, r_{ij} is the distance between particles i and j, and λ is a parameter whose numerical value was fixed so that an analogous calculation using λ would reproduce for He^4 the empirical values of E_0 and the mean square deviation of an atom from its lattice site. The effect of the exponential cutoff at short distances was to avoid the singularities associated with the LJ (12–6) potential as $r_{ij} \to 0$. This procedure has several deficiencies, and in particular has led to a value of the exchange energy J now known to be several orders of magnitude too large. While J contributes but very little to E_0, the magnetic properties of solid He^3 are sensitively dependent upon the exchange term.

In 1962, Saunders [71] published calculations of the ground state of solid He^3. These were enthusiastically received because the properties of the solid predicted by the theory compared favorably with experimental findings. This feeling persisted until 1965, when Garwin and Landesman [72] expressed their disenchantment with the bases of the theory; and since then, both Nosanow [67] and Mullin [73] have severely criticized and thoroughly discredited Saunders' method. We have felt obliged to mention this development, as the literature abounds in references to this theory, which we feel we must now discount.

Nosanow and co-workers ([67,74–76]) have developed a most useful and fruitful microscopic approach for the ground state of quantum crystals [though several other individual calculations ([68,77]) have yielded slightly lower values of E_0]. This is a variational calculation in which the trial wave function was taken in the form

$$\Psi(\mathbf{r}_1, \ldots, \mathbf{r}_N) = \prod_{i=1}^{N} \phi(\Delta_i) \prod_{j<k} f(r_{jk}) \qquad (9.11)$$

Here, $\mathbf{r}_i$ is the coordinate of the ith particle and Δ_i its displacement from its lattice site; $r_{jk} = |\mathbf{r}_j - \mathbf{r}_k|$. The functions ϕ, with Δ localized about respective sites, serve to describe the crystal structure, as in the Hartree approximation, and the f's represent the short-range dynamic correlations. It is significant that Nosanow's method does not require the wave function (9.11) to be separable. To evaluate E_0, the expansion

$$E_0 = E_{01} + E_{02} + E_{03} + \cdots \qquad (9.12)$$

was used, in which E_{0n} represents the energy contribution due to the close clustering of n particles. Except for E_{01}, which depends only on the kinetic energy, each term can be divided into two parts, one involving the kinetic energy, E_{0nT}, the other the potential energy, E_{0nV}. The LJ (12-6) potential was used to describe the pair interaction.

In the first paper ([67]), approximate single-particle solutions, ϕ were found such that all $E_{0nT} = 0$ except for $n = 1$. Then the approximation

$$E_0 \approx E_{01} + E_{02V} \qquad (9.13)$$

was variationally minimized as a function of molar volume V. For He⁴, the calculations of E_0 vs. V (17 to 21.5 cm³/mole) are about 8 cal/mole too high, and for He³ ($V = 20$ to 24.5 cm³/mole) about 10 cal/mole higher than expected from experiment. For both isotopes, the theory indicates that the bcc phases should be energetically more stable than the corresponding hcp phases (though, of course, the stable phase for He⁴ and 0°K is hcp). The importance of the kinetic energy term becomes evident when we examine the components of E_0; for example, for solid He³ at $V \approx 24$ cm³/mole, $E_0 \approx E_{01} + E_{02V} = 31.2 - 21.6 = 9.7$ cal/mole. (From the estimate of $E_0 \approx -1$ cal/mole, it is apparent that in the real crystal, the potential and kinetic energies are even more nearly balanced.)

In a second paper, Hetherington *et al.* ([76]) evaluated E_{03V} to determine the contribution of three-body terms and to test the convergence of the series (9.12). They found that E_{03V} is indeed quite small, and for the case given above, E_{03V} is of the order 0.1 cal/mole; while inclusion of this term in the minimization procedure slightly alters both E_{01} and E_{02V}, the net total energy changes also by only about 0.1 cal/mole. Furthermore, the convergence of the cluster expansion appears assured.

Calculations both with and without the three-body term have been made for such properties of the solids as P, β_S, and sound velocities as functions of molar volume ([75]). Inclusion of E_{03V} affects these calculations more than those for E_0. An example of the agreement obtained with experiment is shown for the volume dependence of the compressibility in Fig. 9.10. Here, the addition of E_{03V} offers an improvement to the fit of the calculation to experimental data, though this is not always the case. In general, the calculated values for P, β_S and sound velocity are considerably more realistic than those for E_0. We may understand this as follows: It is meaningless to say that $E_0^{(calc)}$ is, e.g., 1000% greater than $E_0^{(obs)}$, since agreement with $E_0^{(obs)}$ could be achieved by a theory which lowers both E_{01} and E_{02V} by only $\sim 15\%$; but the principal volume dependence resides in E_{01}, so that the derived quantities should be consistent with experiment to within $\sim 15\%$, which is roughly the case.

The exchange energy in the two-body approximation, $J = E_{02J}$, has been calculated by Nosanow and Mullin ([74]) and in the three-body approximation by Hetherington et al. ([76]). The exchange energy was found to be trivially small compared with $E_{01} + E_{02V}$. Figure 9.15 shows the spin-alignment temperatures T_c vs. particle spacing deduced from this work as compared with the experimental data to be discussed in the following section. Two points with respect to the figure are worth mentioning here. First we see that $|J|$ decreases with increasing density even though initially one might expect that bringing the particles closer together should promote overlap and thereby increase $|J|$. A probable explanation for this comes from the fact that a small change in the average lattice spacing significantly affects the shape of the potential wells in which the nuclei reside (cf. Fig. 9.14). Thus an increase in the density narrows the wells and limits the range over which we may expect to find a given nucleus, thereby decreasing the probability for exchange between the nucleus and its neighbors. Second, the introduction of the three-body term into the calculations makes the comparison with experiment poorer, especially at large densities. Hetherington et al. explained this as due to the extreme sensitivity of one of the variational parameters with respect to the exact amount of overlap between adjacent single-particle functions.

9.3.2. Magnetic Properties of Solid He³

We recall (Section 6.2.3c) that nuclear magnetic resonance measurements may provide information about the susceptibility χ,

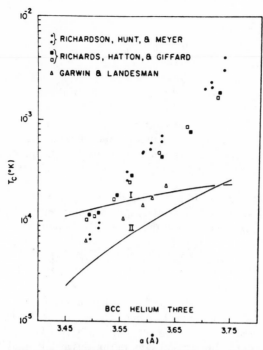

Fig. 9.15. Variation of the spin-alignment temperature T_c in solid He³ with nearest-neighbor distance a. Curve I calculated using two-body clusters; curve II includes the effects of three-body clusters. [From Hetherington *et al.* ([76]).]

the spin-diffusion D, and the relaxation times T_1 and T_2 characterizing the approach of the nuclear spin system to thermodynamic equilibrium with the lattice. Through various modifications of experimental technique, these quantities may be interrelated, as we have already seen for the case of liquid He³. But of particular importance for solid He³ is the evaluation of the exchange integral J from the experimentally determined magnetic parameters. This will be the primary concern of the present section.

Depending on how one chooses to write the exchange part of the Hamiltonian, the exchange parameter may be expressed either as $J/2\pi$ in frequency units or as J/k_B in temperature units. Both Hamiltonians involve pairwise exchange and in all approximations to date, this is considered to occur between a given atom and its z nearest neighbors. Under these conditions, the spin-alignment temperature can be expressed as

$$T_c = \frac{z}{4} \frac{h}{k_B} \left| \frac{J}{2\pi} \right| \qquad (J/2\pi \text{ in sec}^{-1}) \qquad (9.14)$$

$$= \frac{z}{2} \left| \frac{J}{k_B} \right| \qquad (J/k_B \text{ in } °K) \qquad (9.15)$$

The sign of J determines the kind of ordering which takes place at T_c, i.e., positive J indicates parallel alignment of the spins (ferromagnetism) and negative J, antiparallel alignment (antiferromagnetism), corresponding, respectively, to positive and negative deviations from Curie's law.

In passing, we wish to point out that J may in principle be inferred from heat capacity as well as magnetic measurements. The exchange contribution per mole, C_X, to the total heat capacity can be given as

$$C_X = \frac{3N_A}{8} \left(\frac{J}{k_B} \right)^2 \frac{k_B z}{T^2} = 3R \left(\frac{J}{k_B T} \right)^2 \qquad (9.16)$$

for spin $\frac{1}{2}$, $z = 8$ for bcc He^3, and provided that $(J/k_B) \ll T$.

Considerable confusion has marked the history of the magnetic investigations, which is not too surprising in view of the complexity of the subject. On the theoretical side, Bernardes and Primakoff [32] first calculated $J/k_B \approx -0.02°K$ at low densities; with increasing pressure, the exchange was expected to decrease such that the antiferromagnetic solid should ultimately become ferromagnetic.

The first experimental NMR susceptibility measurements in the solid by Fairbank and Walters [35] showed below $0.3°K$ sometimes positive and sometimes negative deviations from Curie's law for separate runs over the same region. Later, using an improved apparatus, Adams et al. [78] measured the susceptibility over the range $T = 0.07$ to $1.2°K$, $P = 36$ to 112 atm. The data for molar volumes greater than ~ 23 cm^3 ($P < 60$ atm) could be interpreted on the basis of the Curie–Weiss law for antiferromagnets, i.e.,

$$\chi = \mathscr{C}/(T + T_c) \qquad (9.17)$$

where $\mathscr{C}$ is the Curie constant; T_c from the measurements was of the order of $0.01°K$. At higher densities ($V < 23$ cm^3, $60 < P < 122$ atm), the Curie law was obeyed down to about $0.3°K$; but at lower T, the susceptibility isobars behaved anomalously, first deviating positively, then passing through maxima, and finally, at the lowest temperatures, tending to a constant χ with a negative deviation. This implied an anomalously high value for J/k_B.

Even in 1960, when the work of Adams et al. ([78]) was reported, several puzzling features were recognized; but as more data accumulated, the confusion grew, particularly over the high-pressure results. From the specific-heat measurements of Edwards et al. ([79]), an upper bound for $|J/k|$ of $2 \times 10^{-3}\,°K$ could be set for all densities in the bcc phase and of $7 \times 10^{-4}\,°K$ for the hcp phase ($V = 19.5\,cm^3$), while lower bounds of from 10^{-4} to $10^{-5}\,°K$ were deduced ([80,81]) from relaxation measurements at $V = 20\,cm^3$. Furthermore, thermal anomalies were expected to be associated with those in χ, but none were detected. Taken together, these results cast suspicion upon the susceptibility measurements; but the final damaging evidence appeared through the discovery that the sample used by Adams et al. was contaminated with $\sim 1\,\%$ He^4 and that even such small amounts might affect the measurements because of phase separation in the solid ([82]). Following this, Thomson et al. ([83]) remeasured χ in a He^3 sample 99.95 % pure. All the data for $V > 22\,cm^3$ could be analyzed in terms of a volume-dependent T_c using equation (9.17), from which J/k_B was found consistent with specific-heat and relaxation data. In addition, significant departures from Curie's law appeared only below about 0.06°K, as contrasted to the higher temperature for the less pure samples of Adams et al. Nevertheless, for $V > 22\,cm^3$, problems with impurities still seemed to plague the results.

For very pure He^3 this confusing situation appears to have been somewhat clarified through the steady-state NMR measurements of Cohen et al. ([84]) on a sample containing but 5 parts He^4 in 10^7. At $V = 21\,cm^3$ the susceptibility followed Curie's law over the temperature range investigated ($0.04° < T < 1°K$), with the experimental error placing a limit of $\pm 0.003°K$ on the extrapolation for T_c. This is consistent with what is expected for a pure He^3 crystal (see below). Cohen et al. also studied solutions with $1/10^4$ and $3/10^3$ He^4, finding T_c to increase in magnitude with both V and He^4 concentration. However, while T_c was positive for the former solution, it was negative for the more impure sample. Hence we are still left with perplexing experimental evidence for the dilute solutions and without an explanation of why He^4 impurities affect the magnetic properties of liquid He^3 as they do.

Measurements of T_1 and T_2 in solid He^3 have been made primarily by the groups working at Duke ([80,85,86]), IBM ([72,81,87–89]), and Oxford ([90–92]). While the exchange integral is important in determining both T_1 and T_2, there are a number of mechanisms by which relaxation may occur; and since it is a very complicated matter to sort these out, this has led to considerable ambiguity in the results. However, it now seems likely that the important difficulties have been satisfactorily resolved, especially through the work of Richardson et al. ([85]) using the spin-echo technique and of Richards *et al.* ([91]) using continuous-wave nuclear magnetic resonance methods. Both of these papers contain useful summaries and bibliographies of the theory for the manner in which the spin system couples with the lattice. We give here only a few of the salient features concerning T_1 and T_2.

The transverse relaxation described by T_2 is believed to occur through two mechanisms. The first of these is by a process of the Arrhenius type, $D = D_0 \exp(-E_D/k_B T)$, where E_D is the density-dependent activation energy for diffusion—e.g., at $V = 20\,\text{cm}^3$, $E_D/k_B \approx 13.5°\text{K}$ ([80,81,87]). Exchange does not play a part here. The second mechanism acts through the magnetic dipole–dipole inter-action, which is affected by exchange. Experimentally, T_2 may be determined as the mean decay time of the spin-echo generated by a 90° pulse followed by a 180° pulse. The decay is exponential. However, the line shape varies with Larmor frequency ω_0, so we must distinguish between two cases. When $\omega_0 \gg J$, the theory ([88]) relates J and T_2 approximately by

$$T_2'(\omega_0 \gg J) = \frac{V^2(J/2\pi) \times 10^{-9}}{17.35} \qquad (9.18)$$

but when $\omega_0 \ll J$, the line is broadened ([93]) by a factor of 10/3, so that

$$T_2(\omega_0 \ll J) = (3/10)T_2' \qquad (9.19)$$

A more complete theory ([94]) of T_2 indicates that the relaxation time should depend upon ω_0. Smoothed results for T_2 by Richardson *et al.* ([85]) for $V \approx 20.4\,\text{cm}^3$ at several frequencies are plotted in Fig. 9.16 as a function of T^{-1}. Above 1°K, the temperature-dependent diffusive mechanism is apparent; but below 1°K, the curves are independent of temperature, as suggested by equations (9.18) and (9.19), and provide means for evaluating J.

To describe adequately the longitudinal or spin-lattice relaxation time T_1, which is far more complicated than T_2, a "three-bath" model is useful for solid He^3 [e.g., see Reich ([87])]. According to this model, each of the three separate subsystems—the Zeeman (or spin), the exchange, and the lattice—may in the absence of interactions be characterized by its own temperature, energy, specific heat, etc. How-ever, when the interactions are turned on, mechanisms become available for achieving equilibrium among the subsystems. Figure 9.17 depicts the relaxation routes possible for this model. Thus, after we perturb the spin system, as, for example by applying an rf field, the Zeeman bath may, depending upon ω_0 and T, equilibrate with the lattice either directly, with characteristic time τ_{ZL}, or by the two-stage process through the exchange bath involving the times τ_{ZX} and τ_{XL}.

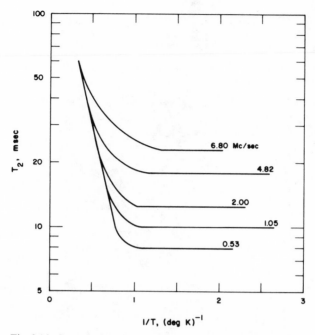

Fig. 9.16. Smoothed curves for the transverse relaxation time for solid He³ at $V \approx 20.4 \, \text{cm}^3$ as a function of T^{-1} and at several frequencies. J is determined from the temperature-independent part of the curves [after Richardson *et al.* ([85])].

Fortunately, the temperature dependence of the overall relaxation time provides some clues as to how this complex situation may be analyzed. As an example, we give in Fig. 9.17 data due to Richards *et al.* ([91]) for solid He³ at $V = 20 \, \text{cm}^3$, showing as a function of T^{-1} the recovery time of the Zeeman system after being fully excited at a resonant frequency $\omega_0/2\pi = 4.8 \, \text{Mc/sec}$. The curve may be divided into five regions:

Region I. Above $\sim 1°\text{K}$, the behavior is typical of the diffusive mechanism of relaxation and is associated almost exclusively with Zeeman-lattice interaction with $T_1 = T_{ZL}$; the descending part of the curve starting at the highest temperature also represents T_2. The minimum occurs at $\omega_0\tau_c \approx 1$ (τ_c being the characteristic time required for one nucleus to diffuse past another) indicating the most favorable conditions for spin-flipping by the magnetic interaction between the two nuclei involved.

Region II. Because of the exponential temperature dependence of diffusion, this process becomes unimportant with decreasing T,

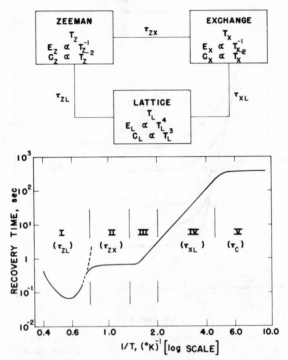

Fig. 9.17. Upper section: the three-bath model for spin equilibration in solid He³: lower section: recovery time of the Zeeman system as a function of T^{-1} [after Richards *et al.* ([91])].

so that beginning near 1°K, the relaxation process must take the alternate route. (For larger ω_0, relaxation via τ_{ZL} would persist to lower T, as shown by the dotted line in the figure.) Of the two mechanisms in series, Zeeman–exchange and exchange–lattice, the former is expected from theory ([88,95]) to be temperature independent. Hence the observed plateau in this region suggests that τ_{ZX} is the rate-determining quantity, and therefore here, $T_1 \approx \tau_{ZX}$. At sufficiently high frequencies, the theoretical expression for τ_{ZX} takes the form

$$1/\tau_{ZX} = (A/JV^2) \exp(-\omega_0^2/BJ^2) \qquad (9.20)$$

with A and B constants. In principle, J can be obtained from both the slope and intercept of a plot of ω_0^2 *vs.* τ_{ZX}. While Richards *et al.* ([91]) were able to use this method, Richardson *et al.* ([85]) could not fit their data to the exponential form, but instead availed themselves of the limiting form as $\omega_0 \to \infty$.

Region III. This is a transition region near 0.7°K, in which τ_{XL} begins to take over the role of the "bottleneck" in the relaxation process, i.e., we pass from $\tau_{ZX} \gg \tau_{XL}$ to $\tau_{XL} \gg \tau_{ZX}$.

Region IV. This region is dominated by the exchange–lattice relaxation time which is accountable [96] primarily in terms of phonon interactions with the exchange bath. Garwin and Landesman [88] have considered the principal mechanism to be a Raman-type process (one phonon is absorbed by the exchange bath and another of different energy emitted). Then

$$1/\tau_{XL} \approx 1/\tau_2 \equiv C\left(\frac{d^2 J}{da^2}\right)\frac{T^7}{\theta^{10}} \qquad (9.21)$$

where a is the nearest neighbor distance, θ the Debye temperature, and C a constant. Richards *et al.* [91] have also considered a one-phonon process $[1/\tau_1 \propto J^2(\partial J/\partial a)^2 T]$ and a diffusion process $[1/\tau_c = 6D/a^2 \propto \exp(-E_D/k_B T)]$ in interpreting their observed relaxation times in this region, although the temperature dependence of the recovery time in this region is predominantly T^{-7}. It then becomes possible to write

$$1/\tau_{XL} = 1/\tau_1 + 1/\tau_2 + 1/\tau_c \qquad (9.22)$$

But the measured quantity is the relaxation of the Zeeman system and not τ_{XL} directly. On the other hand, if the Zeeman system is strongly coupled to the exchange bath and if $T_Z = T_X$, then the recovery time of the Zeeman system may be found as

$$T_1 = \tau_{XL}\left(1 + \frac{C_Z}{C_X}\right) = \tau_{XL}\left[1 + \left(\frac{8}{3}z\right)\left(\frac{\omega_0}{J}\right)^2\right] \qquad (9.23)$$

Measurements of this T_1 by Richardson *et al.* [85] indicate more a T^{-10} than a T^{-7} dependence, although the values of J obtained in this way agree well with other determinations.

Region V. Should some high-power law for τ_{XL} persist to lower temperatures, this would imply extraordinarily long relaxation times and would render meaningless or impossible magnetic measurements on the solid below $\sim 0.1°$K. However, near 0.2°K, it appears as if τ_{XL} stops becoming large and instead remains constant with decreasing temperature. Richards *et al.* [91] found their data in this region to be consistent with the notion that the diffusion process here is more rapid than either the one- or two-phonon processes, and thus governs τ_{XL}.

The experimental situation has been complicated by the fact that even minute traces of He^4 in the sample markedly affect the mechanisms involved in the three-bath model. One of the more perplexing problems that have been resolved through recognition of this fact has been the large discrepancy between the observed values of the exchange bath specific heat and the values of C_X calculated using equation (9.16). Direct magnetic measurements of C_X by Garwin and Reich [89] were about 4000 times larger than expected, a disparity which according to Richards et al. [91] could be traced to a He^4 content of $\sim 1\%$ in the sample used for the former authors. Richards et al. found that the anomalies in C_X disappeared for samples containing less than $0.05\% He^4$. Both the results of Garwin and Reich and the susceptibility data of Adams et al. [78] on impure samples imply high values of J and T_1. Richards et al. have suggested that this might be due to some additional bottleneck process which because of the large C_X would not be detected in relaxation measurements. In the region above about $0.6°K$, where the recovery rate is governed by the Zeeman–exchange process, the system is apparently not sensitive to He^4 impurities; but below this temperature, quite the reverse is true, and it is doubtful that the three-bath model can here satisfactorily describe the relaxation in impure solid He^3.

Recently, Giffard and Hatton [92] have found an additional contribution to τ_{XL} at temperatures below $0.6°K$ and for $X = He^4/He^3$ ranging between 5×10^{-7} and 3×10^{-4}. The new relaxation process is characterized by a rate which increases as T^{-8} or T^{-9} and which is proportional to X. Hence, as the purity is improved and the temperature is lowered, increasingly large values of τ_{XL} are obtained. The measurements were not carried below $0.4°K$, so that the limiting low-temperature behavior for τ_{XL} has not been determined for very pure He^3. While these results are in no way connected with the effects discussed in the preceding paragraph, since X here is far too low, they do have an obvious bearing upon the interpretation of earlier τ_{XL} measurements. As yet, no theoretical explanation for the new process has become available.

From the various NMR experiments and expressions we have just discussed involving the exchange energy, values of J, or, equivalently, T_c, may be obtained. We have plotted some of these results as a function of nearest neighbor spacing in Fig. 9.15 and we see that the data from different sources and methods are, in general, compatible.

We return now to the recent work of Panczyk et al. [47] who have determined $|J|$ from extremely sensitive P–V–T measurements above the melting curve ($V \approx 22.5$–24.5 cm^3). We may consider the coefficient $(\partial P/\partial T)_V$ to be partitioned into two contributions, one from the lattice, the other from the exchange system, and find

$$\left(\frac{\partial P}{\partial T}\right)_V = \left(\frac{\partial P}{\partial T}\right)_{VX} + \left(\frac{\partial P}{\partial T}\right)_{VL}$$

$$= \frac{C_{VX}\gamma_X}{V} + \frac{C_{VL}\gamma}{V} \tag{9.24}$$

where $C_{VX} = 3R(J/k_B T)^2$ from equation (9.16), C_{VL} is the lattice specific heat, γ is the Grüneisen constant (see next section), and

$$\gamma_X = -(\partial \ln|J|/\partial \ln V)_T \tag{9.25}$$

Panczyk et al. measured ΔP (increments in P from some arbitrary P) vs. $1/T$, the slope of which gives $3\gamma_X RJ^2/k_B^2 V$. From this, J and γ_X were obtained self-consistently with the results: $|J/k_B| = 7 \times 10^{-3}$ °K at $V = 24\,\text{cm}^3$ and $\gamma_X = -16.4$. These are in good agreement with the NMR values, especially those of Richardson et al. ([85]); but more importantly, they represent the first *direct equilibrium* measurements of $|J|$.

9.3.3. The Heat Capacity and Related Properties of Solid Helium

Dugdale ([2]) has given a rather extensive survey of the heat capacity measurements made on solid He prior to 1964. Since that time, Sample and Swenson ([97]) have extended and refined the data for He³, and Edwards and Pandorf ([61,98]) have done the same for He⁴. Because several of the uncertainties (though not all) raised by the earlier work have now been resolved, it seems worthwhile to review here the recent investigations and present the most up-to-date picture. In addition, new results are available on such properties related to the heat capacity as the compressibility, expansion coefficient, and sound velocities in the various solid forms.

For He³, Sample and Swenson ([97]) measured C_V at 9 molar volumes as indicated on the V–T phase diagram of Fig. 9.18. In each case, data were taken from $T/\theta_0 < 0.01$ (where θ_0 is the Debye temperature θ extrapolated to 0°K) up to the melting curve, the lowest temperatures being of the order of 0.15°K. Heat capacities of solids may generally be expressed in terms of the Debye temperature as derived from the C_V measurements assuming the T^3 dependence. Figure 9.19 shows a plot of θ vs. T/θ_0 obtained in this way by Sample and Swenson for hcp He³ in comparison with the earlier work of Dugdale and Franck ([99]) at higher temperatures. In the region of overlap both sets of data show the rise of θ with decreasing temperature and are numerically consistent to within about 1%. However, the fact that each low temperature curve (except for $V = 19.05\,\text{cm}^3$) passes through a maximum creates some problems for the θ_0 extrapolation. Previous work on hcp He³ ([41])

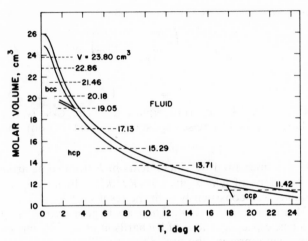

Fig. 9.18. Volume–temperature diagram of compressed He^3 indicating molar volumes at which heat capacity data of Sample and Swenson [97] were taken [after Sample and Swenson [97]].

and on hcp He^4 ([41,100]) had revealed low-temperature anomalies which were analyzed using the relation

$$C_V = AT + 3RD(\theta/T) \tag{9.26}$$

where A is a constant and $D(\theta/T)$ is the Debye function assuming $\theta = \theta_0$, a constant. Franck ([100]) has suggested that the linear term might be associated with annealing effects in the solid, since A appeared to vary for different samples. However, Sample and Swenson could find no evidence of the annealing mechanism and have instead ascribed the low-temperature anomalies to artifacts of the apparatus. Therefore, in determining θ_0, they have ignored the points to the left of the maxima in the figure and have extrapolated as shown by the solid lines, contending that the plateaus in the region $0.04 \gtrsim T/\theta_0 \gtrsim 0.02$ properly indicate the lattice specific heats.

The θ vs. T/θ_0 plots for bcc He^3 appear qualitatively similar to those for hcp He^3 but display significant differences for $T/\theta_0 > 0.05$. In this region, the curves for bcc He^3 fall considerably faster with increasing temperature than those for hcp He^3. In addition, the hcp data for different molar volumes all lie within $\frac{1}{2}\%$ of a single curve when replotted as θ/θ_0 vs. T/θ_0, whereas no such reduced representation is possible for bcc He^3. It is interesting to note that Sample and Swenson have found that on this reduced plot, the data for hcp He^3 are quite compatible with those for the "classical" close-packed crystals argon and krypton.

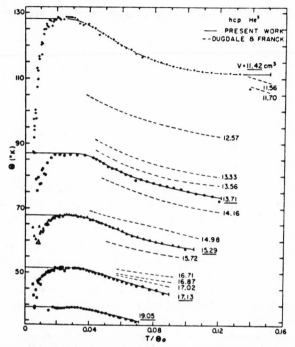

Fig. 9.19. Debye θ vs. T/θ_0 for various molar volumes of hcp He³ as observed by Sample and Swenson ([97]) (solid lines). Vertical bars at right-hand termini of curves indicate the melting line. Dotted curves show earlier data of Dugdale and Franck ([99]). [From Sample and Swenson ([97]).]

Swenson and co-workers ([41,97]) have analyzed the nonconforming behavior of bcc He³ in terms of an excess specific heat, C_{xs}; that is,

$$C_{xs} = C_V^{(\text{obs})} - C^{(\text{Debye})} \qquad (9.27)$$

with the best analytic fit ([97]) to the data given by

$$C_{xs} = R(\phi/T)^2 \exp(-\phi/T) \qquad (9.28)$$

Here, ϕ is a function of volume, which was also fitted numerically, and $C^{(\text{Debye})}$ is determined using $\theta = \theta_0$ for each V. Equation (9.28) indicates that for fixed V, and therefore fixed ϕ, C_{xs} increases rapidly with temperature. An example of how C_{xs} contributes to the observed C_V is shown in Table 9.IV for the case $V = 21.46 \text{ cm}^3$ [data taken from Tables I and II and Fig. 12 of Sample and Swenson ([97])]. Because values of $\phi(V)$ were found to be quite close to those of $E_D(V)$, the activation energy for spin-diffusion, it was thought that C_{xs} could be

Table 9.IV. Analysis of Heat Capacity Data for bcc He³ ᵃ

T/θ_0	$T(°K)$	C_V (cal/mole)	C_{xs} (cal/mole)	C_{xs}/C_V
0.01	0.253	0.000463	~0	~0
0.03	0.759	0.0134	0.002	0.15
0.05	1.265	0.0909	0.035	0.39
0.07	1.771	0.358	0.195	0.54

ᵃ $V = 21.46 \text{ cm}^3$, $\theta_0 = 25.30°K$, $\phi = 10.49°K$.

associated with imperfections in the crystal lattice. However, Sample and Swenson have suggested that because of the large zero-point energy and consequent expansion of the lattice, the classical concept of these imperfections is probably meaningless. We are therefore left without a suitable explanation for the large excess contribution to C_V in bcc He³. Of the several C_V investigations of solid He³, none has uncovered down to the lowest temperatures, i.e., ~0.02°K ([39]), any evidence for a T^{-2} contribution from the exchange system as required by equation (9.16).

Edwards and Pandorf ([61]) have carried the heat capacity measurements of hcp He⁴ to lower temperatures and smaller molar volumes than did earlier authors ([99,101,102]), such that in the new work, θ_0 was well-defined. In addition, Edwards and Pandorf found that all of their C_V data (taken along six isochores at $16.5 < V < 21 \text{ cm}^3$ extending from ~0.3°K to the melting curve) could be represented by a single curve on a reduced plot of $\theta/\theta_{0.05}$ vs. T/θ. Here, $\theta_{0.05}$ is the value of θ when $T/\theta = 0.05$ and the expressions

$$\theta_0 = (7.12 \times 10^4)V^{-2.60}, \qquad \theta_{0.05} = (6.73 \times 10^4)V^{-2.60} \qquad (9.29)$$

fit the data exceedingly well. Figure 9.20 illustrates the results. The earlier data join nicely onto this curve, but for $T/\theta > $ ~0.08, diverge from the unique representation. Also, on a reduced plot of θ/θ_0 vs. T/θ_0, the Edwards and Pandorf measurements are nearly coincident with the hcp He³ data ([97]).

The naturally restricted range in molar volumes of the bcc He⁴ phase has been fully covered by the heat capacity measurements of Ahlers ([102]) and of Edwards and Pandorf ([98]). Debye θ's determined from the two investigations are mutually consistent. Although the bcc phase does not exist at $T = 0°K$, the latter authors have obtained extrapolated values of $\theta_0(V)$ ranging from 21.2°K at $V = 20.927 \text{ cm}^3$ to 20.8°K at 21.028 cm³. Ahlers observed an anomalous increase in C_V for decreasing molar volume and suggested that this might be associated with the existence of anomalous thermal excitations in

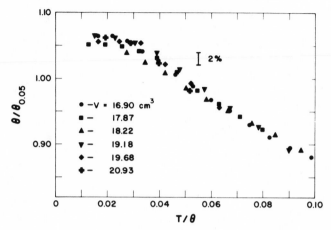

Fig. 9.20. The plot of $\theta/\theta_{0.05}$ vs. T/θ for hcp He⁴ [after Edwards and Pandorf [61]].

solid He⁴. Earlier, Goldstein [52] had been led to invoke such excitations for the solid in order to explain incomplete melting-line data. On the other hand, Edwards and Pandorf found $(\partial C_V/\partial V)_T$ to be positive from direct measurements and, as well, showed that both β_T and α_P behave normally, thereby arguing strongly against anomalous behavior. It seems possible that the Ahlers' results were affected by difficulties in keeping his solid sample at constant volume.

Data for the volume variation of θ_0 for the hcp and bcc phases of both He³ and He⁴ are collected on the log–log plot of Fig. 9.21. It is purely accidental that the hcp He⁴ curve runs into the bcc He³. There are, nevertheless, several interesting correlations evident from the plot. If we examine the ratio $\theta_0(\mathrm{He^3})/\theta_0(\mathrm{He^4})$ at fixed V, we find that for the hcp phases, this is approximately 1.18 and for the bcc phases, about 1.23. In the classical harmonic approximation, the ratio depends only upon the relative masses, and is $(4/3)^{1/2} = 1.155$, not too different from the hcp value just mentioned. We may also see from the figure that for each isotope, θ_0 for the bcc phase is some 20 % lower than for the corresponding hcp phase at the same volume. While this is not unexpected from the theoretical standpoint, it does emphasize the considerable differences between the crystal forms, especially since this variation in θ_0 implies a difference of about 70 % in C_V. Also of considerable interest is the slope, $\gamma_0 = (d \ln \theta_0/d \ln V)$, which for the helium solids varies from about 2.0 to 2.6 and for a given phase increases with increasing molar volume. For the general case (i.e., T not necessarily 0°K), γ is known as the Grüneisen constant, defined by

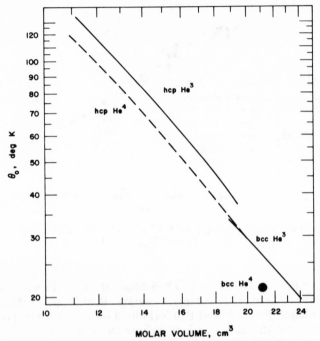

Fig. 9.21. The variation of θ_0 with molar volume for hcp He^3 and He^4
and for bcc He^3 and He^4 [after Sample and Swenson ([97]); θ_0 for bcc
He^4 taken from Edwards and Pandorf ([98]) and Ahlers ([102])].

the relation

$$\gamma = -\alpha_P V / \beta_T C_V = -d \ln \theta / d \ln V \qquad (9.30)$$

Although in principle γ is calculable from theory, it is usually obtained
empirically and found to vary slowly with T and V; for most simple
solids, γ ranges between 1 and 3.

Through equation (9.30) and its various equivalent forms derivable
from thermodynamics, it is possible to test the consistency between the
empirically determined thermal and P–V–T properties of the solids.
For example, Table 9.V lists some properties of bcc He^3 near the
melting curve as compiled by Grilly (private communication). Here,
values of C_V have been taken from Sample and Swenson ([97]). Two
differing sets of data for α_P are available due to Grilly ([43]) and to
Straty ([42]) and these are listed separately as $\alpha_P^{(G)}$ and $\alpha_P^{(S)}$; however,
determinations of β_T by these authors agree, requiring only one entry
for each (T, V) condition. We note that the resulting values of $\gamma^{(S)}$ are

Table 9.V. Thermal and *P–V–T* Properties of Solid He³ Near Melting

T ($^\circ$K)	$\alpha_P^{(G)}$ (10^{-3} deg^{-1})	$\alpha_P^{(S)}$ (10^{-3} deg^{-1})	β_T (10^{-3} atm^{-1})	C_V (cal/mole-deg)	V (cm³/mole)	$\gamma^{(G)} = \dfrac{\alpha_P^{(G)} V}{\beta_T C_V}$	$\gamma^{(S)} = \dfrac{\alpha_P^{(S)} V}{\beta_T C_V}$
1.2	3.60	4.20	3.86	0.210	23.09	2.48	2.89
1.4	4.64	4.90	3.48	0.268	22.48	2.71	2.86
1.6	5.46	5.34	3.08	0.325	21.94	2.90	2.84
1.8	5.96	5.65	2.68	0.380	21.46	3.04	2.88

independent of T and V, whereas $\gamma^{(G)}$ shows a slight variation. Unfortunately, γ cannot be determined with sufficient accuracy from $C_V(V)$ alone to permit a choice between these alternatives. On the other hand, bcc He^3 may be expected to behave similarly to bcc He^4 in this temperature range. In Fig. 9.22, we show the results of γ for bcc He^4 and for hcp He^4 as obtained by Jarvis and Meyer ([46]) from their measurements of $(\partial P/\partial T)_V$ in the solids and from the C_V data of Edwards and Pandorf ([61,98]). On the basis of the observed slow variation of γ for bcc He^4, $\gamma^{(S)}$ for bcc He^3 appears to be favored over $\gamma^{(G)}$. It is also worth noting that Sample and Swenson ([97]) were able to analyze their heat capacity for He^3 in terms of $\gamma(V, T)$ and found a close correspondence with the Jarvis and Meyer values for hcp He^4.

Another link between the thermal and state properties of the solid is provided by measurements of the sound velocities. According to the Debye theory, for an elastically isotropic crystal—i.e., one in which the velocity of sound is independent of the propagation direction in the crystal,

$$\theta = \frac{\hbar}{k_B}\left(\frac{6\pi^2 N_A}{V}\right)\left(\frac{2}{3u_t^3} + \frac{1}{3u_l^3}\right)^{-1/3} \tag{9.31}$$

where u_l and u_t are the velocities of the longitudinal (compressional) and transverse (shear) modes related by

$$u_l^2 = 1/\rho\beta_S + (4/3)u_t^2 \tag{9.32}$$

(β_S here is the adiabatic compressibility coefficient). Equations (9.31) and (9.32) are appropriate for single crystals; when the specimen is

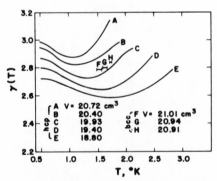

Fig. 9.22. Temperature variation of the Grüneisen constant for bcc He^4 and hcp He^4 at several molar volumes (smoothed curves) [after Jarvis and Meyer ([46])].

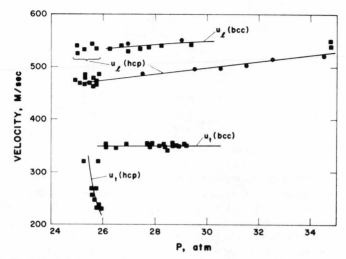

Fig. 9.23. Velocity of sound in solid He⁴ as a function of pressure: ● Vignos and Fairbank ([62]): ■ Lipschultz and Lee ([103]).

polycrystalline, the sound velocities are averaged over all orientations of the crystallites, and the relation

$$u_l^2 = 5/(9\rho\beta_S) \tag{9.33}$$

may be used.

For bcc and hcp He⁴, Vignos and Fairbank ([62]) and Lipschultz and Lee ([103]) have measured u_l, and the latter authors have observed u_t as well. The data are shown in Fig. 9.23. Use of these in equation (9.31) results in values of θ for bcc He⁴ nearly twice as large as those obtained from heat capacity measurements ([98,102]), indicating that the crystal is highly anisotropic. On the other hand, this difference in θ's for hcp He⁴ is only about 10% ([41,61,102]), even though the theoretical calculations by Nosanow and Werthamer ([75]) indicate that the anisotropies should be large for both phases. In general, the measured velocities for bcc He⁴ have shown a smaller spread than for the hcp phase, suggesting that in the former case, the specimens were composed of one or a few crystals, while those for hcp were polycrystalline. Despite the existence of considerable anisotropy, values of β_S computed from the appropriate equation, (9.32) or (9.33), compare favorably with those obtained by other methods (we note that for solid helium, the adiabatic and isothermal compressibilities differ by only a few percent). This is illustrated by the sampling of data taken near the melting condition which is given in Table 9.VI.

Table 9.VI.

	P (atm)	β_S (atm^{-1})	Method	Reference
bcc He^4	~29	3.7×10^{-3}	$P-V-T$	([43])
	~29	3.8×10^{-3}	C_V	([98])
	~29	3.9×10^{-3}	Eq. (9.32)	([103])
hcp He^4	~26	3.6×10^{-3}	$P-V-T$	([43])
	~30	3.3×10^{-3}	C_V	([61])
	~26	3.3×10^{-3}	Eq. (9.33)	([103])

From the preceding discussions, it is apparent that rather satisfactory consistency has been achieved among the various experimentally determined static properties of solid helium. And in a broader sense we may be tempted to conclude that the behavior of these crystals, especially of the hcp forms, is nearly "classical," since in many respects, the dependences found for θ and γ for solid helium appear to be interpretable in terms of reasonable departures from the harmonic approximation. Such a conclusion, however, would be premature lacking detailed knowledge of the true vibration spectra for the crystals as a function of volume. Nor can we work backwards from the observed values of θ and γ to deduce this spectrum, since both θ and γ are highly averaged functions of the individual frequencies of the vibration spectrum. Thus, the averaging processes smooth over such thermodynamically important spectral features as anharmonicities, departures from the Debye frequency distribution—or even singularities in this distribution—and changes in the distribution with volume. We must be content to apply the simple Debye and Grüneisen relations as handy tools for correlating certain properties; but we cannot draw detailed conclusions when they succeed, and we should not be surprised when they fail.

9.3.4. Heat Conduction in Solid Helium: Second Sound

In dielectric crystals, interactions between the acoustic vibrational modes provide the primary mechanism for the transport of energy under a thermal gradient, and, consequently, studies of heat conduction in such crystals offer a direct way of investigating the phonon collision processes. A great many experimental heat conduction results have been successfully interpreted through a model based on an analogy with the kinetic theory of gases which treats the phonons, or carriers of heat, as constituents of a quasiparticle-gas separated from the lattice. To a good approximation, the flow of heat is considered to be a diffusive process, limited by an effective mean free path l_{eff} between phonon collisions. In the steady state this results in a simple kinetic relation for the coefficient of thermal conductivity; that is,

$$\lambda = \tfrac{1}{3}C\bar{u}l_{\text{eff}} \qquad (9.34)$$

where C is the phonon-gas heat capacity per unit volume and $\bar{u}$ is some average sound velocity. For details of the theory, see, for example, Peierls [104] and Ziman [105].

The crucial problems arise in determining l_{eff} and in identifying the processes which limit the phonon lifetimes. It is now well established that phonon interactions can occur only through the anharmonic potential of the real crystal lattice and that the three-phonon process is by far the most important mechanism for energy transfer in a defect-free crystal of infinite extent. These processes may be described in terms of the phonon wave vectors k_i as

$$\mathbf{k}_1 + \mathbf{k}_2 \rightleftharpoons \mathbf{k}_3 + \mathbf{L} \qquad (9.35)$$

They are of two types. The first of these are the normal, or N-processes, for which $\mathbf{L} = 0$. Peierls has shown that N-processes cannot alter the momentum distribution of the phonon gas and therefore can serve neither to establish directly local thermal equilibrium in the crystal nor to impede the flow of heat. The second type of collision according to equation (9.35) results when $\mathbf{L} \neq 0$. Such interactions have been called by Peierls *umklapp*, or U-processes, in which the conservation of momentum in the crystal requires that the total wave vector change, $\mathbf{L}$, be a vector of the reciprocal lattice. (Actually, a phonon in a crystal does not carry momentum, but we may treat the wave vector $\mathbf{k}$ as if it stood for momentum $\hbar\mathbf{k}$.) These processes are peculiar to periodic structures and are forbidden in continuous media. Thus, U-processes have no counterpart in ordinary gases. As contrasted to N-processes, U-processes can effect changes in the momentum distribution of the phonon gas, and, in a crude way, we may imagine that by this mechanism momentum is extracted from the heat flow and transferred to the lattice. In this sense, U-processes may be considered as "momentum-loss" collisions. The important result is that l_{eff} in equation (9.34) is in this approximation determined solely by U-processes.

It is clear that the energies of the interacting phonons must be greater for U-processes than for N-processes, so that the frequency with which the former occur is strongly temperature dependent. At high temperatures, i.e., $T > \theta$, there will be very many high momentum-change collisions, so that the distinction between the two processes is of little consequence in determining l_{eff}. Straightforward arguments lead to l_{eff}, and also λ, being proportional to $1/T$. At low temperatures, $T < \theta$, U-processes are much less probable than

N-processes, and in this region, we may expect ([104]) λ to have the form

$$\lambda = a(T/\theta)^n \exp(\theta/bT) \qquad (9.36)$$

where a, b, and n are to be determined from experiment.

The above conclusions apply to heat conduction in infinite perfect crystals; but other momentum-loss mechanisms become possible when we consider the real situation. Very important among these for low-temperature experiments is the size of the specimen ([106]). Suppose the sample is a rod of diameter D; as T decreases, l_{eff} increases until $l_{eff} \approx D$, at which point scattering of phonons by the boundary cuts short the rise in l_{eff}. For lower temperatures, l_{eff} remains constant, and since $C \propto T^3$, λ should also be proportional to T^3. Following the gas analogy, this behavior when $l_{eff} \approx D$ may be called "Knudsen flow" or "ballistic transport." The temperature dependences for the three regions discussed so far are shown schematically as the solid curve in Fig. 9.24.

Significant effects upon the observed thermal conductivity may also be produced by phonon scattering from crystal imperfections, from internal crystal boundaries (polycrystalline sample), and from isotopic or chemical impurities. Scattering from point defects in the

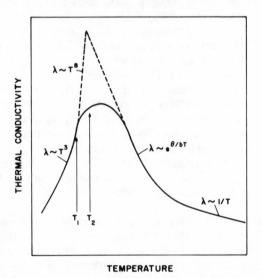

Fig. 9.24. Expected temperature dependence of the thermal conductivity of a crystal. The region between T_1 and T_2 indicates Poiseuille flow for a pure, defect-free single crystal (dotted curve).

crystal leads to a $1/T$ dependence for λ, and, in some cases, even at high temperature, the thermal resistance due to this mechanism is comparable to the effect of the simple U-processes.

Gurzhi [107] has suggested that although N-processes do not directly contribute to the thermal resistance, they may under certain conditions of low temperature and of crystal size and purity limit the momentum transfer from the phonon gas in collisions involving crystal defects and boundaries. In a region characterized by the inequality

$$l_N \ll D \ll l_R \tag{9.37}$$

(l_N and l_R are, respectively, the effective mean free paths for N-processes and for all resistive processes combined), Gurzhi considered l_{eff} to be of the order D^2/l_N. Then, between temperatures T_1, where $l_N \approx D$, and T_2, where $D^2/l_N \approx l_R$, he found that the principal contribution to λ is a term proportional to $D^2 T^8$. The effect of this term upon $\lambda(T)$ is shown in Fig. 9.24 as the dotted curve.

The region between T_1 and T_2 is known as the *Poiseuille flow* regime [also see Sussmann and Thellung [108]], since here, the phonon gas flowing down the sample rod behaves similarly to the viscous flow of an ordinary fluid; that is, the heat flow in the axial direction is only a function of the distance from the axis, and the radial flow at the boundary is zero. As we shall soon see, the conditions for Poiseuille flow have considerable bearing upon the problem of second-sound detection in solids.

We have attempted here to provide some background for understanding the experimental results on the thermal conductivity of solid He. These brief and incomplete remarks should not however be construed as implying that the theoretical aspects of the problem are either elementary or completely understood. Indeed they are not! For the reader who wishes a more rigorous exposition on these problems (in the approximation of the linearized Boltzmann equation), we recommend the articles by Guyer and Krumhansl [109].

In 1952, Webb *et al.* [110] made the first comprehensive experimental study of the steady-state thermal conductivity of solid He⁴. The measurements extended over the range 0.3 to 2.5°K for molar volumes between 18.3 and 20.6 cm³. Most important among the results was the observation of a maximum in λ near 1°K, above which the observed λ could be well fitted by the exponential function (9.36) and l_{eff} by $A \exp(\theta/bT)$, where A and b changed but little with density. Subsequently, Webb and Wilks [111] extended the data to $V = 11.4$ cm³ ($P = 1800$ atm), so that over the entire range, θ varied from 24° to 90°K. These investigations have provided substantial evidence for the correctness of the umklapp theory and in particular have demonstrated the essential role played by θ in these thermal conductivity processes.

(Note that in solid He below $\sim 4°$K, $T \ll \theta$, so that the high-temperature $1/T$ region will not be observed.) With increasing θ, the maximum in λ shifts to higher temperature, and at a fixed temperature, λ increases rapidly with θ (or density). For example, at $2°$K, this increase was found to be 300-fold for the above-mentioned range of θ. On the other hand, the results obtained by Webb and co-workers ([110,111]) for the low-temperature side of the maxima in λ did not quantitatively conform to the T^3 boundary scattering theory.

Since 1960, H. A. Fairbank and co-workers at Duke have experimentally investigated various aspects of thermal conduction processes in pure He^3 and He^4 and in isotropic mixtures. R. Berman and co-workers at Oxford have simultaneously covered much of the same ground. In the following, we summarize some of the important results.

Hcp Phases of the Pure Isotopes. Equation (9.36) with $n = 0$ describes λ quite well for temperatures above the maximum in λ. The parameters of this equation as deduced from the data by Bertman et al. ([112]) for several molar volumes are given in Table 9.VII. Below

Table 9.VII. Parameters for Equation (9.36) for hcp He^3 and hcp He^4 [a]

Isotope	V (cm³)	θ (°K)	$a \times 10^5$ (W/cm-deg)	θ/b	b
	18.6	33.9	3.7	11.7	2.9
	19.4	30.4	3.0	10.3	3.0
He^4	20.0	28.0	1.8	10.2	2.7
	20.2	27.2	2.0	9.4	2.9
	20.6	25.7	1.8	8.9	2.9
	21.0	24.4	1.6	8.4	2.9
He^3	19.5	34.6	5.0	11.2	3.1

[a] From Bertman et al. ([112]).

the maximum, the measurements fit a T^3 law quite accurately; but the magnitude of λ was found to depend markedly upon the state of annealing of the crystal and to increase by as much as a factor of 20 with successive treatments. Figure 9.25 compares λ for He^3 and He^4 both at $V = 19.5$ cm³; above $1.9°$K, the He^3 curve represents the bcc solid.

Bcc Phases of the Pure Isotopes. The initial measurements by Walker and Fairbank ([113]) indicated anomalous behavior of λ for bcc He^3. This has been confirmed by Bertman et al. ([112]). Not only is

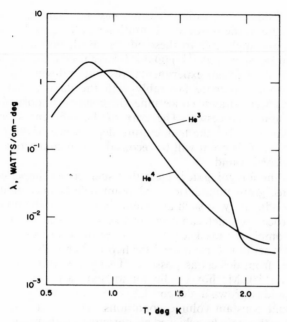

Fig. 9.25. Thermal conductivity of solid He^3 and He^4, both at $V = 19.5 \, \text{cm}^3$. The break in the He^3 curve at $\sim 1.9°$K signals the hcp–bcc transition. [After Bertman et al. ([112]).]

λ for bcc He^3 considerably lower than for hcp He^3, but in the region where umklapps are expected to dominate, the measurements suggest that two independent resistive processes are operative, each described by a relation of the form (9.36). These results are not completely understood. Observations have also been made in bcc He^4 ([112,114]), λ again being lower than in the hcp phase; but because of the restricted temperature region in which bcc He^4 is stable, it was not possible to determine whether anomalies appear in this phase analogous to those in bcc He^3.

Isotopic Mixtures. According to the theory ([115]) of homogeneously distributed point defects, the isotope contribution to the thermal resistance, i.e., λ_i^{-1}, should be proportional to T and to the square of the mass difference (averaged over the crystal unit cell) due to the impurity. However, observations in He ([113]) have indicated λ_i^{-1} to be nearly independent of T between 1° and 2°K and much larger than predicted. Evidently, thermal conduction here is a very complicated matter, since analysis of the data requires sorting out the relative strengths of the scattering processes due to umklapps, normal collisions, boundaries, point defects, mass-fluctuations, and lattice distortion due to the isotopic substitution. Callaway ([116]) has developed a theory applicable to these effects. Both Bertman et al. ([117]) (Duke) and Berman et al. ([118]) (Oxford) have used Callaway's method to interpret their recent experimental results; and while in each case the calculations compare favorably with the data, rather different conclusions were drawn concerning the relative importance of the various phonon processes. The crux of the differences lies in the assumptions made for the temperature dependence of the N-process collision rate. This point will be reconsidered in connection with the work on second sound.

From the foregoing, it is clear that such crystal imperfections as dislocations, grain boundaries, and point defects may influence the thermal conductivity to such an extent that some of the fundamental phonon processes which can occur in a perfect crystal at low temperature are completely masked. To uncover these processes, Mezhov-Deglin ([119]) set out to measure λ for hcp He^4 crystals grown as pure and as free from defects as possible. Using a method developed by Shal'nikov ([120]), Mezhov-Deglin found that vastly improved single crystals could be grown under constant-pressure conditions as opposed to the usual constant-volume conditions. His experimental results attest that in the main he achieved his objective, for they quite definitely display the characteristics of Poiseuille flow as predicted by Gurzhi ([107]). An example of $\lambda(T)$ for a single crystal grown at 85 atm is compared in Fig. 9.26 with several temperature dependences and the conductivity usually observed for a polycrystalline sample. The Mezhov-Deglin single-crystal results on the low T side of the maximum cannot by themselves distinguish between a T^6 or T^8 dependence; moreover, the theoretical T^8 law could also be T^7 or T^6, subject again to the proper choice for the temperature variation of the N-process collision rate.

In 1951, Ward and Wilks ([121]) speculated that the phonon-density fluctuation observed in liquid He II as second sound might under certain conditions also be characteristic of the phonon gas of dielectric solids. Several other authors developed this theme further, and in 1964, Prohofsky and Krumhansl ([122]) listed the criteria for detecting thermal waves in crystals. These turned out to be essentially the same requirement as for detecting Poiseuille flow [equation (9.37)], so that the experiments of Mezhov–Deglin mentioned above directly demonstrated the feasibility of observing second sound in solid helium.

For discussing phonon processes, it is often convenient to use the relaxation times τ (statistical averages weighted over the phonon distribution) for the separate processes. In this terminology, equation

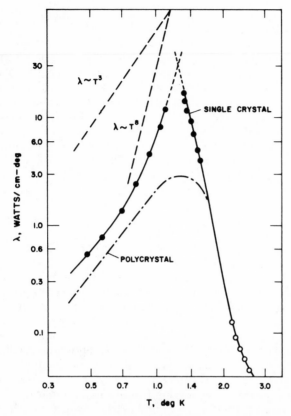

Fig. 9.26. Thermal conductivity of a single crystal of He⁴
grown at 85 atm [data of Mezhov-Deglin ([119])]. Note large
conductivity as compared with polycrystalline sample
[after Ackerman ([125])].

(9.34) may be rewritten as

$$\lambda = \tfrac{1}{3}C\bar{u}^2\tau_{\text{eff}} \tag{9.38}$$

and in the Poiseuille flow region,

$$\tau_{\text{eff}} = 5(D/2)^2/8\bar{u}^2\tau_N \tag{9.39}$$

where τ_N is the N-process relaxation time. Similarly, if ω_T is the
frequency of the thermal wave, the requirements of equation (9.37)
become

$$\tau_N \ll \omega_T^{-1} \ll \tau_R \tag{9.40}$$

so that if a typical sample dimension is $D \approx 1$ cm and $u \approx 10^5$ cm/sec, as for solid He, then ω_T should be of the order 10^5 sec^{-1}.

Thus, for second sound propagation, two requirements must be met: (1) $\omega_R = 1/\tau_R$ must be much smaller than ω_T, or, alternatively, l_R must be long compared with the wavelength of the thermal wave; and (2) l_N must be much shorter than this wavelength, so that the N-processes can establish thermal equilibrium in the wave faster than the passage-time for the wave. If (1) is not satisfied, the wave will be highly attenuated, leading to ordinary diffusive heat conduction; and if (1) is satisfied but (2) is not, the phonons will pass through the crystal at the velocity of first sound. The velocity of second sound has been predicted ([108]) to be given by

$$u_2^2 = \frac{1}{3} \frac{u_l^{-3} + 2u_t^{-3}}{u_l^{-5} + 2u_t^{-5}} \tag{9.41}$$

The dispersion relations have been worked out by Guyer and Krumhansl ([123]) and the attenuation by Guyer ([124]).

The frequency "window" described by equation (9.40) for observing second sound in He^4 is shown in Fig. 9.27. Here we have plotted approximate calculations ([125]) of τ_N^{-1} and τ_U^{-1} against T/θ, assuming that $\tau_U = \tau_R$. The shaded area indicates the region where second sound may be propagated. It is bounded at low frequencies by the onset of Poiseuille flow. We see that the optimum conditions for observing second sound occur near the thermal conductivity maximum, or at $T/\theta \approx 0.025$. The assumption that $\tau_U = \tau_R$ is valid for an infinite ideal crystal, but when scattering from isotopic impurities or crystal boundaries is important, $\tau_U \neq \tau_R$, and τ_R has a temperature dependence much like τ_N, which serves to close the window. The dashed line in the figure indicates the effect schematically. Again we may appreciate the importance of growing large, defect-free, isotopically pure single crystals for second sound work. Fortunately, techniques are available for meeting these requirements in the case of helium.

We wish to emphasize that second sound is not a phenomenon restricted to He^4—or He^3—but may occur in nonquantum solids; and in general, the condition $T/\theta \approx 0.025$ offers the best opportunity for observing thermal waves in crystals ([109]). Some alkali halides such as LiF and NaF are prime candidates for exhibiting the effect; however, the search ([126]) in LiF has been unsuccessful, probably because of difficulties in preparing isotopically pure specimens ([109]).

We also mention that other theoretical approaches to second sound in solids have been developed ([127]).

Phonon processes in solids may be investigated experimentally in two ways, using either thermal pulses or steady state heat flow. Guyer

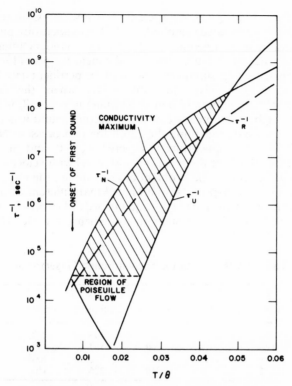

Fig. 9.27. Inverse relaxation times in solid He⁴ as a function of T/θ, showing the frequency window for observing second sound [after Ackerman ([125])].

and Krumhansl ([109]) have summarized the type of information deriv-able from these methods in the various temperature regions of differing thermal conductivity behavior. In particular, the method of choice for measuring the velocity and attenuation of second sound is the thermal pulse.

The first experimental evidence for the propagation of second sound in crystals of He⁴ was reported by Ackerman et al. ([128]) who measured the transit time of temperature pulses (0.1 to 5.0 μsec dura-tion) across a specimen 0.8 cm long ($D = 0.9$ cm) grown at $P = 54.2$ atm. The two important pieces of evidence that second sound was being observed were: (1) transit times were found in reasonable agree-ment with equation (9.41) for temperatures between 0.5° and 0.8°K—above 0.8°K the times corresponded with those expected for U-processes; and (2) an echo, characteristic of a wave mode as opposed to a diffusive mode, was detected in the low-temperature region. Subsequent more detailed examination ([129]) of temperature pulses, in a more favorable crystal geometry (eliminating boundary interference) and over a range of pressures, has added conclusive proof for second-sound propagation. A summary of some of the pertinent data for these latter experiments is given in Table 9.VIII, where the calculated velocities, $u_2^{(calc)}$, have been obtained assuming $u_l = 2u_t$; T_u is approximately the highest temperature at which second sound was observed for a given pressure, signalling the cutoff for U-processes. Note that $u_2 \approx u_1/2$. As the temperature is lowered, $\tau_N \to 0$, and the ballistic region is entered, where the pulses should travel with velocity u_1.

We return now to the problem of determining the characteristic relaxation time for N-processes and recall that different assumptions were made for τ_N by the Duke ([117]) and Oxford ([118]) workers in analyzing their respective steady-state measurements on He^3-He^4 solid

Table 9.VIII. Data for Second Sound Observations^a

P (atm)	V (cm^3)	θ (°K)	$u_2^{(obs)}$ (m/sec)	$u_2^{(calc)}$ (m/sec)	u_1 (m/sec)	T_u (°K)
33	20.5	27.8	130	147	290	0.65
54	19.4	31.8	160	167	330	0.83
100	18.0	38.7	180	202	400	1.05
130	17.2	43.0	210	226	450	1.22

^{a} Ackerman et al. ([129]).

solutions. The former group considered $\tau_N \propto T^{-5}$, implying $\lambda \propto T^8$ in the Poiseuille flow region, whereas the Oxford group chose $\tau_N \propto T^{-4}$, or $\lambda \propto T^7$. More recently, Ackerman and Guyer ([130]) have determined τ_N from the dispersion relations for second sound as applied to the thermal pulse shapes observed by Ackerman and co-workers ([128,129]) and have as well calculated τ_N from Mezhov-Deglin's ([119]) steady-state data using equations (9.38) and (9.39). They found these two sources to yield complementary information: all the results, plotted as τ_N vs. T/θ, defined essentially a single curve

$$\tau_N = 2 \times 10^{-6}(T/\theta)^{-3} \quad \mu\text{sec} \qquad (9.42)$$

with the steady-state data giving the best values of τ_N at high T/θ, just below the maximum in λ, and with the second-sound pulse data providing reliable results at low T/θ. Despite the difference in slope, equation (9.42) fits the magnitude of the Duke measurements near the maximum in λ, but nowhere does this relation approximate the Oxford data.

REFERENCES

1. R. H. Sherman in *Physics of High Pressures and the Condensed Phase* (A. van Itterbeek, ed.), p. 358, North Holland, Amsterdam (1965).
2. J. S. Dugdale, *ibid*, p. 382.
3. L. Goldstein, *Phys. Rev.*, **112**, 1465 (1958); **112**, 1483 (1958).
4. L. Goldstein, *Phys. Rev.*, **117**, 375 (1960).
5. K. A. Brueckner and K. R. Atkins, *Phys. Rev. Letters*, **1**, 315 (1958).
6. E. C. Kerr and R. D. Taylor, *Ann. Phys. (N.Y.)*, **20**, 450 (1962).
7. R. H. Sherman and F. J. Edeskuty, *Ann. Phys. (N.Y.)*, **9**, 522 (1960).
8. E. R. Grilly and R. L. Mills, *Ann. Phys. (N.Y.)*, **8**, 1 (1959).
9. D. F. Brewer and J. G. Daunt, *Phys. Rev.*, **115**, 843 (1959).
10. D. F. Brewer and J. R. G. Keyston, *Nature*, **191**, 1261 (1961).
11. A. C. Anderson, W. Reese, and J. C. Wheatley, *Phys. Rev.*, **130**, 495 (1963).
12. D. M. Lee, H. A. Fairbank, and E. J. Walker, *Phys. Rev.*, **121**, 1258 (1961).
13. J. E. Rives and H. Meyer, *Phys. Rev. Letters*, **7**, 217 (1961).
14. C. Boghosian, H. Meyer, and J. E. Rives, *Phys. Rev.*, **146**, 110 (1966).
15. D. F. Brewer, J. G. Daunt, and A. K. Sreedhar, *Phys. Rev.*, **115**, 836 (1959).
16. L. Goldstein, *Ann. Phys. (N.Y.)*, **8**, 390 (1959); **16**, 205 (1961).
17. O. V. Lounasmaa, *Cryogenics*, **1**, 212 (1961).
18. R. W. Hill and O. V. Lounasmaa, *Phil. Trans. Roy. Soc.*, **A252**, 357 (1960).
19. K. R. Atkins and M. H. Edwards, *Phys. Rev.*, **97**, 1429 (1955).
20. E. C. Kerr and R. D. Taylor, *Ann. Phys. (N.Y.)*, **26**, 292 (1964).
21. R. L. Mills and S. G. Sydoriak, *Ann. Phys. (N.Y.)*, **34**, 276 (1965).
22. H. C. Kramers, J. D. Wasscher, and C. J. Gorter, *Physica*, **18**, 329 (1952); J. Wiebes, C. J. Niels-Hakkenberg, and H. C. Kramers, *Physica*, **23**, 625 (1957).
23. S. G. Sydoriak and R. L. Mills, in *Low Temperature Physics LT-9* (J. G. Daunt, D. O. Edwards, F. J. Milford, and M. Yaqub, eds.), p. 273, Plenum Press, New York (1965).
24. C. Boghosian and H. Meyer, *Phys. Rev.*, **152**, 200 (1966); **163**, 206 (1967).
25. K. R. Atkins and R. A. Stasior, *Can. J. Phys.*, **31**, 1156 (1953).
26. R. L. Mills, *Ann. Phys. (N.Y.)*, **35**, 410 (1965).
27. H. Palevsky, K. Otnes, and K. E. Larsson, *Phys. Rev.*, **112**, 11 (1958); J. L. Yarnell, G. P. Arnold, P. J. Bendt, and E. C. Kerr, *Phys. Rev.*, **113**, 1379 (1959); D. G. Henshaw and A. D. B. Woods, *Phys. Rev.*, **121**, 1266 (1961).
28. D. G. Henshaw and A. D. B. Woods, in *Proceedings of the VII International Conference on Low Temperature Physics* (G. M. Graham and A. C. H. Hallett, eds.), p. 539, University of Toronto Press (1961).
29. C. J. N. van den Meijdenberg, K. W. Taconis, and R. De Bruyn Ouboter, *Physica*, **27**, 197 (1961).
30. J. Wiebes and H. C. Kramers, LT-10, Vol. I, p. 243, Moscow (1967).
31. I. Pomeranchuk, *Zh. Eksperim. i Teor. Fiz.*, **20**, 919 (1960).
32. N. Bernardes and H. Primakoff, *Phys. Rev. Letters*, **2**, 290 (1959); **3**, 144 (1959); *Phys. Rev.*, **119**, 968 (1960).
33. D. W. Osborne, B. M. Abraham, and B. Weinstock, *Phys. Rev.*, **82**, 263 (1951); B. Weinstock, B. M. Abraham, and D. W. Osborne, *Phys. Rev.*, **85**, 158 (1952).
34. T. R. Roberts and S. G. Sydoriak, *Phys. Rev.*, **93**, 1418 (1954).
35. W. M. Fairbank and G. K. Walters, *Bull. Am. Phys. Soc.*, **2**, 193 (1957); *Symposium on Liquid and Solid He^3* (J. G. Daunt, ed.), p. 220, Ohio State University Press (1957).
36. J. L. Baum, D. F. Brewer, J. G. Daunt, and D. O. Edwards, *Phys. Rev. Letters*, **3**, 127 (1959).
37. R. L. Mills, E. R. Grilly, and S. G. Sydoriak, *Ann. Phys. (N.Y.)*, **12**, 41 (1961).

38. A. C. Anderson, G. L. Salinger, W. A. Steyert, and J. C. Wheatley, *Phys. Rev. Letters*, **7**, 299 (1961).
39. A. C. Anderson, W. Reese, and J. C. Wheatley, *Phys. Rev.*, **130**, 1644 (1963).
40. E. D. Adams, G. C. Straty, and E. L. Wall, *Phys. Rev. Letters*, **15**, 549 (1965).
41. E. C. Heltemes and C. A. Swenson, *Phys. Rev.*, **128**, 1512 (1962).
42. G. C. Straty, Thesis, University of Florida (1967); G. C. Straty and E. D. Adams, *Phys. Rev.*, **169**, 232 (1968).
43. E. R. Grilly, LT-10, Vol. I, p. 253, Moscow (1967); also private communication.
44. L. Goldstein, *Phys. Rev.*, **133**, A52 (1964).
45. L. Goldstein, *Phys. Rev.*, **159**, 120 (1967).
46. J. Jarvis and H. Meyer, LT-10, Vol. I, p. 258, Moscow (1967).
47. M. F. Panczyk, R. A. Scribner, G. C. Straty, and E. D. Adams, *Phys. Rev. Letters*, **19**, 1102 (1967).
48. W. R. Abel, A. C. Anderson, and J. C. Wheatley, *Phys. Rev. Letters*, **7**, 299 (1961).
49. A. C. Anderson, W. Reese, and J. C. Wheatley, *Phys. Rev. Letters*, **7**, 366 (1961).
50. H. A. Fairbank, *Phys. Rev. Letters*, **8**, 49 (1962).
51. D. O. Edwards, A. S. McWilliams, and J. G. Daunt, *Physics Letters*, **1**, 101 (1962).
52. L. Goldstein, *Phys. Rev. Letters*, **5**, 104 (1960); *Phys. Rev.*, **122**, 726 (1961); **128**, 1520 (1962).
53. J. Wiebes and H. C. Kramers, *Physics Letters*, **4**, 298 (1963).
54. C. Le Pair, K. W. Taconis, R. De Bruyn Ouboter, and P. Das, *Physica*, **29**, 755 (1963).
55. G. O. Zimmerman, in *Low Temperature Physics LT-9* (J. G. Daunt, D. O. Edwards, F. J. Milford, and M. Yaqub, eds.), p. 240, Plenum Press, New York (1965).
56. S. G. Sydoriak and R. L. Mills, in *Low Temperature Physics LT-9* (J. G. Daunt, D. O. Edwards, F. J. Milford, and M. Yaqub, eds.), p. 273, Plenum Press, New York (1965).
57. C. Le Pair, R. De Bruyn Ouboter, and J. Pit, *Physica*, **31**, 813 (1965).
58. G. C. Straty and E. D. Adams, *Phys. Rev. Letters*, **17**, 290 (1966); **17**, 505 (1966).
59. L. Goldstein and R. L. Mills, *Phys. Rev.*, **159**, 136 (1967).
60. E. R. Grilly and R. L. Mills, *Ann. Phys. (N.Y.)*, **18**, 250 (1962).
61. D. O. Edwards and R. C. Pandorf, *Phys. Rev.*, **140**, A816 (1965); **152**, 494 (1966).
62. J. H. Vignos and H. A. Fairbank, *Phys. Rev.*, **147**, 185 (1966).
63. W. H. Keesom and K. W. Taconis, *Physica*, **5**, 161 (1938).
64. A. F. Schuch and R. L. Mills, in *Advances in Cryogenic Engineering* (K. D. Timmerhaus, ed.), Vol. 7, p. 311, Plenum Press, New York (1962).
65. A. F. Schuch and R. L. Mills, *Acta Cryst. (Suppl.)*, **16**, Part 13, A20 (1963).
66. F. W. de Wette and B. R. A. Nijboer, *Physics Letters*, **18**, 19 (1965).
67. L. H. Nosanow, *Phys. Rev.*, **146**, 120 (1966).
68. T. R. Koehler, *Phys. Rev. Letters*, **17**, 89 (1966); **18**, 654 (1967); *Phys. Rev.*, **144**, 789 (1966); **165**, 942 (1968).
69. L. H. Nosanow and G. L. Shaw, *Phys. Rev.*, **119**, 968 (1962).
70. D. Rosenwald, *Phys. Rev.*, **154**, 160 (1967).
71. E. M. Saunders, *Phys. Rev.*, **126**, 1724 (1962).
72. R. L. Garwin and A. Landesman, *Physics*, **2**, 107 (1965).
73. W. J. Mullin, *Phys. Rev.*, **166**, 142 (1968).
74. L. H. Nosanow and W. J. Mullin, *Phys. Rev. Letters*, **14**, 133 (1965).
75. L. H. Nosanow and N. R. Werthamer, *Phys. Rev. Letters*, **15**, 618, 997 (1965).
76. J. H. Hetherington, W. J. Mullin, and L. H. Nosanow, *Phys. Rev.*, **154**, 175 (1967).
77. W. L. McMillan, *Phys. Rev.*, **138**, A442 (1965); see also Section 5.1.4c of this book.
78. E. D. Adams, H. Meyer, and W. M. Fairbank, in *Helium Three* (J. G. Daunt, ed.), p. 57, Ohio State University Press (1960).
79. D. O. Edwards, A. S. McWilliams, and J. G. Daunt, *Physics Letters*, **1**, 218 (1962).
80. J. M. Goodkind and W. M. Fairbank, in *Helium Three* (J. G. Daunt, ed.), p. 52, Ohio State University Press (1960).

81. H. A. Reich, *ibid*, p. 63.
82. D. O. Edwards, A. S. McWilliams, and J. G. Daunt, *Phys. Rev. Letters*, **9**, 195 (1962).
83. A. L. Thomson, H. Meyer, and P. N. Dheer, *Phys. Rev.*, **132**, 1455 (1963).
84. H. D. Cohen, P. B. Pipes, K. L. Verosub and W. M. Fairbank, *Phys. Rev. Letters*, **21**, 677 (1968).
85. R. C. Richardson, E. Hunt, and H. Meyer, *Phys. Rev.*, **138**, A1326 (1965).
86. R. C. Richardson, A. Landesman, E. Hunt, and H. Meyer, *Phys. Rev.*, **146**, 244 (1966).
87. H. A. Reich, *Phys. Rev.*, **129**, 630 (1963).
88. R. L. Garwin and A. Landesman, *Phys. Rev.*, **133**, A1503 (1964).
89. R. L. Garwin and H. A. Reich, *Phys. Rev. Letters*, **12**, 354 (1964).
90. B. T. Beal, R. P. Giffard, J. Hatton, M. G. Richards, and P. M. Richards, *Phys. Rev. Letters*, **12**, 393 (1964).
91. M. G. Richards, J. Hatton, and R. P. Giffard, *Phys. Rev.*, **139**, A91 (1965).
92. R. P. Giffard and J. Hatton, *Phys. Rev. Letters*, **18**, 1106 (1967); private communication.
93. P. W. Anderson and P. R. Weiss, *Rev. Mod. Phys.*, **25**, 269 (1953).
94. R. Kubo and K. Tomita, *J. Phys. Soc. (Japan)*, **9**, 888 (1954).
95. S. R. Hartmann, *Phys. Rev.*, **133**, A17 (1964).
96. R. B. Griffiths, *Phys. Rev.*, **124**, 1023 (1961).
97. H. H. Sample and C. A. Swenson, *Phys. Rev.*, **158**, 188 (1967).
98. D. O. Edwards and R. C. Pandorf, *Phys. Rev.*, **144**, 143 (1966).
99. J. S. Dugdale and J. P. Franck, *Phil. Trans. Roy. Soc.*, **A257**, 1 (1964).
100. J. P. Franck, *Physics Letters*, **11**, 208 (1964).
101. W. H. Keesom and A. P. Keesom, *Physica*, **3**, 105 (1936).
102. G. H. Ahlers, *Phys. Rev. Letters*, **10**, 439 (1963); *Phys. Rev.*, **135**, A10 (1964).
103. R. P. Lipschultz and D. M. Lee, *Phys. Rev. Letters*, **14**, 1017 (1965): Lipschultz, Thesis, Cornell University (1966).
104. R. Peierls, *Quantum Theory of Solids*, Clarendon Press, Oxford (1955).
105. J. M. Ziman, *Electrons and Phonons*, Clarendon Press, Oxford (1962).
106. H. B. G. Casimir, *Physica*, **5**, 495 (1938).
107. R. N. Gurzhi, *Zh. Eksperim. i Teor. Fiz.*, **46**, 719 (1964) [English translation, *Soviet Phys.— JETP*, **19**, 490 (1964)].
108. J. Sussmann and A. Thellung, *Proc. Phys. Soc. (London)*, **81**, 1122 (1963).
109. R. A. Guyer and J. A. Krumhansl, *Phys. Rev.*, **148**, 766 (1966); **148**; 778 (1966).
110. F. J. Webb, K. R. Wilkinson, and J. Wilks, *Proc. Roy. Soc. (London)*, **A214**, 546 (1952).
111. F. J. Webb and J. Wilks, *Phil. Mag.*, **44**, 664 (1953).
112. B. Bertman, H. A. Fairbank, C. W. White, and M. J. Crooks, *Phys. Rev.*, **142**, 74 (1966).
113. E. J. Walker and H. A. Fairbank, *Phys. Rev.*, **118**, 913 (1960).
114. R. Berman and S. J. Rogers, *Physics Letters*, **9**, 115 (1964).
115. P. G. Klemens, *Proc. Roy. Soc. (London)*, **A208**, 108 (1951); *Proc. Phys. Soc. (London)*, **A68**, 1113 (1955).
116. J. Callaway, *Phys. Rev.*, **113**, 1046 (1959); **122**, 787 (1961).
117. B. Bertman, H. A. Fairbank, R. A. Guyer, and C. W. White, *Phys. Rev.*, **142**, 79 (1966).
118. R. Berman, C. L. Bounds, and S. J. Rogers, *Proc. Roy. Soc. (London)*, **A289**, 66 (1966).
119. L. Mezhov-Deglin, *Zh. Eksperim. i Teor. Fiz.*, **49**, 66 (1965) [English translation, *Soviet Phys.—JETP*, **22**, 47 (1966)].
120. A. I. Shal'nikov, *Zh. Eksperim. i Teor. Fiz.*, **41**, 1056, 1059 (1961) [English translation, *Soviet Phys.—JETP*, **14**, 753, 755 (1962)].
121. J. C. Ward and J. Wilks, *Phil. Mag.*, **42**, 314 (1951).

122. E. W. Prohofsky and J. A. Krumhansl, *Phys. Rev.*, **133**, A1403 (1964).
123. R. A. Guyer and J. A. Krumhansl, *Phys. Rev.*, **133**, A1411 (1964).
124. R. A. Guyer, *Phys. Rev.*, **148**, 789 (1966).
125. C. C. Ackerman, Thesis, Duke University (1966).
126. R. J. von Gutfeld and A. H. Nethercot, *Phys. Rev. Letters*, **12**, 64 (1964).
127. See, for example, P. C. Kwok and P. C. Martin, *Phys. Rev.*, **142**, 495 (1966);
     L. J. Sham, *Phys. Rev.*, **156**, 494 (1967).
128. C. C. Ackerman, B. Bertman, H. A. Fairbank, and R. A. Guyer, *Phys. Rev. Letters*,
     16, 789 (1966).
129. C. C. Ackerman and R. A. Guyer [to be published, *Ann. Phys.* (N.Y.)].
130. C. C. Ackerman and R. A. Guyer, *Solid State Comm.*, **5**, 671 (1967).

Notes on Units, Physical Constants and Notation

1. In this book c.g.s. units are used except where noted.

2. Some useful physical constants:

   k_B (Boltzmann constant) $= 1.3805 \times 10^{-16}$ erg/deg.
   N_A (Avogadro number) $= 6.0225 \times 10^{23}$ mol^{-1}.
   g (standard acceleration of free fall) $= 980.665$ cm/sec^2.
   h (Planck's constant) $= 6.6256 \times 10^{-27}$ erg-sec.
   $\hbar = h/2\pi = 1.0545 \times 10^{-27}$ erg-sec.
   e (elementary charge) $= 1.6021 \times 10^{-20}$ cm$^{1/2}$/g$^{1/2}$.
   m_e (electron rest mass) $= 0.911 \times 10^{-27}$ g.
   m_3 (mass of He^3 atom) $= 3.01700/N_A = 5.0095 \times 10^{-24}$ g.
   m_4 (mass of He^4 atom) $= 4.00390/N_A = 6.6482 \times 10^{-24}$ g.

3. Except where noted, molar quantities for thermodynamic symbols are capitalized (e.g., C_V, joules/mol-deg), and specific, or per gram, quantities are lower case (e.g., c_V, joules/g-deg). For the chemical potential, μ is per particle and $\bar{\mu}$ is per gram.

4. Diamond brackets about a quantum-mechanical operator—e.g., $\langle \Psi(\mathbf{r}) \rangle$—indicate the expectation value or average (with respect to time and/or space) value of the operator. Diamond brackets used as $\langle i|\Phi|j \rangle$ indicate the matrix element between two states i and j connected by the operator Φ.

5. Labels for momentum states, or the value of the momentum, are generally denoted by $\mathbf{p}$ or $\mathbf{q}$ (or when the vector property is not required, by p or q); the corresponding wave vector is denoted by $\mathbf{k}$ or k.

Author Index

Subject Index

415